Integrating ISO 9001:2000 with ISO/TS 16949 and AS9100

Also available from ASQ Quality Press:

Automotive Internal Auditor Pocket Guide: Process Auditing to ISO/TS 16949:2002
J.P. Russell

Failure Mode and Effect Analysis: FMEA from Theory to Execution,
Second Edition
D. H. Stamatis

ISO 9001:2000 A Practical Quality Manual Explained
Kevin R. Grimes

The ASQ ISO 9000:2000 Handbook
Joseph J. Tsiakals, Charles A. Cianfrani, and John E. (Jack) West

Integrating QS-9000 with Your Automotive Quality System, Third Edition
D. H. Stamatis

To request a complimentary catalog of ASQ Quality Press publications, call 800-248-1946, or visit our Web site at http://qualitypress.asq.org.

Integrating ISO 9001:2000 with ISO/TS 16949 and AS9100

D. H. Stamatis

ASQ Quality Press
Milwaukee, Wisconsin

American Society for Quality, Quality Press, Milwaukee 53203
© 2004 by ASQ
All rights reserved. Published 2004
Printed in the United States of America

12 11 10 09 08 07 06 05 04   5 4 3 2 1

Library of Congress Cataloging-in-Publication Data

Stamatis, D. H., 1947–
  Integrating ISO 9001:2000 with ISO/TS 16949 and AS9100 / D. H.
Stamatis.
    p. cm.
  Includes bibliographical references and index.
  ISBN 0-87389-628-9
  1. Quality control—Standards. 2. ISO 9000 Series Standards. I. Title.

  TS156.S72 2004
  658.5'62—dc22   2004008223

ISBN 0-87389-628-9

Publisher: William A. Tony
Acquisitions Editor: Annemieke Hytinen
Project Editor: Paul O'Mara
Production Administrator: Randall Benson
Special Marketing Representative: Matt Meinholz

ASQ Mission: The American Society for Quality advances individual,
organizational, and community excellence worldwide through learning,
quality improvement, and knowledge exchange.

Attention Bookstores, Wholesalers, Schools, and Corporations: ASQ Quality
Press books, videotapes, audiotapes, and software are available at quantity
discounts with bulk purchases for business, educational, or instructional use.
For information, please contact ASQ Quality Press at 800-248-1946, or write to
ASQ Quality Press, P.O. Box 3005, Milwaukee, WI 53201-3005.

To place orders or to request a free copy of the ASQ Quality Press Publications
Catalog, including ASQ membership information, call 800-248-1946. Visit our
Web site at www.asq.org or http://qualitypress.asq.org.

 Printed on acid-free paper

Quality Press
600 N. Plankinton Avenue
Milwaukee, Wisconsin 53203
Call toll free 800-248-1946
Fax 414-272-1734
www.asq.org
http://qualitypress.asq.org
http://standardsgroup.asq.org
E-mail: authors@asq.org

This book is dedicated to Eric and Stacey.

Contents

CD Contents

List of Figures and Tables

Preface

The ISO 9000:1994 family contained some 27 standards and documents. This proliferation of standards was a particular concern of ISO 9000 users and customers. To respond to this concern, the ISO TC 176 committee agreed that the ISO 9000:2000 family would consist of four primary standards supported by a considerably reduced number of other documents (guidance standards, brochures, technical reports, technical specifications). To the extent possible, the key points in the 1994 standard of 27 documents are integrated into the four primary standards. Sector needs are also addressed while maintaining the generic nature of the standards. The four primary standards are:

1. ISO 9000:2000—*Quality management systems—Fundamentals and vocabulary.*

2. ISO 9001:2000—*Quality management systems—Requirements.* (The certifiable standard.)

3. ISO 9004:2000—*Quality management systems—Guidelines for performance improvement.*

4. ISO 19011:2002—*Quality management systems—Guidelines for auditing quality systems.*

The new (2000) ISO 9001 and ISO 9004 standards were developed as a "consistent pair" of standards, although ISO 9004 is really a guideline that may be used for organizations whose top management wishes to move beyond the requirements of ISO 9001, in pursuit of continual performance improvement. Their structure and sequence are identical in order to facilitate an easy and useful transition between them. However, ISO 9004 it is not a "certifiable" standard; rather, it gives guidance on a wider range of objectives of a quality management system than does ISO 9001, particularly for the continuous improvement of an organization's overall performance and efficiency, as well as its effectiveness. This "new consistency" and structure hopefully will contribute to enhanced synergy between the two and will aid organizational efficiency and effectiveness. After all, the new standards are more user-friendly and make it easier for an organization to introduce a quality management system (QMS) into an organization. Furthermore, their common structure should follow the typical format of the main processes of an organization and will enable the QMS to be aligned to its operations.

Whereas the new ISO 9001:2000 more clearly addresses the QMS requirements for an organization to demonstrate its capability to meet customer needs, the revised ISO 9004:2000 is intended to lead beyond ISO 9001:2000, toward the development of a comprehensive QMS designed to address the needs of all interested parties.

Both standards use a common vocabulary as defined in ISO 9000:2000, which also describes the underlying fundamentals. A logical, systematic approach has been adopted in formulating the definitions used in ISO 9000:2000, with the intention of generating a more consistent terminology that is "user-friendly."

The 1994 ISO 9001, ISO 9002, and ISO 9003 standards are consolidated into the single revised ISO 9001:2000 standard. "Permissible exclusions" are allowed to some clauses of ISO 9001:2000 where the related processes are not performed by the organization and these requirements do not affect the organization's ability to provide products that meet customer and applicable regulatory requirements.

The primary contribution of the "consistent pair" is to relate modern quality management to the processes and activities of an organization, including the promotion of continual improvement and achievement of customer satisfaction. Furthermore, it is intended that the ISO 9000 standards have global applicability. Therefore, the factors that drove the 2000 revision process, among others, were:

1. Applicability to all product categories and to all sizes of organizations (Note that the ISO 9000:2000 definition of "product" also includes "services"!)

2. Simple to use, clear in language, readily translatable, and easily understandable

3. Ability to connect quality management systems to organizational processes

4. Provision of a natural stepping stone toward total quality management (TQM)

5. Greater orientation toward continual improvement and customer satisfaction, especially when building team performance is concerned

6. Compatibility with other management systems, such as ISO 14001 for environmental management, BS 8800 health and safety at work

7. Need to provide a consistent basis and address the primary needs and interests of organizations in specific sectors such as aerospace (AS9000, AS9100), automotive (QS-9000, TE 9000, ISO/TS 16949), medical devices, telecommunications (TL 9000), and others

Therefore, with this new ISO 9001 standard, all sizes and types of organizations are being offered tools with which to achieve internal and external benefits. (Note: In this book the author focuses only on the application of ISO 9001 as it relates to automotive and aerospace sector industries. He recognizes that other sectors such as service, health, education, and others may use ISO 9001:2000; however, each of the sectors must modify its application to reflect their own special needs).

Specifically, this book is organized in 12 chapters, each covering different issues of the standard and its derivatives. In summary form the contents of each chapter are:

Preface and Introduction. The process of development, revision, and general comments about the standard are covered.

Chapter 1. Common questions about the basic ISO 9000 series. A general introduction to quality standards via question-and-answer format. The intent is to give the reader a concentrated answer to common questions about the ISO standards.

Chapter 2. ISO 9001:2000—The basic certifiable standard. This chapter explains the basic standard.

Chapter 3. Automotive ISO/TS 16949 requirements. This chapter addresses the generic requirements of the automotive industry beyond the ISO requirements.

Chapter 4. Customer-specific requirements for use with ISO/TS 16949 second edition. This chapter addresses issues, concerns, and additional specific requirements for DaimlerChrysler, General Motors, and Ford Motor Company.

Chapter 5. Transition from ISO 9001:1994 to ISO 9001:2000 and QS-9000 to ISO/TS 16949. The path to the transition from ISO to QS to ISO/TS is identified and explained. In addition, the requirements of upgrading the ISO 9000:1994 to ISO 9000:2000 are discussed.

Chapter 6. AS9100 aerospace requirements. This chapter addresses the generic requirements of the aerospace industry beyond the ISO requirements. In addition to the ISO requirements, the items that concern the aerospace industry for registration are addressed.

Chapter 7. Documentation. The issues of recognizing the importance of documentation and its rationale are discussed. In addition, specific examples are given as to how one goes about documenting a system of quality. A detailed discussion is presented for creating documentation with and without the aid of computer software.

Chapter 8. The five basic pillars to quality. This chapter gives an overview of the five basic methodologies of any "good" quality system and their significant contribution to quality improvement. Specifically, the methodologies covered are: failure mode and effects analysis (FMEA), statistical process control (SPC), advanced product quality planning (APQP), measurement system analysis (MSA), and production part approval process (PPAP).

Chapter 9. Auditing. The issue of auditing (the planning as well as the process) is discussed with a heavy emphasis on "process" orientation.

Chapter 10. Process-oriented audit (assessment). With the introduction of ISO 9000:2000, a new concept is also introduced for auditing. The concept is "process audit." This chapter picks up where chapter 9 left off. It focuses on the mechanics and benefits of a process audit. Included in the discussion are the issues of checklists, corrective actions, and the importance of communication.

Chapter 11. Issues and concerns about auditing. With all audit (assessment) systems there are problems and concerns. The ISO approach to system assessment is no different. In this chapter some of these issues are identified and discussed.

They are identified as pre-audit, during audit, and closure of audit.

Chapter 12. Implementing ISO 9001, AS9100, and ISO/TS 16949. The last chapter of the book covers the process of implementation for ISO, TS, and AS. The implementation process is the execution of the intent of these standards. Therefore, it is of great importance for the organization demonstrating the need of documentation to follow these standards in a very systematic approach. There are many approaches for implementation; however, in this chapter some key approaches are identified and discussed.

Appendix A. Readability Index.

Appendix B. Training.

Appendix C. Aids in helping formulate an FMEA.

Appendix D. Guidelines for process selection and metrics evaluation.

Appendix E. A cross-reference between ISO 9001:1994 and ISO 9001:2000.

Appendix F. Statistics in auditing.

Glossary

Selected Bibliography

CD:

Appendix I. Production Part Approval Process (PPAP).

Appendix II. Advanced Product Quality Planning (APQP).

Appendix III. A Cursory View of Overall Equipment Effectiveness (OEE).

Appendix IV. A Generic Checklist for ISO 9001:2000 Requirements.

Appendix V. ISO/TS 16949 Checklist.

Appendix VI. AS9100 Checklist.

Appendix VII. Typical Procedures.

Appendix VIII. An ISO 9001 Quality Manual (Transition Format)

Acknowledgments

As always, when writing any book, the author is responsible for the content and flow of the book; however, he or she depends on many others to carry out tasks such as research, copying, reviewing, bouncing ideas, encouragement, typing, and so on.

This book is no different! I owe much to many individuals without whose help this work would not have been completed.

In the list of priorities, I must give credit to Mr. P. Jinks for his long, thought-provoking discussions about audits; Mr. Gene Thomlinson for his always provocative questions in reference to the five pillars; Mr. Marvin Holmberg for his availability to bounce ideas off in reference to the checklists; Mr. Anastasios Anastasiou for his willingness to discuss AS9100 and its ramifications in the aerospace industry. (I have tried to incorporate his comments and ideas in both the quality manual and the checklist); and Dr. Rod Munro for his willingness to help at all sorts of times with reviews and questions.

I want to thank Ms. J. Stockhouse for the opportunity to work in her plant to implement ISO/TS 16949.

I want to thank Mr. C. Tsavos for his insights in developing a better understanding in the automotive business of the transition process from ISO 2001:1994 to ISO/TS 16949. His insight was instrumental in developing the quality manual in appendix O—a novel approach indeed! Simple and to the point.

I want to thank all the participants in my public seminars, for I owe them a very strong "thank you" for offering suggestions and specific recommendations for improvement. I have tried to incorporate as many as possible. Without their comments and input, this book would not have been possible.

I want to thank the editors of ASQ Quality Press not only for an outstanding—as usual—job of expediting the publishing of the book but also, most importantly, for the "nuggets" of suggestions to improve the final work.

I want to thank Marcel Dekker, Inc., for granting me permission to use material published by them. Specifically, the material is from the following two books:

1. Som, R. K. 1996. *Practical Sampling Techniques,* 2nd ed.: 19–21, 31, 147, 229.

2. Willburn, J. 1984. *Practical Statistical Sampling for Auditors:* 55–67.

I want to thank ASQ Quality Press for granting me permission to use the ANSI/ASQ ISO 9001:2000 standard.

Finally, I want to thank Carla for always being there and always being ready to listen to my frustrations. Carla, without you I would not be able to do what I have been doing. We did it together. Thanks. You are truly the greatest!!

Introduction

The ISO 9000:2000 standards are a set of international quality management standards and guidelines. Since their initial publication in 1987, they have earned a global reputation as the basis for establishing quality management systems.

Fundamentally, the impetus for this quality management system (QMS) has been the philosophy of W. Edwards Deming. Table I.1 shows the Deming philosophy as it relates to the overall organizational goals and their respective objectives. It is imperative to note that the philosophy is concentrated in four areas: 1) management objectives, 2) production objectives, 3) training objectives, and 4) objectives for the entire workforce.

The success and acceptance of the initial ISO standard initiated an avalanche of interest in many industries, and in 1994 we were introduced to the first revision. At that time, the three 1994 standards—ISO 9001, 9002 and 9003—were used extensively as the basis for independent (third-party) quality system certification. This resulted in the certification of around 350,000 organizations in 150 countries worldwide, with many more in the process of setting up and implementing quality management systems.

Since ISO protocol requires that all standards be reviewed at least every five years to determine whether they should be confirmed, revised, or withdrawn, the 1994 versions of ISO 9000 were revised and published in 2000. This last revision (the 2000) is the current standard and indeed is the basis for ISO/TS 16949, AS9100, and other industry-specific related standards.

BACKGROUND TO THE CHANGES

Extensive surveys were carried out on a worldwide basis in order to better understand the needs of all user groups. The revised standards took into account all previous experience with quality management systems. They

Table I.1   Deming philosophy as it relates to the overall organization.

Overall Organizational Goals	Corresponding Quality Objectives	Remarks, Difficulties, Challenges, and/ or Opportunities
Quality Assurance Management Objectives		
1. Achieve consistency and continuity 2. Eliminate fear and encourage communication 3. Encourage teamwork 4. Define management's permanent commitment to quality and productivity 5. Provide realistic goals 6. Remove barriers to pride of workmanship	1. Create corporate creed 2. Create an employee program 3. Develop process for corrective-action programs 4. Develop quality philosophy program (work with all corporate functions) 5. Work with R&D to improve process and to set R&D schedules 6. Create an outstanding employee recognition program	
Quality Assurance Production Objectives		
1. Don't depend on mass inspection 2. Make purchases based on statistical evidence, not price (reduce number of suppliers) 3. Don't allow commonly accepted levels of mistakes, defective materials, and defective workmanship	1. Plan an SPC policy (work with production) 2. Develop an outside sourcing plan (work with production) 3. Create processes that improve quality levels for continuous improvement (work with production)	
Quality Assurance Training Objectives		
1. Train workforce in statistics 2. Focus supervisor to help people do a better job 3. Institute training and educational methods on new methodology and technology	1. Plan training programs (work with human resources department) 2. Plan supervisory training program (work with human resources department) 3. Investigate video programs or programs online for cost-effectiveness	
Quality Assurance Objectives Pertaining to Entire Workforce		
1. Search for better ways to improve system 2. Use statistical methods	1. Develop process for corporate field failure reporting (this alone will begin the process for instituting corporate knowledge database) 2. Implement SPC in QA to identify processes that are out of control (the focus here is to develop stable processes so that we may predict capability, production, and so on	

are the result of a closer alignment of the QMS with the needs of the day to day operation of the organization.

It has long been recognized that investment in quality management systems, in addition to responding to customer expectations, has resulted in benefits to the efficiency of the organization, its operations, and economic performance, as well as to the quality of its products and services. Specifically, the revised 2000 standards are expected to be of great help for organizations wishing to go beyond simple compliance with QMS requirements for certification purposes. They can be readily applied to small, medium, and large organizations in the public and private sectors, and will be equally applicable to users in industrial, service, software, and other areas.

As such, the new standards follow a very strict structure and are in tandem with the environmental standards (ISO 14000). This structure is:

1. Quality management system, which includes the old elements of 4.1, 4.2, and 4.16 in addition to some other new items

2. Management responsibility, which includes the old elements of 4.1, 4.2, 4.5, and 4.16 in addition to some other new items

3. Resource management, which includes the old elements of 4.1, 4.9, and 4.18 in addition to some other new items

4. Product realization, which includes the old elements of 4.2, 4.3, 4.4, 4.6, 4.7, 4.8, 4.9, 4.10, 4.11, 4.12, 4.15, and 4.19 in addition to some other new items

5. Measurement, analysis and improvement, which includes the old elements 4.10, 4.13, 4.14, 4.17, and 4.20 in addition to some other new items

The reader should notice that there are overlaps from the old elements to the new categories. That is because the new categories are more finely defined and explained better than the 1994 revision standards. This change is expected to facilitate a better understanding and easier implementation of the 2000 version. For a more detailed comparison of the standards see appendix E.

THE REVISION PROCESS

The revision process is the responsibility of ISO's Technical Committee TC 176, and is conducted on the basis of consensus among quality and industry experts, nominated by ISO member bodies, and representing all interested parties. For the year 2000 revision, TC 176 adopted a project management approach in order to cope with the complexity of the task. Initial project specifications and goals were established after extensive user surveys had been carried out to determine needs and expectations for the revisions. Furthermore, an essential part of the revision was the verification and user validation process, to ensure that the standards met the user needs. The revision process schedule was as follows:

- Fourth quarter 1997—First working draft (WD1) for use by TC 176 WG18 (complete)

- First quarter 1998—Second working draft (WD2) for use by TC 176 WIG 18 (complete)

- Second quarter 1998—Third working draft (WD3) for use by TC 176 WG18 (complete)

- Third quarter 1998—Committee draft (CD1) issued for comment by member countries (complete)

- First quarter 1999—Committee draft (CD2) issued for vote by TC 176 member countries (complete)

- Fourth quarter 1999—Draft international standard (DIS) for vote by member countries (complete)

- Third quarter 2000—Final draft international standard (FDIS) for vote by member countries (complete)

- Fourth quarter 2000—Publication of international standard (ISO): December 2000

THE CORE ESSENTIALS
OF THE STANDARD

All standards, without exception, are minimum performance standards. ISO 9001, TS 16949, AS9100, and all the other derivatives of these standards are not any different. The focus of the standards is to make sure that customer requirements are followed and also to make a profit for the organization. In that sense then, ISO, ISO/TS 16949, AS9100, and all other standards provide the definition—the direction—of these requirements for the system. The implementation methods are up to the organization itself. However, the specificity is generally identified through three items. They are:

1. *QMS (the general requirements).* In this fundamental requirement the *organization* is called on to establish, document, implement, and maintain a quality management system. Furthermore and perhaps most importantly is that the system is to continually improve its effectiveness. The effectiveness must be evaluated based on several mandatory items (in the standard they are identified by the word "shall"), such as:

   a. Identify the processes needed for the QMS and their application throughout the organization. (Processes needed for the quality management system referred to here should include processes for management activities, provision of resources, product realization, and measurement. Where an organization chooses to outsource any process that affects product conformity with requirements, the organization shall ensure control over such processes. Control of such outsourced processes shall be identified within the quality management system.)

   b. Determine the sequence and interaction of these processes.

   c. Determine criteria and methods needed to ensure that both the operation and control of these processes are effective.

   d. Ensure the availability of resources and information necessary to support the operation and monitoring of these processes.

   e. Monitor, measure, and analyze these processes.

   f. Implement actions necessary to achieve planned results and continual improvement of these processes.

2. *Documentation requirements.* In order for the management system to exist, a quality management system of documentation must also exist. (The extent of the quality management system documentation, which can be in any form or type of medium, can differ from one organization to another due to: a) size of the organization and type of activities, b) the complexity of the processes and their interactions, and c) the competence of personnel.) This system must include:

   a. Documented statements of a quality policy and quality objectives.

   b. A quality manual.

    c. Documented procedures required in this international standard (where the term "documented procedure" appears within this international standard, this means that the procedure is established, documented, implemented, and maintained).

    d. Documents needed by the organization to ensure the effective planning, operation, and control of its processes.

    e. Quality records required by this international standard.

3. *Audit.* The third and final requirement is the audit. With an audit the organization can identify the gaps in the quality system and what the organization is doing or to what extent the organization is following its own system. The audit, if done correctly, can prove an invaluable tool in both the effectiveness and the improvement areas of any organization.

With this new standard there is a single quality management system requirements standard, ISO 9001:2000, applicable to all organizations, products, and services, that has replaced the three quality assurance standards ISO 9001:1994, ISO 9002:1994, and ISO 9003:1994. This may be used for the certification of quality management systems and may also be the basis for contractual agreements. ISO 9004:2000 is the quality management system guidance standard. ISO 9004 is designed to go beyond quality management requirements to a holistic approach to quality management in pursuit of operational improvement and benefits to all interested parties.

Major changes in the ISO 9000:2000 standards are the increased focus on top management commitment and customer focus/satisfaction (through appropriate and applicable feedback), the emphasis on processes within the organization, emphasis on effectiveness, and the introduction of continual improvement concepts.

Key features include the continuity and compatibility between the old and new versions of the standards. This means that in ISO 9001:2000, the QMS will cover those activities of an organization that provide assurance to customers that their needs are being addressed. This is accomplished by focusing both ISO 9001 and ISO 9004 on eight quality management principles that reflect best management practices. These eight principles are:

1. *Customer-focused organization.* Organizations depend on their customers and therefore should understand current and future customer needs, meet customer requirements, and strive to exceed customer expectations.

2. *Leadership.* Leaders establish unity of purpose and direction for the organization. They should create and maintain the internal environment in which people can become fully involved in achieving the organization's objectives.

3. *Involvement of people.* People at all levels are the essence of an organization and their full involvement enables their abilities to be used for the organization's benefit. Key issues here are concerns about building team performance. Some considerations are: 1) establish urgency, demanding performance standards and directions that are doable, 2) select members who have the skill(s) or the potential for the necessary skill(s) to do the task (do not select individuals strictly on personality), 3) pay attention to verbal and body language during the first meeting and the actions of the individuals involved, 4) set and follow the rules of behavior and make sure everyone is aware of them, 5) set and seize upon a few immediate performance tasks and goals, 6) challenge the group regularly with fresh facts and information that is relevant to the task, 7) spend as much time together as possible—it cultivates comradeship, and 8) exploit the power of positive feedback.

4. *Process approach.* A desired result is achieved more efficiently when related resources and activities are managed as a process.

5. *System approach to management.* Identifying, understanding, and managing a system of interrelated processes for a given objective improves the organization's effectiveness and efficiency.

6. *Continual improvement.* Continual improvement should be a permanent objective of the organization.

7. *Factual approach to decision making.* Effective decisions are based on the analysis of data and information.

8. *Mutually beneficial supplier relationships.* An organization and its suppliers are interdependent, and a mutually beneficial relationship enhances the ability of both to create value.

MAJOR CHANGES

The new standard provides for some major changes in both structure and content. They are:

1. *Structure.* The new ISO quality management standards include a significant change to the structure of ISO 9001 and ISO 9004. While both retain the essence of the original requirements, the changes are in the repositioning of the certified 20 elements of the ISO 9001:1994 into five main sections, and the level of detail in the ISO 9004: 2000 has increased dramatically, especially where customer satisfaction and management commitment are concerned. The five sections that ISO 9001:2000 identifies are:

   a. Quality management system

   b. Management responsibility

   c. Resource management

   d. Product realization

   e. Measurement, analysis and improvement

2. *Process model.* A process model, which is based on the plan, do, check (study), act [PDC(S)A] philosophy, is used to ensure that the standard follows a more logical sequence.

3. *Top management.* More emphasis is placed on the role of top management, which includes its commitment to the development and improvement of a quality management system with a customer focus, consideration of legal and regulatory require-ments, and establishment of measurable objectives at relevant functions and levels.

4. *Continual improvement.* The enhancement in ISO 9001:2000 of the "continual improvement" concept is intended to help an organization respond to the changing needs of its customers, while stimulating the efficiency of the organization and improving its competitive position. The consistency of the two standards will also support a smooth transition for organizations wishing to go beyond ISO 9001 to ISO 9004. The focus of this "continual improvement" is on effectiveness of the QMS. Typical issues with continual improvement are:

   a. Ways to conduct improvement:

      • Breakthrough projects

         – Lead to revision and improvement of existing processes

         – Implementation of new processes

       – Usually carried out by cross-functional teams outside of routine operations

       – Involve significant redesign of existing processes

b. Breakthrough projects should include at least the following:

- Definition of the objectives and the outline of the improvement project

- An analysis of current processes as they exist before any changes

- Identifying opportunities to improve the processes

- Plan the improvement activities

- Implement the improvement plan

- Verify and validate the results of the plan and any process improvements

- Evaluate the improvements realized, including any lessons learned

c. Ways to conduct continual improvement

- Small-step ongoing improvement activities

       – Conduct within existing processes

       – Sources of ideas often come from people in the organization participating in groups

       – People are provided the authority, technical support, and necessary resources

d. All continual improvement methods should involve at least the following:

- A reason for improvement

- An evaluation of the current situation or process

- A root-cause analysis of the identified problem

- The identification of possible solutions

- An evaluation of the effects of the selected solution

- Implementing and standardizing the solution

- Evaluating the effectiveness and efficiency of the process after the improvement action is complete

Top management should consider the following activities to promote involvement and awareness of continual improvement:

- Formation of small groups with leaders elected by the group members

- Empowering people to control and improve their workplaces

- Developing people's knowledge, experience, and skills

e. Manufacturing process improvement

- Manufacturing process improvement shall focus continually on control and reduction of variation in product characteristics and process parameters (8.5.1.2)

  – Controlled characteristics are identified in the control plan.

  – Continuous improvement begins once manufacturing processes are stable and meet customer requirements.

5. *Permissible exclusions.* The concept of "permissible exclusions" to the ISO 9001:2000 requirements is introduced as a way to cope with the wide spectrum of organizations and activities that will be using the new standard.

6. *Customer satisfaction.* Another new item that is introduced into ISO 9001:2000 is the requirement for the organization to monitor information on customer satisfaction and/or dissatisfaction as a measure of system performance.

7. *Resources.* Attention has been placed on top management to provide and make available the necessary resources. Requirements now include evaluation of the effectiveness of training, provision of relevant information, internal and external communication, facility needs, and human and physical factors of the work environment.

8. *Communication.* Top management is to communicate awareness of the quality policy and objectives, and the importance of meeting customer requirements to all organization staff. The communication should extend to the customer to obtain customer

requirements and expectations, and determine customer satisfaction levels.

9. *Terminology.* The most important changes concern the use of the term "organization" instead of "supplier," still used in the ISO 9000:1994 standards, and the use of the term "supplier" instead of "subcontractor." These changes respond to the need to be more consistent and friendly with the normal use and meaning of the words. Furthermore, the new standard includes the quality vocabulary (old ISO 8402) as part of ISO 9001. This change introduces the quality concepts and addresses the vocabulary issues based on a formal approach to the definition of terms.

10. *Documentation.* The number of requirements for documented procedures is reduced in ISO 9001:2000, and the emphasis is placed on the organization demonstrating effective operation. With the new standard there is a minimum of six procedures required. They are:

    a. Control of documents

    b. Control of quality records

    c. Internal quality system audits

    d. Control of nonconforming product

    e. Corrective action

    f. Preventive action

11. Some of the organization's processes can also be documented in the form of procedures. It must be emphasized that ISO 9001:2000 does not specify requirements on the layout or structure of an organization's QMS documentation. In other words, it imposes no rules on the presentation of a quality manual. This flexibility allows organizations to document their QMS in a manner that reflects their own ways of doing business.

12. *Compatibility with ISO 14001.* Significant improvements in compatibility of structure, content language, and terminology have been incorporated into the standard. The intent and goal of this effort was to ensure that common elements of the two series of standards could be readily implemented in a shared manner in whole or in part by organizations without unnecessary duplications or the imposition of conflicting requirements.

1

Common Questions About the Basic ISO 9000 Series

Q. What is ISO?

A. Contrary to popular understanding, *ISO* is not an acronym. It is a product of the International Organization for Standardization based in Geneva, Switzerland, but if it was the acronym for that organization, it would be the French acronym OIN (Organisation Internationale de Normalisation). Rather, *ISO* is a Greek word meaning equal, harmonize. The intent of the International Organization for Standardization is indeed to harmonize standards all over the world with minimum effort and maximum efficiency. Consequently, there are many standards that this organization produces covering products, processes, services, and business systems and quality is one of these standards. Specifically the ISO 9000:2000 series is a bundle of quality standards that is globally recognized as a quality management system (QMS) framework with a commonsense, documented system focusing on consistency, reliability, and improving the way the business operates. It is a standard that focuses on organizational processes, the customer, and improvement. Furthermore, it provides guidance, and what is required to achieve an internationally recognized standard. As important and thorough as the standard is, *it does not tell an organization how to operate.*

ISO 9000:2000 is a series of three standards (ISO 9000, ISO 9001, and ISO 9004), but, generally speaking, when most people make reference to this they mean ISO 9001, a standard designed to specify requirements for a QMS where an organization:

1. Aims to enhance customer satisfaction through the effective application of the system, including processes for continuous business improvement.

2. Needs to demonstrate its ability to provide products and services that constantly meet customer and applicable regulatory requirements. More than 350,000 companies worldwide use one of the certifiable standards in the ISO 9000 series to help them run their organization. The benefits they find include:

   - Improved consistency of service/product performance and therefore higher customer satisfaction levels

   - Improved customer perception of the organization's image, culture, and performance

   - Improved productivity and efficiency, which lead to cost reductions

   - Improved communications, morale, and job satisfaction—staff members understand what is expected of them and each other

   - Competitive advantage and increased marketing and sales opportunities

Q. When one talks about ISO 9001, invariably the discussion will turn to QMS. What is a QMS?

A. It's a commonsense, documented business management system that can be applied to all business sectors and all sizes of companies. If you think of a business as a set of processes, it identifies the key process areas that need to be addressed to ensure that quality is managed effectively. The *ISO 9001:2000 Quality management systems—Requirements,* is based around the management of individual processes which, when put together as a whole, help you to *effectively* manage your entire business. To do that the PDC(S)A model is used because it helps manage the individual processes. Then the continual improvement model shows the different areas where process management can be applied, including the organization's interaction with customers, and how, when these are working together, continual improvement can be achieved.

To appreciate the QMS, the ISO has identified eight quality management principles. They are:

1. *Customer focus*. If you look at the continual improvement model in the standard itself, it is fairly simple. On the left-hand side of the model as inputs to the QMS we have customer requirements and on the right-hand side we have customer satisfaction. It's all about meeting our customer's needs with the aim of enhancing their satisfaction level with our products and services.

2. *Leadership*. We need to demonstrate and practice sound leadership skills within our organization, that is to say "lead by example."

3. *Involvement of people*. People are our most valuable resource, and it is therefore of vital importance that they are party to any decisions and activities affecting the QMS.

4. *The process approach*. The application and management of a system of processes and their interaction.

5. *A system approach to management*. Being aware of what systems are in place and improving our systems is a sure way of enhancing our products and services and, ultimately, the satisfaction levels of both internal and external customers.

6. *Continual improvement*. By knowing what we do and how well we do it, we can identify ways to improve both our systems and our processes.

7. *Factual approach to decision making*. By analysis of data, and conducting internal audits and management reviews we can improve business performance and the quality of our products and services.

8. *Mutually beneficial supplier relationships*. By communicating and working with our suppliers we can ensure that, in the process of them satisfying our needs, they can also gain benefits in terms of decreased cost and improved performance. A typical well-thought-out and implemented quality system will:

   a. Increase competitiveness

   b. Improve staff morale

   c. Reduce waste

   d. Improve awareness of improvement opportunities

Q. One of the key structural changes in the new ISO 9001:2000 standard is section 4.0: Quality management system. What is that all about?

A. Clause 4.0 sets the scene for the rest of the ISO 9001:2000 standard. It emphasizes the need to document, implement, and maintain a QMS and continually improve its effectiveness. Notice that Section 4.0 has a strong relationship with the other four clauses. Section 4.0 covers documentation requirements, including the need to create a quality manual and documented procedures. Section 4.0 also requires documented statements of quality policy and objectives.

As important as these items are, they are not enough to fulfill the QMS requirements. It is also a requirement to control documents we create and to control records that demonstrate we have followed our system. At this juncture, one may think that ISO is nothing but a lot of documentation. It does not have to be that way. In fact, many companies are getting very smart in how they present their quality system and manual. A quality system could be a creative one-page or very large document. Organizations need to look at what is best for their business. They should avoid creating over-burdensome documentation, as this is not the intent of the standard. Many companies are using process mapping software and business mapping to clearly identify what documentation is critical in the application of their QMS. Many others are placing their quality system on intranets or referencing material on the Internet.

Q. What is document and data control?

A. Quality manual, procedures, instructions, and other information that identifies, supports, or substantiates the quality system (for example, blueprints, drawings, and so on). Generally, if the documents are important and significant in the process, only selected individuals have access to them, and they are given only to those who really need them. When that happens, those documents are said to be "controlled documents" and a record is kept as to "what" has been issued to "whom." Obviously, when things change, the information is updated and the relevant people are informed as part of the formal system. Upon the completion of the change, obsolete documents are archived or destroyed.

Q. What about control of quality records?

A. If we need to retain information that demonstrates that activities carried out within the quality system were to our satisfaction, then we are interested in control of records. Typical quality activities that need to be verified are: training records, inspection records, test procedures, calibration records, legal and regulatory compliance, and many more.

Q. ISO 9001:2000 places an enormous emphasis on management. What is it about section 5.0: Management responsibility that is unique about the ISO 9001:2000 standard?

A. In the context of ISO 9001, senior management includes the people responsible for setting quality policy for a given location or activity. They could be the CEO, a site manager, or a corporate quality director. Their primary responsibility should be in communicating the need to continually improve, and meet customer, regulatory, and statutory requirements, as well as organizational structure. This means that the organizational structure must support and ensure efficiency, effectiveness, and profitability throughout the organization. Furthermore, management must make sure that all staff members are aware of the lines of responsibility and understand what impact their decisions have on the organization.

So, for all intents and purposes this management clause involves formalizing the QMS and giving it legitimacy. This legitimacy is supported by the management representative who is responsible for implementing the quality system and reporting back to management on performance, through management review meetings. There is also a requirement for a statement of commitment to quality from senior management, through the quality policy.

Q. Another "new" item in ISO 9001:2000 is section 6.0: Resource management. What is this all about?

A. All functions in any organization need to be managed on a day-to-day basis. This element focuses on management of quality and effectiveness that relies on using the appropriate resources for each task. Appropriate and applicable resources include the people conducting activities, the tools they have, and supporting services including preventive maintence. This implies that management must recognize the importance of and provide a working environment that is ergonomically correct as well as appropriate and applicable training for the employees. This is very important because this section of the standard provides the link of "continual improvement" not only for the quality system but also for the organization.

Q. How important is training?

A. Very important. Without appropriate and applicable training there is no guarantee that employees know and/or do their task(s) as the task(s) were designed and whether they are effective. One way to measure training effectiveness is to review "the training itself" before and after the training. Upon completion of the training, it is easy to demonstrate whether a person is more effective as a result. Competence may be gained through: a) formal education, b) on-the-job training, c) years of experience, or d) a prescribed combination of all three.

It is imperative here to separate what is being done from the tools that are being used. In element 6.0 only the tools are addressed. What they do is addressed in element 7.0. Of course, as already mentioned, this includes the equipment and environment in which they work.

Q. In the ISO 9000:2000 version of the standard, the section 7.0: Product realization is mentioned. What is that all about?

A. Product realization is indeed mentioned in the 2000 version of the standard and, in fact, it has produced some misconceptions and mis-interpretations about the quality system and its specific meaning. To understand it, you must first understand what the customer requires. Then, and only then, you must proceed to think about the processes you need in place to ensure these requirements are met and their effectiveness is measured. This means that the new ISO standard does not give the organization the option of choosing, as was the case with the ISO 1994 version. (If you recall, in the 1994 version the organization had to decide whether to include design, which not all companies do, so it was not always included as part of a quality system. If it is, records should be kept, so a corporate knowledge database is created and may be used in future programs or projects.) Design, however, is not the only thing that you should worry about. You must think about the entire production process. That means planning, scheduling resources, and purchasing, which are, of course, all part of this process. Once these have been accounted for then you have to ensure that service provision, work instructions (people know what they are doing), traceability, preservation, monitoring, and measurement devices are all in place.

Q. Perhaps one of the most difficult aspects of section 7.0 is to define what the customer requires. How do we know what a customer requires?

A. You need to establish customer requirements from the outset. And you also need to understand their unstated requirements, such as what the product or service is going to be used for. At the same time you must also meet statutory and regulatory requirements. But that is not all. You (the organization) must seek, gather, and evaluate "customer feedback." It is part of the QMS, both negative and positive. Based on this evaluation the organization may modify the requirements or continue the improvement.

Q. Section 8.0: Measurement, analysis and improvement sounds like the old version of the standard. What is its significance?

A. Whereas in section 7.0 the issue of evaluation is raised, in this element the issue of measurement, analysis, and improvement is discussed. The assumption of the standard is that recording actual performance and analyzing it helps to identify areas for improvement. In other words, this element is for all intents and purposes the key to a successful business. It involves those measurements being made that can help us to improve our business and demonstrate conformity of product. Usually it involves the use of statistical techniques if appropriate and applicable.

Q. If measurement is important, what does the organization have to measure and analyze?

A. There are many areas where the organization may want to measure and analyze data. For example: warranty costs, customers' complaints, levels of customer satisfaction, scrap rates, rework, internal audits, and others. Obviously, there are many possibilities here, including monitoring and measuring of the processes and product. If the appropriate and applicable measurement occurs, then your organization needs to ensure that any resulting product is prevented from unintended use. A documented procedure is needed to ensure that action is taken to eliminate the defective, nonconforming product, and that the resulting product is dealt with in an appropriate manner.

What is important here is that the standards provide minimum requirements that the organization must measure: customer satisfaction, conformity to product requirements, characteristics, and trends of processes and products as well as suppliers. The result of this measurement will help the organization in at least the following areas: a) improvement, b) corrective and preventive actions, c) quality policy, d) setting objectives, e) audit results, f) analysis of data, and g) management review. Of this list, the most common item to provoke a spirited discussion is "corrective and preventive action." One must remember that the aim of the standard is the prevention of nonconformity. This can be done in two ways: a) through corrective action or b) through preventive actions. Corrective actions are put into place once something has been identified as having gone wrong. It is an appraisal approach. Preventive actions, on the other hand, are more proactive and are put in place once something has been identified as possibly going wrong. It is a planning approach. Of course, it is necessary to keep records of any corrective or preventive actions taken.

Q. What are the most common tools in pursuing quality improvement with the ISO 9000 series of standards?

A. The most common tools in the improvement process are:

- Brainstorming (generate ideas about a process and or a problem)
- Cause-and-effect diagram (relate the cause and effect of the problem and categorize the problem in predefined categories— people, machine, material, measurement, method, and environment)
- Process map (identify the "as is" process)
- Histogram (identify the distribution of the process)
- Pareto chart (identify the priority of concerns)
- Critical-to-quality tree (things that the customer is considering as value)
- Process summary worksheet (evaluating the process)
- Scatter diagram (identify relationships)
- Affinity diagram (identify the categories of the problems)
- Run chart (identify trends)
- Control chart (identify the behavior of the process)

Q. What is a process?

A. A process is an activity, supported by resources and management, for enabling the transformation of inputs into outputs. The outputs from one process often form the input to the next. A process may be defined with internal boundaries and/or external boundaries.

ISO 9001:2000 suggests that the application and management of a system of processes is an effective way to ensure good quality management. To adopt this *process approach,* ISO 9001 includes a PDCA methodology that can be applied to all processes and can briefly be described as follows:

- *Plan.* Establish the objectives and processes necessary to deliver results in accordance with customer requirements and the organization policies.

- *Do.* Implement the processes.

- *Check.* Monitor and measure processes and products against policies, objectives, and requirements for the product and report the results.

- *Act.* Take actions to continually improve process performance. The visual representation of the continual improvement model is shown in page vi of the actual standard document.

Q. So, is this process unique to ISO 9001:2000?

A. No, it is not. To the contrary, many businesses do these things without realizing, as they are common sense. Where ISO 9001:2000 can help is by providing a framework to build on these principles. At the end of the day, ISO 9001:2000 is an excellent tool for improving your business performance.

Q. How do we implement ISO 9001:2000?

A. There are a number of key steps to consider in implementation. The following are typical:

1. Familiarity with the standard is imperative.

2. Assemble and form a team, including senior management, and agree on a strategy.

3. Develop a quality manual reflecting your own organizational needs rather than just repeating the standard in the language of the organization.

4. Develop documentation, typically procedures supporting the quality manual. The emphasis here is on "what is" rather than "what will" or "what should" be.

5. Implement the QMS. This requires communication and training throughout the organization.

In the case of pursuing registration (registration is optional—the standard does not require registration) the following steps are necessary:

6. Select a registrar.

7. Gain registration through a third party.

Typically, the quest for registration is dependent upon the customer or the desire of the organization to demonstrate, by use of an external party, the compliance of their quality management system to the standard.

Q. What does registration to ISO 9001:2000 mean?

A. A (any) registration involves a third party. That means an independent registrar will have to evaluate your QMS and assess it for conformity to the ISO 9001:2000 standard. This involves visiting the organization, and assessing the relevant systems and processes. All registrations by all registrars involve periodic reassessments, usually one or two per year. Ultimately, registration means that an organization has and adheres to a quality system and that system is independently verified for its customers and other stakeholders. In other words, the organization is a quality company based on the ISO 9001:2000 scheme. To gain registration, an organization must have an audit that verifies the entire system for effectiveness. This is done as an initial exposure to the registration process and every three or so years thereafter. On the other hand, a surveillance audit (a limited audit) is required every six to twelve months to make sure the organization follows the standard and to verify the effectiveness to the organization on a continual basis.

ISO 9001:2000 indicates that a quality system is in place that is capable of meeting customer requirements. A common misconception is that it indicates that every product or service will be defect-free—this is more the realm of product certification, and has nothing to do with a system orientation. It is precisely why ISO/TS 16949 and AS9100 came to be, as they are not only system- but product-oriented as well.

Q. Why does an organization need registration?

A. Registration serves as proof or rather demonstration to customers that the organization has a commitment to quality, and through regular and independent assessments ensures that the organization continually uses, monitors, and improves their processes. Registration also can improve business performance, reduce uncertainty, and increase market opportunities.

Q. Who adopts the ISO 9001:2000 standard?

A. The ISO 9001 quality standard is globally renowned with certificates awarded in 161 countries. It is a leading QMS with more than a half million certificates awarded. In fact, based on 2000 information, the following statistics are available (ISO survey 1999). This is the most recent *complete* information available as of this writing:

	1999	2000
Manufacturing	173,048	193,302
Service	98,523	120,051
Primary	2,469	3,773

ISO 9001 is so well received worldwide that the statistics from the McGraw survey are astonishing. They report the following:

	January 1993	December 2001
Issued certificates	27,816	510,616
North America		
United States	893	37,026
Mexico	16	2,233
Canada	292	11,635

By contrast, the transition to ISO 9001:2000 as of November 12, 2003, and reported on www.qualitydigest.com, shows that the majority of the companies are not anywhere near fulfilling the requirements. The statistics are shown in Table 1.1.

(This is the reason why we have chosen to include transition quality manuals on the CD-ROM as well as the 2000-format appendixes I–XII.)

Table 1.1   Companies that have transitioned to ISO 9001:2000.

Region	Percentage of ISO 9001:2000 Registrations	Total ISO 9001 Registrations	ISO 9001:2000 Registrations
United States	33.7%	42,351	14,265
Canada	34.8%	13,007	4,520
Mexico	31.7%	2,428	752
North America	33.8%	57,786	19,537

Q. Is there a relationship between implementation and benefits of the ISO 9001:2000 experience?

A. Experiences with registration can vary greatly. Some companies have achieved substantial gains, while others have suffered large losses. The way the requirements are implemented critically affects these results. For example, the McGraw survey identified the following implementation strategies which result in a more positive return on investment:

1. *Customization.* Customization is the extent to which the standard is tailored to specific company circumstances. Among its components are:

    a. Customized to company needs

    b. Integrated with practices already in place

    c. Based on an analysis of internal processes and performance

    d. A springboard to introduce new practices

    e. Coordinated and led by external consultants

    f. Based upon learning from other companies already registered

    g. Coordinated with customers

    h. Coordinated with suppliers

2. *Routinization.* Routinization is the extent to which ISO 9001:2000 is used in daily practice. Among its components are:

    a. Documents are used in daily practice.

    b. Documents are regularly updated.

    c. It has become part of a regular routine.

    d. It has resulted in changing daily practice.

    e. Managers see value in internal audits.

    f. ISO 9001 has led to the discovery of improvement opportunities.

    g. Changes have been made since registration.

    h. The system is not regularly ignored.

    i. The system is not an unnecessary burden.

     j. The system is applied to operations such as marketing, and so on.

     k. Preparations for the surveillance audit are not made at the last minute.

3. *Learning.* Learning is the extent to which the standard is used to make improvements. Among its components are:

     a. Audit findings are incorporated into training.

     b. ISO 9001 has helped prevent problems.

     c. Top management uses the data to find solutions to the company's business problems.

     d. Top management uses the data to find solutions to the company's technical problems.

4. *Going beyond.* Going beyond is the extent to which implementation moves beyond the minimum requirements. Among its components are:

     a. ISO 9001 is understood as an opportunity to innovate.

     b. ISO 9001 is a catalyst for rethinking the way you do business.

  c. ISO 9001 is a starting point for introducing other more advanced practices.

    Furthermore, the survey found that the benefits are commensurate with the size, effort, and commitment of the organization as a whole toward improvement and customer satisfaction. Some of the benefits found are:

- Companies with high savings (> $125,000) have significantly higher internal registration costs (mean and sigma are about 3.5 times higher) than companies with low savings and companies with no savings.

- Companies with high savings (> $125,000) have significantly higher external registration costs (mean and sigma are about 2.25 and 1.5 times higher respectively) than companies with low savings.

- Companies with high savings (> $125,000) have a significantly higher savings-to-costs ratio (mean = 4.6, sigma = 7) compared to companies with low savings (mean = .8, sigma = 1).

Q. What kind of support strategies do most organizations use for a successful ISO 9001 program?

A. Generally speaking, companies use three support strategies in the implementation process:

1. Consultant conventional involvement

2. Training provider involvement

3. Internal training and self-development

Of the three strategies, the least successful is consultant conventional involvement; the most successful is consultant–training provider involvement. This is substantiated by the results of the McGraw survey, which found that consultant–training provider involvement focused on the development of internal implementation leaders whose involvement continues throughout the process, significantly increases the likelihood for:

• High levels of total satisfaction

• High return on investment

• Best savings-to-costs ratios

• The greater the reliance on training that enables internal employees to lead the process and a consultant–training provider that remains highly involved in the process, the greater the level of total satisfaction, the higher the return on investment, and the better the savings-to-costs ratio.

Q. What are the drivers for ISO 9001:2000 registration?

A. A number of common drivers have been identified for ISO 9001:2000 registration. In the McGraw survey, three of the most important are:

1. Customer and regulatory demand:

   a. Thirty-eight percent of respondents identified customer demands as the key driver, the foremost driver for ISO 9001 registration by far.

   b. Five percent identified government requirements.

2. Quality benefits:

   a. 26.9 percent identified perceived quality benefits (for example, reduced rework).

   b. Increased quality/reduced cost of quality.

   c. Cost savings.

   d. Customer focus.

   e. Employee-related benefits.

   f. Operational benefits (process-related benefits).

3. Market advantage:

   a. 15.9 percent felt ISO 9001 provided a competitive advantage and could increase sales and market share.

Q. What are the benefits of pursuing ISO 9001:2000 or its derivatives?

A. There are many benefits both internal and external to the organization. Some of the most important generic benefits are:

• Greater emphasis on quality objectives

• Improved staff communication and satisfaction

• Improved new products introduction process

• Unified customer quality system requirements

Some facts and figures on the benefits of ISO 9001 from the ISO 9000 Survey (McGraw-Hill 1999):

• Average ongoing savings: $124,128.

• 64 percent of respondents saw a reduction in the defect rate.

• 73 percent attributed some improvement in customer satisfaction to ISO 9000.

• 67 percent said ISO 9000 was a catalyst for rethinking the way the business was run.

• 72 percent said ISO 9000 was seen as an opportunity to innovate.

Specific benefits have also been reported by individual registrars. For example, BSI (www.bsiamericas.com) has reported the following:

1. Increased quality/reduced cost of quality

   • British Gas: Reductions in unnecessary rework of $750,000.

   • Hibbert Group: Cost of quality reduced by 67 percent.

   • J W Suckling Transport: Delivery failure rates down by 79 percent to 83 percent.

- Glasgow City Council Land Services: Clients' defects dropped by 87 percent.

- Reduced inspection of tankers has saved substantial sums.

2. Significant improvements in customer focus, with increases in satisfaction, and a reduction in complaints:

   - Average response time to clients reduced by 16 percent.

   - Customer complaints decreased by 34 percent from 1993 to 1999.

   - Increase in the level of customer satisfaction.

3. On-time delivery to top-10 clients at almost 100 percent:

   - Implementation has had an important effect of increasing/ maintaining sales, and improving market share.

   - Documentation has led to ease of training new staff, and employee training is more structured.

   - A formalized training review system has helped to identify requirements, resulting in flexibility, reduced risk, and improved levels of achievement.

   - Staff members increasingly adhere to professional standards.

4. Operational benefits:

   - 36 percent of respondents said improved documentation was the most significant benefit.

   - 66 percent said they had achieved shorter lifecycles in new product introductions.

   - Reduction in process nonconformities.

   - Reduction in process cycle.

   - Audits help in ensuring continual improvement.

5. ISO 9001 audits cause consistency in processes:

   - ISO 9001 resulted in an electronic process-based system.

   - Reduced all procedures to one page in length.

6. Reduced its operational downtime through ISO 9001:

- Streamlined and improved the rigor of its processes.

- Improved operational procedures and coordination between businesses.

- Means to identify best practice across the business.

- Documentation system is a handbook for best practice.

- Reexamination of processes and resulting improvements.

Q. Why is the audit necessary?

A. An audit is the proof of conforming to the standard and the organization's documentation. A good audit, therefore, should:

- Aid your success.

- Provide assessments to bring added value.

- Provide honest and thorough evaluation.

- Encourage nonadversarial roles and processes.

- Focus on conformance versus effectiveness.

- Help you move toward your goal.

Q. What is the difference between a traditional audit and a process audit?

A. There is a major difference between the two approaches. A traditional audit focused on verification of activities. The thrust of the questioning process was: " Do you . . . ?" and followed with "Could you show me?" The new approach of auditing is focused on conformance to "a" system, and the effectiveness of that system. The thrust of the questioning process is: "How do you . . . ?" followed by "Why do you . . . ?"

Q. What is a "surveillance audit" and how does it differ from the "process audit?"

A. An audit is a formal activity that examines and verifies something by reference to witnesses and standards. On the other hand, a surveillance audit is a continuing evaluation of the status found in the audit, and that is why it is conducted between major audits for registration. Also, a surveillance audit may follow the traditional or process methodology. Finally, what makes it a surveillance audit is the scope and definition of the audit.

Q. What is the process for selecting a registrar?

A. The registrar is the third party who assesses the effectiveness of your QMS, and issues a certificate if you meet the requirements of the standard. Primary considerations in the selection process are: industry experience, geographic coverage, price, whether the registrar is accredited (by a recognized national accreditation body, and in the case of a sector-specific registrar, whether the registrar is accredited by the sector-specific party process), and service level. The typical steps are:

1. Initial inquiry

2. Quotation provided

3. Application completed

4. Client manager appointed

5. Preassessment (optional)

6. Initial assessment

7. Registration confirmed

8. Continual assessment

Q. Can an organization change a registrar even after registration? If so, what is the process?

A. Yes, any organization can change a registrar at any time. However, changing registrars may be an expensive activity, as the process requirements for registration may be slightly different for each registrar. A typical process for changing is the following:

1. Send a completed QMS company profile form to the prospective registrar so that they may have all the information that is needed to give you a quotation.

2. Once the information is received by the registrar, they will send you a quotation and application form.

3. It is your responsibility to return your completed application form along with a copy of:

   • Your current registration details

   • Your last assessment report

   • The corrective-action plan generated from the last assessment report (if applicable)

Upon receiving the detailed information, the registrar will review the documents, issue you a new certificate, and commence the continuing assessment program, picking up where your previous registrar left off. More often than not, most registrars do not charge a fee for transferring certification. There is no application fee and you will only be charged as your assessment visits are conducted, plus an annual management fee. (Of course, you should contact the individual registrar for specific instructions and requirements.)

REFERENCES

ISO. 1999. *ISO 9000 Survey: An Analytical Tool to Assess the Costs, Benefits, and Savings of ISO 9000 Registration.* New York: McGraw-Hill.

www.qualitydigest.com. 2003. ISO 9000 registered company database.

2

ISO 9001: 2000—The Basic Certifiable Standard

I n order to reflect modern management approaches and to improve organizational practices, it was useful and necessary to introduce structural changes to the ISO 9001 standard while maintaining the essential requirements of the original ISO intent. In summary form, the following are the structural changes:

1. *Quality management system.* The organization must have a quality management system that is documented, implemented, maintained, and continuously improved.

2. *Management responsibility.* Top management has an ongoing commitment to the QMS. They are responsible for identifying all of the relevant business requirements, communicating organizational policy, and providing resources to ensure implementation, maintenance, and continuous improvement of the QMS.

3. *Resource management.* The day-to-day management of quality and effectiveness relies on using the appropriate resources for each task. These include competent staff with relevant (and demonstrable) training, the correct tools, and supporting services.

4. *Product realization.* This is the design (where applicable) and production of the products and services you provide. In addition to production planning and scheduling resources, product realization includes determining and measurably meeting customer requirements.

5. *Measurement, analysis, and improvement.* This is a key requirement for a successful business. It involves those measurements being made to help improve your organization and demonstrate product conformity. Statistical techniques should be used where appropriate.

6. *The terms* "subcontractor," "supplier," and "purchaser" have been replaced by supplier, organization, and customer, respectively.

These core structural items are supported by details within each category. The details are indeed the actual "standard statements" that make up ISO 9001:2000, and they may be purchased through the American Society for Quality (ASQ) or the ISO organization directly. While the majority of the elements are pretty much self-explanatory, there are some specific elements (clauses) that need further explanation. A review of these clauses follows, with a short commentary on these selected items.

0 INTRODUCTION

Clarification on clause 0.1:

The QMS itself constitutes evidence of the strategic decision having been taken by the organization's management, and there is no need for any particular, separate records of this.

Clarification on clause 0.3:

ISO 9004:2000 may be used to better understand the requirements of the standards, but whatever guidance or explanation provided therein is not mandatory and must not be considered as part of the audit criteria.

Clarification on clause 0.4:

During the audit of an integrated management system for the purpose of ISO 9001:2000 certification, only the components specific to the QMS, and those shared components used by the QMS, may be audited.

1 SCOPE

Clarification on clause 1.1:

a. See section 7.2.1 (c) for the interpretation of applicable statutory requirements.

Clarification on clause 1.2:

a. Whenever the organization designs or develops any product(s), or modifies the design, then requirements of clause 7.3 must not be excluded.

b. Product design or development is to be understood as a set of processes that translate the identified requirements for the product into specified detailed product characteristics.

c. Design and/or development of processes and associated tooling or machinery used for product realization do not have to be covered by clause 7.3.

d. Organizations may choose to follow the requirements of clause 7.3 in the development of product realization processes and associated tooling.

e. Planning and development of production processes and associated tooling and equipment need to be carried out, as required by clause 7.1 in relation to 7.5.1 and 7.5.2, and should be audited against these requirements.

f. In the case of outsourcing the design/development of the product, the organization retains overall responsibility for product conformance and must therefore establish effective control to ensure suitability of the design to meet requirements through effective control over purchasing/outsourcing, as referred to in 7.4.

g. The interpretation of (e) above applies to all outsourced processes required to adhere product conformance (clause 4.1).

Any exclusion must be detailed and justified in the quality manual (4.2.2 c). It should be noted that permissible exclusions do not apply only to entire clauses; there may be circumstances where only a portion of the requirements of one of the clauses of section 7 of ISO 9001:2000 can be excluded.

The fact that a specific activity (such as design and development, or purchasing) is outsourced, or carried out by a different entity, is not in itself adequate justification for the exclusion of that activity from the QMS. Overall responsibility for and/or coordination of that activity may remain with the organization. Any exclusions that do not meet the criteria established in clause 1.2 of ISO 9001:2000 are not "permissible exclusions," and conformity to ISO 9001:2000 may not be claimed. This includes the following situations:

a. Where an organization has simply discarded a requirement in section 7 as being irrelevant just because they do not want to do it.

b. Where an organization excludes a requirement because they have not previously addressed it in their QMS. The fact that they have not previously carried out what the requirement calls for does not mean that the requirement is not applicable to the organization's activities.

c. Where clauses from outside of section 7 have been excluded from the QMS because regulatory bodies do not require them.

d. Where requirements in section 7 have been excluded that are not required by regulatory bodies but do affect the organization's ability to meet customer requirements.

e. Where requirements in section 7 have been excluded that are required by regulatory bodies even though they do not affect the organization's ability to meet customer requirements.

3 TERMS AND DEFINITIONS

Clarification on clause 3:

ISO 9000:2000 contains definitions and interpretations of terms which, by virtue of the reference in clause 2, become the mandatory and binding interpretation of the terms.

4 QUALITY MANAGEMENT SYSTEM

4.1 General requirements

The organization shall establish, document, implement and maintain a QMS and continually improve its effectiveness in accordance with the requirements of this international standard. The organization shall:

a. Identify the processes needed for the QMS and their application throughout the organization (see 1.2).

b. Determine the sequence and interaction of these processes.

c. Determine criteria and methods needed to ensure that both the operation and control of these processes are effective.

d. Ensure the availability of resources and information necessary to support the operation and monitoring of these processes.

e. Monitor, measure, and analyze these processes.

f. Implement actions necessary to achieve planned results and continuous improvement of these processes.

These processes shall be managed by the organization in accordance with the requirements of this international standard. Where an organization chooses to outsource any process that affects product conformity with requirements, the organization shall ensure control over such processes. Control of such outsourced processes shall be identified within the QMS.

Note: Processes needed for the QMS referred to here should include processes for management activities, provision of resources, product realization, and measurement.

Clarification on clause 4.1:

a. Clause 4.1 includes the general requirements that must be met in order to establish and implement an effective QMS, meeting the requirements of the standard. These requirements are referenced in Table 2.1 and further elaborated in appendix E.

b. In case of deficiencies in fulfillment of any of the cross-linked requirements, the auditor should consider which could be the most value-adding attribute.

c. The auditor should not require the organization to produce system maps, flowcharts, lists of processes, and so on, as evidence to demonstrate that the processes, their sequence, and their interactions were identified. Such documents may be used by organizations should they deem them useful, but are not mandatory. The interactions of the processes must, however, be described in the quality manual (4.2.2 (c)).

d. The auditors must use their judgment in assessing the whole of the objective evidence collected throughout the audit to determine if the requirements of clause 4.1 have been met.

4.2 Documentation requirements

4.2.1 General

The quality management system documentation shall include:

Table 2.1 Requirements of standard.

4.1 General requirements	Relevant further clauses
a) Identify the processes, including outsourcing, needed for the QMS, and its application throughout the organization (see 1.2)	5.4.2 QMS planning 7.1 Planning of product realization 8.1 General
b) Determine the sequence and interaction of these processes	5.4.2 QMS planning 7.1 Planning of product realization 4.2.2 (c)
c) Determine criteria and methods required to ensure that both the operation and control of these processes are effective	7.1 (c) 7.3.3 (c) 7.4.1 (Criteria for selection) 7.5.2
d) Ensure availability of resources and information necessary to support the operation and monitoring of these processes	Entire 6
e) Measure, monitor, and analyze these processes	Entire 8.2

f) Implement actions necessary to achieve planned results and continual improvement of these processes.
   These processes shall be managed by the organization in accordance with the requirements of this international standard.
   Note: Where an organization chooses to outsource any process that affects product conformity with requirements, the organization should ensure control over such processes.
	Entire 5, 6, 7, and 8

    a. Documented statements of a quality policy and quality objectives

    b. A quality manual

    c. Documented procedures required by this international standard

    d. Documents needed by the organization to ensure the effective planning, operation, and control of its processes

    e. Records required by this international standard (see 4.2.4)

Note 1: Where the term "documented procedure" appears within this international standard, this means that the procedure is established, documented, implemented, and maintained.

Note 2: The extent of the QMS documentation can differ from one organization to another due to:

a. The size of organization and type of activities

b. The complexity of processes and their interactions

c. The competence of personnel

Note 3: The documentation can be in any form or type of medium.

4.2.2 Quality manual

The organization shall establish and maintain a quality manual that includes:

a. The scope of the QMS, including details of and justification for any exclusions (see 1.2)

b. The documented procedures established for the QMS, or reference to them

c. A description of the interaction between the processes of the QMS.

Clarification of clause 4.2.2:

a. Auditors must be prepared to accept that there are many ways of documenting the QMS, and organizations may and should adopt the approach that is most useful for effective operation of their system. Such as: a) flowcharts, b) written text, c) diagrams, d) system maps, and e) process maps.

b. Auditors must also remember that the quality manual may have many forms. Although many organizations structure their documentation in a typical pyramid, it is not the only, and not always the most suitable, way. A quality manual doesn't have to exist as a separate document. The quality manual may be:

- A direct collection of QMS documents, including procedures

- A grouping or a section of QMS documentation

- More than one document or level

- In one or more volumes

- A stand-alone document or otherwise

- A collection of separate documents

c. The organization should document its QMS in a way that best suits their mode of operation and is the most user-friendly for their personnel. Auditors must not direct organizations into any rigid standardization approaches. This new edition of the standard offers the users a possibility to establish effective, user-friendly systems. The transition to this edition offers the current users a unique opportunity to streamline their QMS documentation. Auditors should encourage the organizations to use this opportunity wherever applicable and practicable.

d. The interactions between the QMS processes do not have to be separately described, nor illustrated by charts, tables, or maps. Although many organizations may choose such a form, it is not a mandatory method. Interaction between processes may be described, for instance, by way of references and/or cross-references within the procedures, where the procedures form part of the quality manual.

e. A separate document "addressing" the clauses of the standard is not required by the standard—neither does the standard require the quality manual to "address" or "cover" the requirements of the standard.

4.2.3 Control of documents

Documents required by the QMS shall be controlled. Records are a special type of document and shall be controlled according to the requirements given in 4.2.4.

A documented procedure shall be established to define the controls needed to:

a. Approve documents for adequacy prior to issue,

b. Review and update as necessary and reapprove documents,

c. Ensure that changes and the current revision status of documents are identified,

d. Ensure that relevant versions of applicable documents are available at points of use,

e. Ensure that documents remain legible and readily identifiable,

f. Ensure that documents of external origin are identified and their distribution controlled, and

g. Prevent the unintended use of obsolete documents, and to apply suitable identification to them if they are retained for any purpose.

4.2.4 Control of records

Records shall be established and maintained to provide evidence of conformity to requirements and of the effective operation of the QMS. Records shall remain legible, readily identifiable, and retrievable. A documented procedure shall be established to define the controls needed for the identification, storage, protection, retrieval, retention time, and disposition of records.

5 MANAGEMENT RESPONSIBILITY

5.1 Management Commitment

Much has been discussed about management commitment in past quality initiatives. ISO/TS 16949 makes management commitment the driving force to accomplish quality excellence trough clear definition and communication policies in such a way that the goal of "meeting requirements," rather than the nebulous "quality" is indeed the focus of management. As such, the standard calls for top management to (shall) provide evidence of its commitment to developing, implementing, and improving the QMS by:

- Communicating the importance of meeting customer, statutory, and regulatory requirements

- Establishing the quality policy

- Ensuring that quality objectives are established

- Conducting management reviews

- Ensuring availability of resources

Clarification on clause 5.1 (a):

There are a number of ways in which this can be communicated. Typical ways are: a) training, including statutory and regulatory, b) briefings, c) mission statements, and d) cascade dissemination of mission, policy statements, or similar declarations.

The auditor has to accept any effective approach. Effectiveness of the approach taken by an organization can be verified by assessing the degree of awareness (clause 6.2.2). See also clause 5.5.2 (c) promotion of awareness and 5.5.3 Internal communication.

5.2 Customer focus

Top management shall ensure that customer requirements are determined and are met with the aim of enhancing customer satisfaction (see 7.2.1 and 8.2.1).

5.3 Quality policy

Top management shall ensure that the quality policy:

a. Is appropriate to the purpose of the organization,

b. Includes a commitment to comply with ISO requirements and continually improve the effectiveness of the quality management system,

c. Provides a framework for establishing and reviewing quality objectives,

d. Is communicated and understood within the organization, and

e. Is reviewed for continuing suitability.

Clarification on clause 5.3:

a. Quality policy must be documented (4.2.1 (a)).

b. Quality policy does not have to include objectives but should create a framework for establishing them.

c. Quality policy has to be assessed in relation to clauses 5.1 and 8.5.1.

5.4 Planning

5.4.1 Quality objectives

Top management shall ensure that quality objectives, including those needed to meet requirements for product [see 7.1 a)], are established at relevant functions and levels within the organization. The quality objectives shall be measurable and consistent with the quality policy, are included in the business plan, and are used to deploy the quality policy.

Clarification on clause 5.4.1:

Objectives have to be documented (4.2.1 (a)). The auditor has to assess if the objectives are measurable. The only criteria that are available in assessing the objectives are whether they are measurable and consistent with the quality policy. Auditors may see compatibility of these requirements with those in ISO 14001:1996. It is the management of an organization that determines the relevant functions and levels at which these objectives need to be set. There are no generic patterns or rules as to what those should be and yet again auditors must use their judgment to assess if the approach taken by the organization is suitable and implementation of the quality policy effective, including commitment to comply with the requirements and to the continual improvement of the effectiveness of the QMS.

5.4.2 Quality management system planning

Top management shall ensure that the:

a. Planning of the quality management system is carried out in order to meet the requirements given in 4.1, as well as the quality objectives, and

b. Integrity of the QMS is maintained when changes to the QMS are planned and implemented.

Clarification on clause 5.4.2:

a. Planning includes:

- All those planning activities undertaken to establish the QMS in accordance with clause 4.1.

- The existence of an effective, documented, and implemented QMS provides collective evidence demonstrating that these planning activities have been performed effectively.

- Deficiencies in the quality system may indicate that these planning activities were not quite effective.

- Auditors are recommended to attribute such QMS deficiencies to the relevant clause (be specific as possible), requirements of which were contravened, rather than to clause 5.4.2.

- Auditors have to use their judgment in evaluating the entire collected audit evidence in order to assess effectiveness of the planning activities.

b. Planning includes:

- Another aspect of quality management planning is that planning must be undertaken from time to time in order to achieve any quality objectives established by an organization.

- The evidence of effective planning may include: a) any program(s) or plan(s), documented or not, b) minutes of meetings, c) memos, d) internal communication.

- Where there is lack of documented evidence, an auditor may satisfy him or herself that the planning was done by interviewing the personnel at those levels and functions involved in achieving particular objectives.

- Another methodology allowing assessment of effective planning involves review of the progress in implementation of such plans aimed at adhering to individual objectives.

5.5 Responsibility, authority and communication

5.5.1 Responsibility and authority

Top management shall ensure that: Responsibilities and authorities are defined and communicated throughout the organization.

Clarification on clause 5.5.1:

a. There is no specific requirement for any form of documentation in this area.

b. An auditor has to use her or his judgment in evaluating the collective audit evidence to establish if roles, responsibilities, authorities, and their interrelation have been defined and communicated. A wealth of information may be obtained and verified by way of interviewing individuals within the organization.

c. In most of the organizations, there will be documentation available outlining the responsibilities, authorities, and interrelation. It may take the form of: a) organizational charts, b) job descriptions, c) responsibility matrix, or it may, which is very likely, be documented within the procedures and/or other instructions.

5.5.2 Management representative

Top management shall appoint a member of management who, irrespective of other responsibilities, shall have responsibility and authority that includes:

a. Ensuring that processes needed for the QMS are established, implemented, and maintained,

b. Reporting to top management on the performance of the QMS and any need for improvement, and

   c. Ensuring the promotion of awareness of customer requirements throughout the organization.

Note: The responsibility of a management representative can include liaison with external parties on matters relating to the QMS.

Clarification on clause 5.5.2:

   a. Top management must appoint a person to have responsibility and authority as outlined in 5.5.2 a–c.

   b. Such a person, when appointed, becomes a member of management regardless of his or her other position in the organization. Auditors must remember that management is not limited to the board of directors.

   c. This position need not be a full-time responsibility.

   d. A person from outside of the company may be appointed on a part-time management basis (or otherwise), fulfilling responsibility and authority specified in 5.5.2 (a–c). For instance, a consultant may be appointed to undertake this responsibility. When a management representative is not a full-time member of the organization, the QMS must ensure continuity in fulfilling the management representative's responsibilities as stipulated previously.

   e. It is not required that the function of management representative need be separated from that of the top manager. The top manager (CEO) may therefore decide to appoint him or herself to assume the responsibility and authority of management representative. The standard also clearly states that these responsibilities and authorities may be conferred on a person in addition to and irrespective of other responsibilities. As long as the responsibilities and authority of the top manager (CEO) in fulfilling the role of the management representative are clearly defined and communicated within the organization, such a solution is compliant with the requirements of the standard.

5.5.3 Internal communication

Top management shall ensure that:

- Appropriate communication processes are established within the organization.

- Communication takes place regarding effectiveness of the QMS.

Clarification on clause 5.5.3:

- There is no requirement for any documented procedures or other documents outlining the internal communication system.

- Internal communication may take many forms and a variety of processes may be used.

- Auditors must use their judgment in evaluating the entire audit evidence to determine if effective communication has been established.

5.6 Management Review

5.6.1 General

Top management at planned intervals shall review the performance of the QMS:

- To ensure continuing suitability, adequacy, and effectiveness

- To determine if changes to the QMS are needed

- To identify opportunities for improvement

- To maintain records summarizing items reviewed and actions taken

Typical items of this element, even though they are not specifically identified, are:

- Include all elements of the QMS

- Review performance trends

- Monitor performance to objectives

- Evaluate cost of quality data

- Records must include, at a minimum, evidence of the achievement of: a) objectives in the business plan and b) customer satisfaction

5.6.2 Review input

The input to management reviews shall include:

- Results of internal and external (third-party and customer) audits

- Customer feedback

- Process performance

- Product conformity

- Corrective and preventive action status

- Follow-up actions from previous management reviews

- Planned changes that could affect the QMS

- Recommendations for improvement

- Analysis of field failures

- Review the impact of field failures on quality, safety, and environment

5.6.3 Review output

The output from management review shall include any decisions and actions related to:

- Improvement of the effectiveness of the QMS and its processes

- Improvement of the product related to customer requirements

- Resource needs

Clarification on clause 5.6:

a. Performing management review is one of the ways by which top management demonstrates their commitment (5.1.d).

b. It is the top management who determine the planned intervals for such reviews.

c. The reviews need to be carried out frequently enough to ensure ongoing effectiveness, suitability, and adequacy of the system.

d. The auditors must not question the frequency of management reviews unless evidence is available to show deterioration of the system due to lack of management attention and action.

e. The management review may be performed by the CEO alone and need not be done collectively. Such a method of management review obviously does not instill team spirit within an organization. Auditors need to assure themselves that the management review performed in this manner achieves its objectives.

f. The management review may be carried out stagewise or as an ongoing process, reviewing different information, aspects, or elements of the system at different times.

g. The management review is, in such cases, a collection of processes.

h. There is no requirement for a documented procedure covering management review. Whether or not a documented procedure exists, the auditor must ensure that the management review consistently meets the requirements of the standard.

i. Records of management review have to be maintained and controlled (clause 4.2.4).

j. The management review may take documentary form and there is no requirement to carry it out by way of a meeting.

It is not necessary that the whole of the management review be recorded in a single document. Record of a complete management review may take the form of a collection of documents.

6 RESOURCE MANAGEMENT

6.1 Provision of resources

The organization shall determine and provide the necessary resources:

- To implement and maintain the QMS

- To continually improve it

- To enhance customer satisfaction by meeting customer requirements

Clarification on clause 6.1:

Auditors should be mindful that it is the organization's management who determine the adequacy of the resources provided by an organization. Auditors should not raise a nonconformity unless solid objective evidence has been found to demonstrate that: a) the QMS was not effectively implemented, or that its effectiveness was not being improved due to lack of resources, or b) agreed customer requirements were not met due to lack, or insufficiency, of all resources.

6.2 Human resources

6.2.1 General

Personnel affecting product quality shall be competent on the basis of education, training, skills, and/or experience.

6.2.2 Competence, awareness and training

The organization shall:

a) Determine the necessary competence for personnel performing work affecting product quality

b) Provide training or take other actions to satisfy these needs

c) Evaluate the effectiveness of the actions taken

d) Ensure that its personnel are aware of the relevance and importance of their activities and how they contribute to the achievement of the quality objectives

e) Maintain appropriate records of education, training, skills, and experience (see 4.2.4)

Clarification on clause 6.2.2 (a):

Identification of competence needed is not "one off" activity. Changes in the business and its environment may necessitate new competencies, which may not be available. Therefore, the identification of competencies may need to be revisited as and when required.

The need for reevaluation of the competencies required may arise for a number of reasons. Auditors should not require any particular frequency (such as rereview). However, many companies will conduct periodic reviews at defined intervals.

Auditors should be mindful that it is management's responsibility to identify the competency required and should not raise a nonconformity against the process unless there is solid objective evidence of a failure to identify competence needed.

Clarification on clause 6.2.2 (b):

Training includes all those activities where a learning opportunity avails itself. It may take a number of forms:

- Classroom-style, instructor-led training
- Hands-on experience training
- Individual or group coaching
- Mentoring
- Briefings
- Distance learning

- Technology-based training (CD-ROMs, Web-based, and so on)

- Workshops and so on

Organizations will choose whichever form best suits their needs at any particular instance.

Other actions to satisfy competency needs may include:

- Recruitment

- Outsourcing

- Acquisitions

- Use of experts and/or consultants

All such means are acceptable as long as an organization has ensured the availability of the competencies needed.

Clarification on clause 6.2.2 (c):

There are many ways by which organizations can assess the effectiveness of training, depending on its form: a) assessment of delegate performance during training and progression in achieving learning objectives during the course of the training program, b) examinations, and c) assessment of performance at work, focusing, for example, on:

- Productivity

- Reduction of rejects

- Efficiency

- Interviews with the persons

- Annual appraisal

Organizations may choose any methodology that suits a given purpose. Effectiveness of other actions may be evaluated by a variety of means, and organizations should select what best suits their purpose. The measures may include: a) performance reviews, b) discussions, c) evaluation of performance, quality, or other indicators, d) cost reviews, and e) customer satisfaction assessment (see 8.2.1).

Clarification on clause 6.2.2 (e):

There are a variety of ways to record and provide evidence of training, education, skills, and experience. Records may include: diplomas, certificates, training log, annotations in shift logs, toolbox meeting notes, attendance lists, resumés, employment history, test results, and so on.

Such records are typically filed in the personnel files but there may be a number of other locations where such records are kept (requirements of 4.2.4 must be observed).

Auditors need to be aware that in some organizations, particularly in those that are smaller and have been in business longer, there may be a very limited number of personal records available. Auditors must be prepared to accept, in such cases, any relevant records demonstrating the skills and experience of the staff. Auditors should not demand records of the complete history of education and training of an individual. However, all relevant records of education, training, skills, and experience need to be available when asked for.

6.3 Infrastructure

The organization shall provide the necessary infrastructure to meet product requirements, including:

- Buildings, workplaces, and associated utilities

- Process equipment including software

- Supporting services—transportation, communication

- Equipment maintenance

Clarification on clause 6.3:

See item under 6.1.

6.4 Work environment

The organization shall:

- Determine the work environment necessary to meet product requirements.

Typical items for this element, even though they are not identified are:

- Manage the environment
- Address product safety:
  - In the design and development process
  - In the manufacturing process
- Maintain order, cleanliness, and repair of premises
  - Consistent with product and manufacturing needs

Clarification on clause 6.4:

The organization must identify and manage all those factors of the work environment that are needed to supply a conforming product. These factors may include, among others:

Human Factors	Physical Factors
Creative work methods	Heat
Opportunities for greater involvement of personnel	Noise
	Light
Safety rules and guidance	Hygiene
Ergonomics	Humidity
Special facilities for people	Cleanliness
	Vibration
	Pollution
	Airflow

This requirement relates only to those factors that need to be managed in order to achieve conforming products and does not relate to any legislative requirements related to occupational health and safety, protection of the environment, and so on, save as explained in comments to clause 7.2.

7 PRODUCT REALIZATION

7.1 Planning of product realization

The organization shall plan and develop the processes for product realization:

- Considering the other processes of the supplier's QMS

- Developing product requirements and quality objectives

- Providing necessary resources, processes, and documents specific to the product

- Identifying the verification, validation, monitoring, inspection, testing, and product acceptance criteria

- Establishing the records necessary to provide evidence that the realization process and the product meet requirements

- Including customer requirements in the planning process (7.1.1)

- Identifying acceptance criteria; obtaining customer approval if required (7.1.2)

- For attribute data sampling, utilizing n = 0 as the criterion

- Ensuring the confidentiality of customer-contracted planning processes (7.1.3)

- Having a process for controlling changes to the product realization process (including both product and manufacturing process changes, 7.1.4):

  - Assess the effects of the change—Define the verification and validation activities

  - Review changes on proprietary designs with customer prior to incorporation

  - Obtain prior customer approval on any product realization change affecting customer requirements

  - Validate changes prior to implementation

  - Understand and meet any customer requirements for verification or identification, for example, for new product launch

Clarification on clause 7.1:

There is no specific requirement for the output of this planning to be documented. Organizations should choose such a form of planning output that will suite best their mode of operation. A planning output needs to include all the procedures, whether documented or not, defining how the processes and or activities are performed, as well as any other controls required to manage the sequence and interactions for the product realization process.

7.2 Customer-related processes

7.2.1 Determination of requirements related to the product

The organization shall determine:

a) Requirements specified by the customer

- Including delivery and postdelivery (servicing)

b) Requirements not stated by the customer, but necessary for the specified or intended use (where knowable)

c) Statutory and regulatory requirements applicable to the product

- Includes government, safety, and environmental regulations

- Covers acquisition, storage, handling, recycling, and disposal

d)   Additional requirements determined by the organization

Clarification on clause 7.2.1 (a):

Postdelivery activities may include among others:

- Product support

- Servicing where applicable

Clarification on clause 7.2.1 (c):

Statutory requirements are those that are stipulated by statutory instruments that form part of national, regional, and international legislation.

Regulatory requirements are those imposed by regulatory bodies. These requirements are not necessarily part of national legislation.

Compliance with regulatory requirements issued by national regulators (for example, EPA, FTA, FAA, and so on) may be mandatory for the organizations to whom they apply if a statutory instrument requires so.

Organizations are required to comply with a number of legal requirements to be allowed to operate; however, the auditor is concerned only with those statutory and/or regulatory requirements that apply to the organization's product(s) unless a failure to comply with other such requirements impairs the organization's ability to supply conforming product in accordance with contractual requirements.

Auditors have to be aware that as the regulations may apply to product intended for the domestic market, in the case of export sales, organizations will be required to consider the statutory and/or regulatory requirements in the target country that may apply to (a) product(s) supplied.

Organizations are not required to maintain the lists of applicable statutory and/or regulatory requirements, nor need they maintain copies of these documents except as required by clause 7.3.2(b). Organizations must ensure that they have adequate access to or knowledge of applicable statutory and regulatory requirements when determining the requirements related to the product.

Auditors are not required to notify the authorities of any breaches of the regulations, unless it is their legal obligation as a citizen of a country. In many countries, law imposes such an onus on a citizen, and sometimes on visitors as well, with regard to criminal offenses.

7.2.2 Review of requirements related to the product

Prior to commitment to supply product, the organization shall ensure that:

- Product requirements are defined

- Contract requirements different from those previously expressed are resolved

- The organization can meet the defined requirements

- Records are maintained of this review process

- If the customer doesn't provide documented requirements, the supplier has confirmed the requirements prior to acceptance

- In case product requirements are changed, the supplier shall ensure that:

  - Relevant documents are updated

  - Relevant personnel are made aware of the changes

- Waiver of the formal review of requirements requires customer authorization (7.2.2.1)

- Manufacturing feasibility analysis is conducted, including risk analysis, and documented (7.2.2.2)

Clarification on clause 7.2.2 note:

In the case of e-commerce, the systems used must ensure that: a) product requirements are defined, and b) the organization has the ability to supply the product(s).

7.2.3 Customer communication

The organization will develop and implement a process for communicating with customers concerning:

- Product information

- Enquiries, contracts, order handling, amendments

- Customer feedback including complaints

- Using a customer-specified language and format: including digitized data for design (CAD data) and EDI (7.2.3.1)

7.3 Design and development

7.3.1 Design and development planning

These requirements apply to both product and manufacturing process development. The organization shall plan and control the design and development of the product, identifying:

- The design and development stages

- The review, verification, and validation stages that are appropriate to each stage

- The responsibilities and authorities for each design and development stage

- A process to manage the interfaces between various groups involved in the design and development process

- Updates to the planning output as the design and development progresses

7.3.2 Design and development inputs

Inputs relating to product requirements shall be determined and records maintained. Design inputs shall include:

- Functional and performance requirements

- Applicable statutory and regulatory requirements

- Information from similar previous designs, where applicable

- Other requirements essential for design and development

Design inputs shall be reviewed to ensure they are complete, clear, and not in conflict with each other. Typical inputs may be: competitive analysis; customer requirements; regulatory/statutory; functional/performance; similar designs; other essential requirements; and product targets.

Clarification on clause 7.3.2 note:

See clarification for clause 7.2.1.

7.3.3 Design and development outputs

- Permit verification against design inputs

- Shall be approved prior to release

- Meet the input requirements

- Provide appropriate information for purchasing, production, and servicing

- Contain or reference product acceptance criteria

- Specify characteristics key to safe and proper use

7.3.4 Design and development review

Conduct a systematic design and development review at stages identified in the design and development plan:

- To evaluate the ability of the design to meet requirements

- To identify problems and propose actions

- Shall include representatives of functions concerned with the design stage being reviewed (should include manufacturing process design and development personnel)

- Shall be documented

- Shall include monitoring (7.3.4.1) of key measurables, which become input to the management review. Measurables include: quality risks; costs; lead times; critical paths, and others as appropriate

7.3.5 Design and development verification

- Conducted per plan to ensure that the outputs satisfy input requirements

- Records maintained, including any necessary actions

- Applies to both product design and process design

7.3.6 Design and development validation

- Conducted per plan to ensure that the product meets the specified requirements

- Complete prior to delivery or implementation of the product

- Results documented

- Should include analysis of field reports

- Applies to both product design and process design

- Must meet customer requirements including program timing (7.3.6.1)

7.3.7 Control of design and development changes

The organization shall identify and maintain records of design and development changes. All changes shall be:

- Reviewed

- Verified and validated as appropriate

- Approved before implementation

- Include an evaluation of the effects of the change on constituent parts and product already delivered

Records shall be maintained of results of the reviews and any actions taken.

7.4 Purchasing

7.4.1 Purchasing process

The organization shall:

- Ensure that purchased product conforms to specified purchase requirements

- Apply controls consistent with the effect of the purchased product on product realization or the final product

- Evaluate and select suppliers on the basis of their ability to meet requirements

  - Criteria for evaluation, selection, and reevaluation shall be established.

  - Records of evaluation, selection, and related actions shall be maintained.

- Ensure that all purchased products meet applicable regulatory requirements (7.4.1.1)

- Utilize suppliers that, at a minimum, are registered to ISO 9001:2000 unless otherwise specified by the customer (7.4.1.2)

  - Required by December 15, 2003

  - Customer may mandate alternative requirements

- Develop suppliers with the goal of conformance to ISO/TS 16949

  - Prioritize development-based quality history and criticality of the product supplied

- Purchase the product only from the approved source specified by the customer (7.4.1.3)

- Other than selection, treat customer-approved sources like all others

Notes: Purchased products includes all products and services that affect compliance with customer requirements (subassembly, sequencing, sorting, rework, calibration). The organization should verify continuity of the supplier's QMS through mergers, acquisitions, affiliations, and ownership changes.

7.4.2 Purchasing information

Purchasing information shall describe the product to be purchased, including as applicable:

- Approval requirements for product, procedures, processes, and equipment
- Personnel qualification requirements
- QMS requirements
- Provision for verification at the supplier's premises

The organization shall ensure adequacy of requirements prior to issuance.

7.4.3 Verification of purchased product

Implement actions necessary for ensuring that purchased product meets specified purchase requirements. (Special distinction: Validation is the process of evaluating a product/service at the end of its development process to ensure compliance with its requirements. Verification is the process of determining whether the product/service fulfills the requirements established during design of the product/service).

- Arrangements and methods for verifications to be conducted at the supplier shall be stated in the purchasing information.

Typical acceptable methods, although not identified in the standard are:

- Receipt and analysis of statistical data
- Receiving inspection/testing
  - Includes sampling based on quality performance
- Second- or third-party assessment coupled with records of acceptable quality performance
- Product evaluated by a designated laboratory
- Other method agreed upon by the customer

7.5 Production and service provision

7.5.1 Control of production and service provision

Product and service provision (production) shall be carried out under controlled conditions, including as applicable:

- Availability of information that describes product characteristics

- Availability of work instructions at the workstation

  – For all employees responsible for operating processes that impact product quality (7.5.1.2)

  – Derived from the control plan, the quality plan, and the product realization process

- Use of suitable equipment

- Availability and use of monitoring and measuring devices

- Implementation of monitoring and measurement activities

- Implementation of release, delivery, and postdelivery activities

7.5.2 Validation of processes for product and service provision

The organization shall have an established method to validate all production processes, using it as applicable. The following is a typical checklist:

- Defined criteria for review and approval

- Approval of equipment

- Qualification of personnel

- Use of specific methods and procedures

- Documentation via appropriate records

- Establishment of revalidation requirements

7.5.3 Identification and traceability

- The organization shall identify product throughout product realization. (The ISO 9001 "where appropriate" language does not apply. The implication here is that if you cannot identify the product, the process realization would be very difficult to control and or evaluate.)

- The organization shall identify monitoring/measurement status.

- When traceability is a (specified) requirement, the organization will control and record the unique status identification. [Note: location in the process flow does not indicate product status, unless the process itself (for example, automated transfer systems) makes the status obvious.]

7.5.4 Customer property

The organization shall exercise care with customer property.

- Identify, verify, and safeguard customer property provided for use or incorporation into the product.

- If any such property is lost or damaged, it shall be recorded and reported to the customer.

Customer-owned packaging is included in this requirement. Customer-owned manufacturing, testing, and inspection tooling and equipment shall be permanently marked so that ownership is visible and can be determined.

7.5.5 Preservation of product

The organization shall preserve product conformity during production and delivery, including:

- Identification

- Handling

- Packaging

- Storage

- Protection

To detect deterioration, condition of inventory shall be assessed at appropriate planned intervals (7.5.5.1).

The organization shall use an inventory management system to assure stock rotation (for example, first in/first out, or FIFO). Obsolete stock shall be controlled as nonconforming material.

7.6 Control of monitoring and measuring devices

The organization shall:

- Determine the monitoring and measurement to be undertaken

- Determine the monitoring and measurement devices required to determine product conformity to requirements
- Establish a process to ensure that monitoring and measurement can be carried out consistently with requirements

When necessary for valid results, measuring equipment shall:

- Be calibrated at specific intervals or prior to use:
  - Against national or international standards, if available
  - Otherwise, the basis for calibration shall be recorded
- Be adjusted or readjusted as necessary
- Be identified to show calibration status (an identification number is satisfactory)
- Be safeguarded against adjustments that would invalidate results
- Be protected from damage during handling, maintenance, and storage
- Assess and record the validity of previous measurements when out-of-calibration equipment is identified

In addition, the organization shall:

- Take appropriate action on the equipment and affected product
- Maintain records of calibration and verification. Record all calibration activity including:
  - Equipment identification.
  - The standard used for calibration.
  - Any as-received out-of-calibration readings.
  - Assessment of impact of out-of-calibration readings.
  - Statements of conformance to specification after calibration.
  - Notification to customer if suspect material has been shipped.
  - Prior to use, confirm the ability of any software to satisfy the intended application. Reconfirm as necessary.

Clarification on clause 7.6:

Monitoring devices are such devices or measuring systems that enable monitoring, that is, regular surveillance. This includes all sorts of different recording devices (for example, temperature or pressure recorders—see also clause 8).

8 MEASUREMENT, ANALYSIS AND IMPROVEMENT

8.1 General

The organization shall plan and implement the processes for monitoring, measurement, analysis, and improvement in order to: a) demonstrate conformity of the product, b) ensure conformity of the QMS to this standard, and c) to continually improve the effectiveness of the QMS, including determination of the methods to be used, including statistical methods, and the extent of their use.

Clarification on clause 8.1:

To monitor means to maintain regular surveillance over an activity or entity. For instance, monitoring of operatives' performance may take the form of regular periodic observation of a person at work. Process monitoring may, for example, take the form of regular periodic verifications of process parameters.

Measurement (ISO 9000:2000) is defined as a "set of operations having the object of determining the value of a quantity." In other words, to measure means to ascertain the extent or quantity of an entity by comparison with a fixed unit or known standard. Typical examples of measurements are inspections and tests.

8.2 Monitoring and measurement

8.2.1 Customer satisfaction

The organization shall monitor customer *perception* to determine if the organization has met customer satisfaction. The process for obtaining and using this information shall be documented.

Customer satisfaction shall be monitored through continual evaluation of performance of the realization process, based on data, including but not limited to:

- Delivered part quality performance

- Customer disruptions, including field returns

- Delivery performance, including use of premium freight

- Customer notifications concerning quality or delivery

Manufacturing processes must be monitored (recorded data + statistical analysis) to demonstrate:

- Compliance with customer requirements

- Efficiency

Clarification on clause 8.2.1:

The organization must monitor how customers perceive the degree to which their requirements were met.

There are a large variety of methods that can be used, and organizations may choose whichever best suits their mode of operation, nature of product(s), type of clients, and market segment. An auditor must therefore use her or his judgment to accept any approach that allows an organization to monitor information or customer perception of whether the organization has met the requirements (in other words, information on customer satisfaction or dissatisfaction) and to analyze this information.

Although organizations may decide to base their methodology on analyzing only the negative comments, auditors should encourage management to consider the potential benefits of adopting more proactive approaches.

8.2.2 Internal audit

The organization shall conduct internal audits at planned intervals to determine if the QMS:

- Conforms to the plans made per section 7.1 and to the QMS requirements established by the organization

- Is effectively implemented and maintained

The internal audit program:

1. Shall be planned

2. Shall consider:

   - The status and importance of each process

   - The results of previous audits

3. Shall define:

   - Criteria

   - Scope

- Frequency

4. Shall select auditors and conduct audits objectively and impartially

5. Shall preclude auditors auditing *their own work*

6. Shall have documented responsibilities for planning, conducting, and reporting the audits

Management responsible for the area being audited shall ensure timely correction and follow-up for all nonconformities identified. Follow-up includes verification of effectiveness of corrective action and appropriate reporting.

Clarification on clause 8.2.2:

Procedures must ensure that the complete audit results are reported and recorded.

8.2.3 Monitoring and measurement of processes

The organization shall:

- Apply suitable methods for monitoring QMS processes (where applicable, measurement of QMS processes) to achieve desired results.

- When desired results are not achieved, apply correction and corrective action to ensure product conformity.

- Perform process capability studies on all new processes to verify process capability and to provide additional input for process control

- Document results, including objectives for manufacturing process capability, reliability, maintainability, availability, and acceptance criteria.

- Maintain process capability/performance per customer part-approval requirements

- Ensure that the control plan and process flow diagram are implemented, including adherence to:

  - Measurement techniques

  - Sampling plans

  - Acceptance criteria

– Reaction plans, when acceptance criteria are not met

- Note significant events on the control charts, such as tool change or machine repair

- Initiate the control plan's reaction plan for characteristics that are unstable or not statistically capable.

- Include containment and 100 percent inspection as appropriate. Complete a corrective-action plan with specific dates and responsibilities.

- Review plans with customer(s) when required.

- Maintain effective dates of process changes.

A typical monitoring process may follow this path:

Step 1. Monitor QMS process

Step 2. Measure where applicable

Step 3. Conduct process capability studies on new processes

> *Step 3a.* Document

> *Step 3b.* Input to process control

Step 4. Maintain process capability

Step 5. Implement control plan and process flowchart

Step 6. Note significant events on control charts

Clarification on clause 8.2.3:
Refer to comments on clause 8.1 General.

8.2.4 Monitoring and measurement of product

The organization shall:

- Monitor and measure the characteristics of the product to verify that requirements have been met (at appropriate stages of the product realization processes as planned).

- Maintain evidence of conformity with acceptance criteria.

  – Indicate person(s) authorizing release of the product.

  – Product release shall not proceed until planned arrangements have been satisfactorily completed, unless approved by a relevant authority and the customer where applicable.

- Determine product characteristics for monitoring compliance to requirements considering:

  - The types of measurement

  - Suitable means of measurement

  - The capability and skills required

- Conduct layout inspection and functional testing at sufficiently frequent intervals per control plan.

  - Document results for customer review.

- For products designated as "appearance items," provide:

  - Appropriate resources for evaluation, including lighting

  - Masters for color, grain, gloss, metallic brilliance, texture, distinctness of image, as appropriate

  - Maintenance and control of appearance masters and evaluation equipment

  - Verification that personnel making evaluations are qualified

In essence, the monitoring and measurement of product is defined in five steps. They are:

Step 1. Determine characteristics for monitoring

Step 2. Measure characteristics at appropriate stages

Step 3. Maintain evidence of conformity

Step 4. Layout and functional test per control plan

Step 5. Appearance item requirements

Clarification on clause 8.2.4:

Refer to comments on clause 8.1 General.

8.3 Control of nonconforming product

The organization shall:

- Identify nonconforming product and prevent its delivery to customers

- Define controls and responsibilities in a documented procedure

- Deal with nonconforming product by:

  – Taking action to eliminate the detected nonconformity

  – Authorizing its use under concession by the relevant authority (for example, the customer)

  – Precluding its original use (scrapping it)

- Maintain records of nonconformities and actions taken, including any concessions

- Reverify corrected product for conformance to requirements

- Take action appropriate to the nonconformance when nonconforming product is detected after shipment

- Classify unidentified or suspect product as "nonconforming" (8.3.1)

- Provide instructions to applicable personnel for rework and reverification (8.3.2)

- Notify the customer(s) promptly when nonconforming material has been shipped (8.3.3)

- Obtain a customer concession (deviation) for any product or process different from that presently approved (8.3.4)

  – Maintain a record of the authorized quantity or expiration date

  – Assure compliance with original or superseding specifications when authorization expires

  – Identify material shipped under authorization on each shipping container

  – Concur with any requests for concession on material from suppliers before submitting these requests to the customer

8.4 Analysis of data

The organization shall:

- Determine, collect, and analyze data to demonstrate the suitability and effectiveness of the QMS

- Determine where continual improvement of the effectiveness of the QMS can be made

- Shall consider input from monitoring and measurement and other sources

- Analyze data to provide information on customer satisfaction, conformance to product requirements, characteristics and trends of products and processes (including opportunities for improvement), and suppliers

- Compare trends in quality and operational performance with objectives (8.4.1)
- Lead to action to support:

  - Development of prompt solutions to customer-related problems

  - Determination of key customer-related trends to support status review, decision making, and longer-term planning

  - An information system for timely reporting of product usage information

Note: The implication here is effectiveness. Therefore, data should be compared with competitors and benchmarks. A typical process for looking at the QMS effectiveness is:

Step 1. Determine where to get data on QMS effectiveness

Step 2. Gather and analyze data

Step 3. Determine where improvements can be made

Step 4. Compare with objectives

Clarification on clause 8.4:

Organizations are likely to operate a series of activities and/or processes of analyzing the data. These normally include ongoing analysis and will not be limited to the process of formal management review. (See comment on clause 8.1 General).

8.5 Improvement

8.5.1 Continual improvement

The organization shall:

- Continually improve the effectiveness of the QMS through the use of:

  - Quality policy

  - Quality objectives

- Audit results

- Data analysis

- Corrective and preventive action

- Management review

• Define a process for continual improvement of the organization

[Special note: Continual product improvement means: reduction of variation; characteristics in control plan; starts with stable processes that meet customer requirements]

Clarification on clause 8.5.1:

There are a variety of ways to implement the principle of and to achieve continual improvement.

Continuous means consistently or frequently recurring, always happening, as opposed to *continual,* which means unbroken, uninterrupted, connected throughout time and space.

Continuous improvement normally happens in discrete steps. One can visualize it as a step function. On the other hand, continual improvement can be visualized as a positive exponential function.

The auditors must use their judgment in assessing the whole of objective evidence collected throughout the audit to determine if the requirements of clause 8.5.1 have been met.

8.5.2 Corrective action

The organization shall:

• Take action to eliminate the cause of nonconformities to prevent recurrence

• Take corrective action appropriate to the nonconformities encountered

• Develop a documented procedure defining requirements for:

a) Reviewing nonconformities and customer complaints

b) Determining the causes of nonconformities

c) Evaluating the need for preventive action

d) Determining and implementing the actions needed

e) Maintaining records of the results of actions taken

f) Reviewing corrective action taken

- Have a defined process for problem solving leading to root-cause identification and elimination

  - Utilize a customer-prescribed problem-solving format if available

- Utilize error-proofing methods in its corrective-action process

- Apply corrective actions to other similar products and processes

- Analyze all parts returned by the customer(s):

  - Minimize cycle time for determination of root cause, corrective action, and monitoring effectiveness

  - Maintain records of analysis and make them available upon request

  - Initiate corrective action based on the analysis

Clarification on clause 8.5.2:

There is a contradiction within the standard. Auditors should apply point c) rather than the opening sentence of this section of the standard, which requires corrective action to always be taken. Auditors should be mindful that there are situations where taking corrective action is not practical, physically possible, or economically viable. Root cause in this instance should be viewed as an "actionable cause."

8.5.3 Preventive action

The organization shall:

- Determine action to eliminate the causes of potential nonconformities to prevent their recurrence

- Take preventive actions appropriate to the effects of the potential problems

- Establish a documented procedure for:

  - Determining potential nonconformities and their causes

  - Evaluating action to prevent occurrence of nonconformities

  - Determining and implementing the actions needed

  - Recording results of actions taken

  - Reviewing preventive actions taken

[Special note: A nonconformity requires a corrective action and ultimately a preventive action so that this particular nonconformity does not repeat itself. The very basic approach to prevention is: review failure mode and effects analysis (FMEA), review documented procedures, evaluate defective parts, identify actionable cause, eliminate cause, determine corrective action, provide error-proofing for that cause, determine actions on similar processes, and implement preventive actions]

Clarification on clause 8.5.3:
See clarification point on clause 8.5.2.

REFERENCE

ANSI/ISO/ASQ Q9001:2000—Quality management systems—Requirements.
    Milwaukee: ASQ Quality Press, 2000.

3

Automotive ISO/TS 16949 Requirements

QS-9000 is a set of quality system requirements for suppliers that provide production materials, production or service parts, heat treating, plating, painting, and other finishing services directly to automakers that subscribe to the document. It is a standard that was originated with the North American automotive companies with the intent to standardize some of the most common requirements of their supply base.

On the other hand, ISO/TS 16949 is an automotive standard that originated in Europe but is more global and tries to minimize differences between the original equipment manufacturers (OEMs) in their pursuit of quality from their supplier base. Therefore, registration to ISO/TS 16949 will satisfy the quality system requirements of ISO as well as QS-9000 when coupled with individual customer-specific quality requirements.

Specifically, QS-9000 was developed by DaimlerChrysler, Ford, and General Motors as a means to combine their individual supplier quality requirements into a common quality standard for the automotive industry. On the other hand, the ISO/TS 16949 was developed by the International Automotive Task Force (IATF)—with members from BMW AG, Daimler Chrysler, Fiat S.P.A., Ford, General Motors (including Opel-Vauxhall), PSA Peugeot-Citroen SA, Renault SA, Volkswagen AG, and the trade associations AIAG (Automotive Industry Action Group), ANFIA (Associazione Nazionale fra Industrie Automobilistiche of Italy), FIEV (Federation des Industries des Equipments pour Vehicules of France), SMMT (The Society of Motor Manufacturers and Traders, Ltd. of the United Kingdom), and VDA (Verband der Automobilindustrie of Germany).

Ultimately, ISO/TS 16949 will replace the QS-9000 third edition. The replacement is scheduled as follows (until the actual replacement QS-9000 is in effect). The QS-9000 third edition will expire on December 14, 2006. The QS-9000 Tooling & Equipment Supplement and Semi-Conductor Supplement will remain in effect until December 14, 2006. Please note that if that is the case in your organization, the ISO 9001 that is followed is still ISO 9001:1994 and not ISO 9001:2000. Even though the North American OEMs have specific dates for implementing the ISO/TS in their supply base, all of them encourage their suppliers to adopt it as soon as possible].

- DaimlerChrysler Corporation, by December 2003

- Ford Motor Company by July 2004

- General Motors Corporation by December 2006

By implementing the ISO/TS 16949 quality system, suppliers benefit by:

- Eliminating the plethora of individual standards thereby helping to reduce costs.

- Identifying a number of drivers that are responsible for a company seeking ISO/TS 16949 registration.

- The need to broaden the customer base across European and North American OEMs.

- OEMs either mandate ISO/TS 16949 or accept it as an alternative to the automotive versions of ISO 9001 including QS-9000, VDA 6.1, EAQF, and AVSQ. Suppliers registered to ISO/TS 16949 therefore avoid multiple registrations to the various automotive derivatives of ISO 9001.

- Registration to ISO/TS 16949 reduces the amount of first-party audits from some automotive clients.

- Most European OEMs' enthusiasm for ISO/TS 16949 has made registration to ISO/TS 16949 mandatory for all of their first-tier suppliers. The trend worldwide continues to be in the direction of the Europeans.

- ISO/TS 16949 standard is written in a more user-friendly format than QS-9000. It avoids QS-9000's multiple explanatory notes.

- The requirement for senior management to take greater responsibility for quality raises the profile of this activity during the business planning process. Individual responsibilities and action plans for achieving the objectives are set out in individual departmental operating statements.

- Employee involvement, empowerment, and satisfaction have been extensively reviewed. Regular staff meetings include senior managers reporting performance against quality objectives. Staff satisfaction is measured and used to amend the communication process.

Just like QS-9000, so does ISO/TS 16949 have its base in ISO 9001. However, it presents itself with much more detail. This chapter will address these additions. In addition, just like in ISO 9001, the word "shall" indicates a *must* requirement and the word "should" indicates a recommendation. Paragraphs marked "Note" are for guidance in understanding or clarifying the associated requirement. Where the term "such as" is used, any suggestions given are for guidance only.

MAJOR CHANGES

ISO/TS 16949 has 12 "shall" statements that include the words "top management." These include:

1. Provide evidence of commitment through:

    - Communicating the importance of meeting customer/ regulatory requirements

    - Establishing the quality policy

    - Ensuring quality objectives are established

    - Conducting management reviews

    - Ensuring availability of resources

2. Monitor effectiveness of the product realization process.

3. Ensure that customer requirements are determined and fulfilled.

4. Ensure that the quality policy:

    - Is appropriate

- Includes a commitment to meet requirements

- Provides for establishing and reviewing quality objectives

- Is communicated and understood throughout the organization

- Is reviewed for continuing suitability

5. Ensure that measurable quality objectives are established.

6. Define quality objectives and measurements to be included in the business plan.

7. Ensure that:

   - Planning of the QMS is carried out to meet requirements.

   - The integrity of the QMS is maintained through any organizational changes.

8. Ensure that responsibilities are defined and communicated.

9. Appoint a member of management as a management representative who reports to top management on the performance of the QMS.

10. Designate individual(s) to represent the needs of the customers.

11. Ensure communication processes are established and ensure that communications take place on the effectiveness of the QMS.

12. Review the effectiveness of the QMS.

On the other hand, QS-9000 requires a quality manual and procedures, but the major difference is that, in addition to the these, ISO/TS 16949 focuses on processes. Specifically the requirements are:

4.1.1 General requirements—Supplemental. Ensuring control over outsourced processes shall not absolve the organization of the responsibility of conformity to all customer requirements.

Note: See also 7.4.1 and 7.4.1.3.

4.2.3.1 Engineering Specifications. The organization shall have a process to assure the timely review, distribution, and implementation of all customer engineering standards/specifications and changes based on customer-required schedule. Timely review should be as soon as possible, and shall not exceed two working weeks. The organization shall maintain a record of the date on which each change is implemented in production. Implementation shall include updated documents.

Note: A change in these standards/specifications requires an updated record of customer production part approval when these specifications are referenced on the design record or if they affect documents of the production part approval process (PPAP), such as control plans, FMEAs, and so on.

1. Timely review, distribution, and implementation of changes per customer's schedule

2. Record of implementation dates

3. Included document revision in implementation

New requirement: Review not to exceed two working weeks.
Note: Updated PPAP required. Frequently verification of the changes only is required.

4.2.4 Control of Records (All requirements for records are carryover from QS-9000). Records established and maintained to:

- Provide evidence of conformity to requirements

- Demonstrate effective operation of the QMS

Records must be:

- Legible

- Identifiable

- Retrievable

A procedure must state the process for meeting these requirements, especially the retention and disposition period. 1) "Disposition" includes disposal, and 2) customer-specified records are included in these requirements. Of course, retention periods meet applicable regulatory and customer requirements. While QS-9000 devotes elements 4.5 and 4.16 to documentation, ISO/TS 16949 combines these two in the QMS process. In other words, the actual requirements are unchanged, simply relocated. A final comment here is the need to emphasize the importance of documentation. Whereas in both standards (ISO 9001:2000 and ISO/TS 16949) documentation is a requirement, in ISO/TS 16949 it plays a minor role in the overall quality system.

4.2.4.1 Records retention. The control of records shall satisfy regulatory and customer requirements.

5.1.1 Process efficiency. Top management shall review the product realization processes and the support processes to assure their effectiveness and efficiency.

5.4.1.1 Quality objectives—Supplemental. Top management shall define quality objectives and measurements that shall be included in the business plan and used to deploy the quality policy.

Note: Quality objectives should address customer expectations and be achievable within a defined time period.

5.5.1.1 Responsibility for quality. Managers with responsibility and authority for corrective action shall be promptly informed of products or processes that do not conform to requirements. Personnel responsible for product quality shall have the authority to stop production to correct quality problems. Production operations across all shifts shall be staffed with personnel in charge of, or delegated responsibility for, ensuring product quality.

5.5.2.1 Customer representative. Top management shall designate personnel with responsibility and authority to ensure that customer requirements are addressed. This includes selection of special characteristics, setting quality objectives and related training, corrective and preventive actions, and product design and development.

5.6.1.1 Quality management system performance. These reviews shall include all requirements of the QMS and its performance trends as an essential part of the continual improvement process.

Part of the management review shall be the monitoring of quality objectives, and the regular reporting and evaluation of the cost of poor quality (see 8.4.1 and 8.5.1).

These results shall be recorded to provide, as a minimum, evidence of the achievement of the quality objectives specified in the business plan, and customer satisfaction with product supplied.

5.6.2.1 Review input—Supplemental. Input to management review shall include an analysis of actual and potential field failures and their impact on quality, safety, or the environment.

6.2.2.1 Product design skills. The organization shall ensure that personnel with product design responsibility are competent to achieve design requirements and are skilled in applicable tools and techniques. Applicable tools and techniques shall be identified by the organization.

6.2.2.2 Training. The organization shall establish and maintain documented procedures for identifying training needs and achieving competence of all personnel performing activities affecting product quality. Personnel performing specific assigned tasks shall be qualified, as required, with particular attention to the satisfaction of customer requirements.

Note 1: This applies to all employees having an effect on quality at all levels of the organization.

Note 2: An example of the customer-specific requirements is the application of digitized mathematically based data.

6.2.2.3 Training on the job. The organization shall provide on-the-job training for personnel in any new or modified job affecting product quality, including contract or agency personnel. Personnel whose work can affect quality shall be informed about the consequences to the customer of nonconformity to quality requirements.

6.2.2.4 Employee motivation and empowerment. The organization shall have a process to motivate employees to achieve quality objectives, to make continual improvements, and to create an environment to promote innovation. The process shall include the promotion of quality and technological awareness throughout the whole organization. The organization shall have a process to measure the extent to which its personnel are aware of the relevance and importance of their activities and how they contribute to the achievement of the quality objectives [see 6.2.2 d)].

6.3.1 Plant, facility, and equipment planning. The organization shall use a multidisciplinary approach (see 7.3.1.1) for developing plant, facility, and equipment plans. Plant layouts shall optimize material travel, handling, and value-added use of floor space, and shall facilitate synchronous material flow. Methods shall be developed and implemented to evaluate and monitor the effectiveness of existing operations.

Note: These requirements should focus on lean manufacturing principles and the link to the effectiveness of the QMS.

6.3.2 Contingency plans. The organization shall prepare contingency plans to satisfy customer requirements in the event of an emergency such as utility interruptions, labor shortages, key equipment failure, and field returns.

6.4.1 Personnel safety to achieve product quality. Product safety and means to minimize potential risks to employees shall be addressed by the organization, especially in the design and development process and in manufacturing process activities.

6.4.2 Cleanliness of premises. The organization shall maintain its premises in a state of order, cleanliness, and repair consistent with the product and manufacturing process needs.

7.1 Planning of product realization. Note: Some customers refer to project management or advanced product quality planning as a means to achieve product realization. Advanced product quality planning embodies the concepts of error prevention and continual improvement as contrasted with error detection, and is based on a multidisciplinary approach.

7.1.1 Planning of product realization—Supplemental. Customer requirements and references to its technical specifications shall be included in the planning of product realization as a component of the quality plan.

7.1.2 Acceptance criteria. Acceptance criteria shall be defined by the organization and, where required, approved by the customer. For attribute data sampling, the acceptance level shall be zero defects (see 8.2.3.1).

7.1.3 Confidentiality. The organization shall ensure the confidentiality of customer-contracted products and projects under development, and related product information.

7.1.4 Change control. The organization shall have a process to control and react to changes that impact product realization. The effects of any change, including those changes caused by any supplier, shall be assessed, and verification and validation activities shall be defined to ensure compliance with customer requirements. Changes shall be validated before implementation. For proprietary designs, impact on form, fit, and function (including performance and/or durability) shall be reviewed with the customer so that all effects can be properly evaluated. When required by the customer, additional verification and/or identification requirements, such as those required for new product introduction, shall be met.

Note 1: Any product realization change affecting customer requirements requires notification to, and agreement from, the customer.

Note 2: The aforementioned requirement applies to product and manufacturing process changes.

7.2.1 Determination of requirements related to the product. Note 1: Post-delivery activities include any after-sales product service provided as part of the customer contract or purchase order.

Note 2: This requirement includes recycling, environmental impact, and characteristics identified as a result of the organization's knowledge of the product and manufacturing processes (see 7.3.2.3).

Note 3: Compliance to item c) includes all applicable government, safety, and environmental regulations, applied to acquisition, storage, handling, recycling, elimination, or disposal of materials.

7.2.1.1 Customer-designated special characteristics. The organization shall demonstrate conformity to customer requirements for designation, documentation, and control of special characteristics.

7.2.2.1 Review of requirements related to the product—Supplemental. Waiving the requirement stated in 7.2.2 for a formal review (see note) shall require customer authorization.

7.2.2.2 Organization manufacturing feasibility. The organization shall investigate, confirm, and document the manufacturing feasibility of the proposed products in the contract review process, including risk analysis.

7.2.3.1 Customer communication—Supplemental. The organization shall have the ability to communicate necessary information, including data, in a customer-specified language and format (for example, computer-aided design data, electronic data exchange).

7.3 Design and development. Note: The requirements of 7.3 include product and manufacturing process design and development, and focus on error prevention rather than detection.

7.3.1.1 Multidisciplinary approach. The organization shall use a multidisciplinary approach to prepare for product realization, including:

- Development/finalization and monitoring of special characteristics

- Development and review of FMEAs, including actions to reduce potential risks

- Development and review of control plans

Note: A multidisciplinary approach typically includes the organization's design, manufacturing, engineering, quality, production, and other appropriate personnel.

7.3.2 Design and development inputs. These inputs shall be reviewed for adequacy. Requirements shall be complete, unambiguous, and not in conflict with each other.
Note: Special characteristics (see 7.2.1.1) are included in this requirement.

7.3.2.1 Product design input. The organization shall identify, document, and review the product design input requirements, including the following:

- Customer requirements (contract review) such as special characteristics (see 7.3.2.3), identification, traceability, and packaging.

- Use of information: the organization shall have a process to deploy information gained from previous design projects, competitor analysis, supplier feedback, internal input, field data, and other relevant sources, for current and future projects of a similar nature.

- Targets for product quality, life, reliability, durability, maintainability, timing, and cost

7.3.2.2 Manufacturing process design input. The organization shall identify, document, and review the manufacturing process design input requirements, including:

- Product design output data

- Targets for productivity, process capability, and cost

- Customers requirements, if any

- Experience from previous developments

Note: The manufacturing process design includes the use of error-proofing methods to a degree appropriate to the magnitude of the problems and commensurate with the risks encountered.

7.3.2.3 Special characteristics. The organization shall identify special characteristics [see 7.3.3 (d)] and:

- Include all special characteristics in the control plan

- Comply with customer-specified definitions and symbols

- Identify process control documents including drawings, FMEAs, control plans, and operator instructions with the customer's special characteristic symbol or the organization's equivalent symbol or notation to include those process steps that affect special characteristics

Note: Special characteristics can include product characteristics and process parameters

7.3.3.1 Product design outputs—Supplemental. The product design output shall be expressed in terms that can be verified and validated against product design input requirements. The product design output shall include:

- Design FMEA, reliability results

- Product special characteristics and specifications

- Product error-proofing, as appropriate

- Product definition including drawings or mathematically based data

- Product design reviews results

- Diagnostic guidelines where applicable

7.3.3.2 Manufacturing process design output. The manufacturing process design output shall be expressed in terms that can be verified against manufacturing process design input requirements and validated. The manufacturing process design output shall include:

- Specifications and drawings

- Manufacturing process flowchart/layout

- Manufacturing process FMEAs

- Control plan (see 7.5.1.1)

- Work instructions

- Process approval acceptance criteria

- Data for quality, reliability, maintainability, and measurability

- Results of error-proofing activities, as appropriate

- Methods of rapid detection and feedback of product/manufacturing process nonconformities (7.3.4)

Note: These reviews are normally coordinated with the design phases and include manufacturing process design and development.

7.3.4 Design and development review. These reviews are normally coordinated with the design phases and include manufacturing process design and development.

7.3.4.1 Monitoring. Measurements at specified stages of design and development shall be defined, analyzed, and reported with summary results as an input to management review.

Note: These measurements include quality risks, costs, lead-times, critical paths, and others, as appropriate.

7.3.6 Design and development validation. Note 1: The validation process normally includes an analysis of field reports for similar products.

Note 2: The requirements of 7.3.5 and 7.3.6 apply to both product and manufacturing processes.

7.3.6.1 Design and development validation—Supplemental. Design and development validation shall be performed in accordance with customer requirements including program timing.

7.3.6.2 Prototype program. When required by the customer, the organization shall have a prototype program and control plan. The organization shall use, wherever possible, the same suppliers, tooling, and manufacturing processes as will be used in production. All performance-testing activities shall be monitored for timely completion and conformity to requirements.

While services may be outsourced, the organization shall be responsible for the outsourced services, including technical leadership.

7.3.6.3 Product approval process. The organization shall conform to a product and manufacturing process approval procedure recognized by the customer.

Note: Product approval should be subsequent to the verification of the manufacturing process. This product and manufacturing process approval procedure shall also be applied to suppliers.

7.3.7 Control of design and development changes. Note: Design and development changes include all changes during the product program life (see 7.1.4).

7.4.1 Purchasing process. Note 1: Purchased products include all products and services that affect customer requirements such as subassembly, sequencing, sorting, rework, and calibration services.

Note 2: When there are mergers, acquisitions, or affiliations associated with suppliers, the organization should verify the continuity of the supplier's QMS and its effectiveness.

7.4.1.1 Regulatory conformity. All purchased products or materials used in product shall conform to applicable regulatory requirements.

7.4.1.2 Supplier quality management system development. The organization shall perform supplier quality management system development with the goal of supplier conformity with this technical specification. Conformity with ISO 9001:2000 is the first step in achieving this goal.

Note: The prioritization of suppliers for development depends upon, for example, the supplier's quality performance and the importance of the product supplied.

Unless otherwise specified by the customer, suppliers to the organization shall be third-party registered to ISO 9001:2000 by an accredited third-party certification body.

7.4.1.3 Customer-approved sources. Where specified by the contract (for example, customer engineering drawing, specification), the organization shall purchase products, materials, or services from approved sources. The use of customer-designated sources, including tool/gauge suppliers, does not relieve the organization of the responsibility for ensuring the quality of purchased products.

7.4.3.1 Incoming product quality. The organization shall have a process to assure the quality of purchased product (see 7.4.3) utilizing one or more of the following methods:

- Receipt of, and evaluation of, statistical data by the organization

- Receiving inspection and/or testing such as sampling based on performance

- Second- or third-party assessments or audits of supplier sites, when coupled with records of acceptable delivered product quality

- Part evaluation by a designated laboratory

- Another method agreed with the customer

7.4.3.2 Supplier monitoring. Supplier performance shall be monitored through the following indicators:

- Delivered product quality

- Customer disruptions including field returns

- Delivery schedule performance (including incidents of premium freight)

- Special status customer notifications related to quality or delivery issues

The organization shall promote supplier monitoring of the performance of their manufacturing processes.

7.5.1.1 Control plan. The organization shall:

- Develop control plans (see annex A) at the system, subsystem, component, and/or material level for the product supplied, including those for processes producing bulk materials as well as parts, and have a control plan for pre-launch and production that takes into account the design FMEA and manufacturing process FMEA outputs.

The control plan shall:

- List the controls used for the manufacturing process control, include methods for monitoring of control exercised over special characteristics (see 7.3.2.3) defined by both

- Include the customer-required information, if any, and initiate the specified reaction plan (see 8.2.3.1) when the process becomes unstable or not statistically capable.

Control plans shall be reviewed and updated when any change occurs affecting product, manufacturing process, measurement, logistics, supply sources, or FMEA (see 7.1.4).

Note: Customer approval may be required after review or update of the control plan.

7.5.1.2 Work instructions. The organization shall prepare documented work instructions for all employees having responsibilities for the operation of processes that impact product quality. These instructions shall be accessible for use at the work station. These instructions shall be derived from sources such as the quality plan, the control plan, and the product realization process.

7.5.1.3 Verification of job set-ups. Job set-ups shall be verified whenever performed, such as an initial run of a job, material changeover, or job change. Work instructions shall be available for set-up personnel. The organization shall use statistical methods of verification where applicable.

Note: Last-off-part comparisons are recommended.

7.5.1.4 Preventive and predictive maintenance. The organization shall identify key process equipment and provide resources for machine/equipment maintenance and develop an effective planned total preventive maintenance system. As a minimum, this system shall include the following:

- Planned maintenance activities

- Packaging and preservation of equipment, tooling, and gauging

- Availability of replacement parts for key manufacturing equipment

- Documenting, evaluating, and improving maintenance objectives

The organization shall utilize predictive maintenance methods to continually improve the effectiveness and the efficiency of production equipment.

7.5.1.5 Management of production tooling. The organization shall provide resources for tool and gage design, fabrication, and verification activities.

The organization shall establish and implement a system for production tooling management including:

- Maintenance and repair facilities and personnel

- Storage and recovery

- Set-up

- Tool-change programs for perishable tools

- Tool design modification documentation, including engineering change level

- Tool modification and revision to documentation

- Tool identification, defining the status, such as production, repair or disposal

The organization shall implement a system to monitor these activities if any work is outsourced.

Note: This requirement also applies to the availability of tools for vehicle service parts.

7.5.1.6 Production scheduling. Production shall be scheduled in order to meet customer requirements, such as just-in-time supported by an information system that permits access to production information at key stages of the process and is order driven.

7.5.1.7 Feedback of information from service. A process for communication of information on service concerns to manufacturing, engineering, and design activities shall be established and maintained.

Note: The intent of the addition of "service concerns" to this subclause is to ensure that the organization is aware of nonconformities that occur external to its organization.

7.5.1.8 Service agreement with customer. When there is a service agreement with the customer, the organization shall verify the effectiveness of:

- Any organization service centers

- Any special-purpose tools or measurement equipment

- The training of service personnel

7.5.2.1 Validation of processes for production and service provision— Supplemental. The requirements of 7.5.2 shall apply to all processes for production and service provision.

7.5.3 Identification and traceability. Note: Inspection and test status is not indicated by the location of product in the production flow unless inherently obvious, such as material in an automated production transfer process. Alternatives are permitted, if the status is clearly identified, documented, and achieves the designated purpose.

7.5.3.1 Identification and traceability—Supplemental. The words "where appropriate" in 7.5.3 shall not apply.

7.5.4 Customer property. Note: Customer-owned returnable packaging is included in this clause.

7.5.4.1 Customer-owned production tooling. Customer-owned tools, manufacturing, test, inspection tooling, and equipment shall be permanently marked so that the ownership of each item is visible and can be determined.

7.5.5.1 Storage and inventory. In order to detect deterioration, the condition of product in stock shall be assessed at appropriate planned intervals. The organization shall use an inventory management system to optimize inventory turns over time and assure stock rotation, such as first in/first out (FIFO). Obsolete product shall be controlled in a similar manner to nonconforming product.

7.6 Control of monitoring and measuring devices. Note: A number or other identifier traceable to the device calibration record meets the intent of requirement c) in this clause.

7.6.1 Measurement system analysis. Statistical studies shall be conducted to analyze the variation present in the results of each type of measuring and test equipment system. This requirement shall apply to measurement systems referenced in the control plan. The analytical methods and acceptance criteria used shall conform to those in customer reference manuals on measurement systems analysis. Other analytical methods and acceptance criteria may be used if approved by the customer.

7.6.2 Calibration/verification records. Records of the calibration/verification activity for all gages, and measuring and test equipment needed to provide evidence of conformity of product to determined requirements, including employee- and customer-owned equipment, shall include:

- Equipment identification, including the measurement standard against which the equipment is calibrated
- Revisions following engineering changes

- Any out-of-specification readings as received for calibration/ verification

- An assessment of the impact of out-of-specification condition

- Statements of conformity to specification after calibration/verification

- Notification to the customer if suspect product or material has been shipped

7.6.3.1 Internal laboratory. An organization's internal laboratory facility shall have a defined scope that includes its capability to perform the required inspection, test, or calibration services. This laboratory scope shall be included in the QMS documentation. The laboratory shall specify and implement, as a minimum, technical requirements for:

- Adequacy of the laboratory procedures

- Competency of the laboratory personnel

- Testing of the product

- Capability to perform these services correctly, traceable to the relevant process standard (such as ASTM, EN)

- Review of the related records

Note: Accreditation to ISO/IEC 17025 may be used to demonstrate supplier in-house laboratory conformity to this requirement, but it is not mandatory.

7.6.3.2 External laboratory. External/commercial/independent laboratory facilities used for inspection, test, or calibration services by the organization shall have a defined laboratory scope that includes the capability to perform the required inspection, test, or calibration, and either:

- There shall be evidence that the external laboratory is acceptable to the customer, or

- The laboratory shall be accredited to ISO/IEC 17025 or national equivalent.

Note 1: Such evidence may be demonstrated by customer assessment, for example, or by customer-approved second-party assessment that the laboratory meets the intent of ISO/IEC 17025 or national equivalent.

Note 2: When a qualified laboratory is not available for a given piece of equipment, calibration services may be performed by the equipment manufacturer. In such cases, the organization should ensure that the requirements listed in 7.6.3.1 have been met.

8.1.1 Identification of statistical tools. Appropriate statistical tools for each process shall be determined during advance quality planning and included in the control plan.

8.1.2 Knowledge of basic statistical concepts. Basic statistical concepts, such as variation, control (stability), process capability, and overadjustment shall be understood and utilized throughout the organization.

8.2.1 Customer satisfaction. Note: Consideration should be given to both internal and external customers.

8.2.1.1 Customer satisfaction—Supplemental. Customer satisfaction with the organization shall be monitored through continual evaluation of performance of the realization processes. Performance indicators shall be based on objective data and include, but not be limited to:

- Delivered part quality performance

- Customer disruptions, including field returns

- Delivery schedule performance (including incidents of premium freight)

- Customer notifications related to quality or delivery issues

The organization shall monitor the performance of manufacturing processes to demonstrate compliance with customer requirements for product quality and efficiency of the process.

8.2.2.1 Quality management system audit. The organization shall audit its QMS to verify compliance with this technical specification and any additional QMS requirements.

8.2.2.2 Manufacturing process audit. The organization shall audit each manufacturing process to determine its effectiveness.

8.2.2.3 Product audit. The organization shall audit products at appropriate stages of production and delivery to verify conformity to all specified requirements, such as product dimensions, functionality, packaging, and labeling, at a defined frequency.

8.2.2.4 Internal audit plans. Internal audits shall cover all quality management-related processes, activities, and shifts, and shall be scheduled according to an annual plan. When internal/external nonconformities or customer complaints occur, the audit frequency shall be appropriately increased.

Note: Specific checklists should be used for each audit.

8.2.2.5 Internal auditor qualification. The organization shall have internal auditors who are qualified to audit the requirements of this technical specification (see 6.2.2.2).

8.2.3.1 Monitoring and measurement of manufacturing processes. The organization shall perform process studies on all new manufacturing (including assembly or sequencing) processes to verify process capability and to provide additional input for process control. The results of process studies shall be documented with specifications, where applicable, for means of production, measurement and test, and maintenance instructions. These documents shall include objectives for manufacturing process capability, reliability, maintainability, and availability, as well as acceptance criteria. The organization shall maintain manufacturing process capability or performance as specified by the customer part approval process requirements. The organization shall ensure that the control plan and process flow diagram are implemented, including adherence to the specified:

- Measurement techniques

- Sampling plans

- Acceptance criteria

- Reaction plans when acceptance criteria are not met

Significant process events, such as tool change or machine repair, shall be recorded.

The organization shall initiate a reaction plan from the control plan for characteristics that are either not statistically capable or are unstable. These reaction plans shall include containment of product and 100 percent inspection as appropriate. A corrective-action plan shall then be completed by the organization, indicating specific timing and assigned responsibilities to assure that the process becomes stable and capable. The plans shall be reviewed with and approved by the customer when so required. The organization shall maintain records of effective dates of process changes.

8.2.4 Monitoring and measurement of product. Note: When selecting product parameters to monitor compliance to specified internal and external requirements, the organization determines the types of product characteristics, leading to:

- The types of measurement

- Suitable measurement means

- The capability and skills required

8.2.4.1 Layout inspection and functional testing. A layout inspection and a functional verification to applicable customer engineering material and performance standards shall be performed for each product as specified in the control plans. Results shall be available for customer review.

Note: Layout inspection is the complete measurement of all product dimensions shown on the design records.

8.2.4.2 Appearance items. For organizations manufacturing parts designated by the customer as "appearance items," the organization shall provide:

- Appropriate resources including lighting for evaluation

- Masters for color, grain, gloss, metallic brilliance, texture, distinctness of image (DOI), as appropriate

- Maintenance and control of appearance masters and evaluation equipment

- Verification that personnel making appearance evaluations are competent and qualified to do so

8.3.1 Control of nonconforming product—Supplemental. Product with unidentified or suspect status shall be classified as nonconforming product (see 7.5.3).

8.3.2 Control of reworked product. Instructions for rework, including reinspection requirements, shall be accessible to and utilized by the appropriate personnel.

8.3.3 Customer information. Customers shall be informed promptly in the event that nonconforming product has been shipped.

8.3.4 Customer waiver. The organization shall obtain a customer concession or deviation permit prior to further processing whenever the product or manufacturing process is different from that which is currently approved. The organization shall maintain a record of the expiration date or quantity authorized. The organization shall also ensure compliance with the original or superseding specifications and requirements when the authorization expires. Material shipped on an authorization shall be properly identified on each shipping container. This applies equally to purchased product. The organization shall agree with any requests from suppliers before submission to the customer.

8.4.1 Analysis and use of data. Trends in quality and operational performance shall be compared with progress toward objectives and lead to action to support the following:

- Development of priorities for prompt solutions to customer-related problems

- Determination of key customer-related trends and correlation for status review, decision making, and longer-term planning

- An information system for the timely reporting of product information arising from usage

Note: Data should be compared with those of competitors and/or appropriate benchmarks.

8.5.1.1 Continual improvement of the organization. The organization shall define a process for continual improvement (see examples in annex B of ISO 9004:2000).

8.5.1.2 Manufacturing process improvement. Manufacturing process improvement shall continually focus upon control and reduction of variation in product characteristics and manufacturing process parameters.

Note 1: Controlled characteristics are documented in the control plan.

Note 2: Continual improvement is implemented once manufacturing processes are capable and stable, or product characteristics are predictable and meet customer requirements.

8.5.2.1 Problem solving. The organization shall have a defined process for problem solving leading to root-cause identification and elimination. If a customer-prescribed problem-solving format exists, the organization shall use the prescribed format.

8.5.2.2 Error-proofing. The organization shall use error-proofing methods in their corrective-action process.

8.5.2.3 Corrective-action impact. The organization shall apply to other similar processes and products the corrective action, and controls implemented, to eliminate the cause of a nonconformity.

8.5.2.4 Rejected product test/analysis. The organization shall analyze parts rejected by the customer's manufacturing plants, engineering facilities, and dealerships. The organization shall minimize the cycle time of this process. Records of these analyses shall be kept and made available upon request. The organization shall perform analysis and initiate corrective action to prevent recurrence.

Note: Cycle time related to rejected product analysis should be consistent with the determination of root cause, corrective action, and monitoring the effectiveness of implementation.

REFERENCE

ISO/TS 16949: Quality management systems—Particular requirements for the application of ISO 9001:2000 for automotive production and relevant service part organizations. 2002. ISO.

4

Customer-Specific Requirements for Use With ISO/TS 16949 Second Edition

As we said earlier, ISO 9001:2000 is a generic quality standard that attempts to facilitate, through enhanced synergy, both productivity and efficiency for all kinds of organizations. In the case of the automotive industry, however, some of the companies thought the standard did not sufficiently cover their requirements and started to think of more precise requirements. The first wave of these was QS-9000 and the second one is the current ISO/TS 16949:2000.

In ISO/TS 16949 the key players [DaimlerChrysler, General Motors (GM), and Ford Motor Company], at least in the United States, have some additional requirements as they relate to their quality systems. Table 4.1 summarizes some of the individual parameters of their quality expectations.

To appreciate the additional requirements of the American automotive industry, it is imperative that one understands their special vocabulary. It is also important to recognize that if there is a discrepancy between ISO/TS and the specific requirements, the specific requirements will take precedence. In Table 4.2 we summarize some of the special language that is used in the American automotive sector.

Now that we have addressed the expectations and the special vocabulary for the key American automotive companies, we are ready to address their additional requirements. We begin with DaimlerChrysler, and follow with GM and Ford Motor Company.

Table 4.1 Summary of parameters and expectations for DaimlerChrysler, General Motors, and Ford Motor Company.

DaimlerChrysler

After July 1, 2004, ISO/TS 16949:2002 replaces QS-9000 and VDA 6.1 for organizations supplying production and/or service parts. These requirements shall be included in any scope of registration/certification to ISO/TS 16949 issued by an IATF-recognized and IATF-contracted certification body in order for the ISO/TS 16949 certificate to be recognized as satisfying DaimlerChrysler organization criteria for third-party registration/certification.

ISO/TS 16949 is also applicable to assemblers of production parts or materials and to vehicle assembly plants. Service parts and materials applicability does not include aftermarket parts or organizations. All ISO/TS 16949 requirements and the requirements of this document shall be documented in the organization's quality system. The English language version of ISO/TS 16949 and this document shall be the official version for purposes of third-party registration. Translations of ISO/TS 16949 published by SMMT (British), VDA (German), AFNOR (French), ANFIA (Italian), JAMA (Japanese), and STTG (Spanish) are acceptable for purposes of third-party registration. Sanctioned translations of this document shall:

- Be for reference only
- Reference the English version as the official language
- Include DaimlerChrysler, Ford, and GM in the copyright statement

Any other translations are not authorized.

Copies of this document are available from AIAG.

General Motors (GM)

ISO/TS 16949:2002, Second Edition, March 1, 2002, *Quality management systems—Particular requirements for the application of ISO 9001:2000 for automotive production and relevant service part organizations,* and the following requirements define GM's fundamental quality system requirements for organizations where automotive customer-specified parts, for production and/or service are manufactured. To satisfy supplier quality system requirements, GM will accept, as optional to QS-9000, a third-party certification to ISO/TS 16949 that meets the following conditions:

- The certification scope must include both ISO/TS 16949 and the accompanying ISO/TS 16949 GM Customer-Specific Requirements,
- The certification must be conducted in compliance with the IATF recognized automotive certification scheme by a certification body contracted with an IATF Oversight office.

Note: The Quality System Requirements, QS-9000, 3rd Edition, expires on December 14, 2006. All ISO/TS 16949:2002 requirements and the requirements of this document shall be documented in the organization's quality system.

continued

continued

Ford Motor Company

ISO/TS 16949:2002 and the specific requirements define the fundamental quality system requirements for Ford Motor Company suppliers as an alternative to QS-9000 3rd edition. After December 14, 2006, QS-9000 registration will no longer be accepted by Ford Motor Company. The company-specific requirements are supplemental to Technical Specification ISO/TS 16949:2002. These supplemental requirements shall be included in the scope of the registration/certification audit in order to be recognized as satisfying the Ford Motor Company supplier criteria for third-party certification by an IATF-recognized and contracted certification body.

ISO/TS 16949:2002 is applicable to manufacturing sites of suppliers to Ford Motor Company (production and service parts and materials), and to assemblers of production parts or materials supplying to Ford Vehicle Assembly Plants.

Tooling and equipment suppliers to Ford Motor Company are not eligible to be registered to ISO/TS 16949:2002. However, they are eligible for registration to QS-9000 TE Supplement until December 14, 2006.

Semiconductor suppliers may register to ISO/TS 16949:2002, providing they meet the scope requirements. They may also be eligible to register to QS-9000 Semiconductor Supplement.

See the SQRTF (Supplier Quality Requirements Task Force) letter on QS-9000 supplements at https://web.bli.ford.com.

The QS-9000 supplements are available through AIAG: http://www.aiag.org.

Service parts and materials applicability does not include aftermarket or remanufactured parts. All ISO/TS 16949:2002 requirements and the requirements of the specific requirements shall be documented in the organization's quality system.

Similar to QS-9000, ISO/TS 16949 may have sanctioned interpretations (SIs). If there are any SIs for ISO/TS 16949, they would be available on http://www.iaob.org.

The U.S. English language version of this document shall be the official version for purposes of third-party registration.

Any translations of this document shall:

- Be for reference only
- Reference the English (AIAG) version as the official language
- Be acceptable only if translated by organizations authorized by TS 16949 Oversight (see http://www.iaob.org)
- Include Ford Motor Company in the copyright statement

Copies of the special requirements are available from Ford Motor Company at https://web.bli.ford.com and International Automotive Oversight Board at http://www.iaob.org.

Note: To have access to the Web sites you must be an authorized supplier, must have a current ID, and must have the appropriate password.

Table 4.2 Summary of special terms used in the automotive industry.

DaimlerChrysler

---

active part: An active part is one currently being supplied to DaimlerChrysler for original equipment or service applications. The part remains active until tooling scrap authorization is given by the appropriate DaimlerChrysler activity. For parts with no DaimlerChrysler-owned tooling or situations where multiple parts are made from the same tool, written confirmation from the appropriate DaimlerChrysler activity is required to deactivate a part.

aftermarket parts: Replacement parts not procured or released by DaimlerChrysler for service part applications, which may or may not be produced to original equipment specifications.

consulting: For the purpose of ISO/TS 16949 and supporting documents, consulting is the provision of training, documentation development, or assistance with implementation of quality systems to a specific customer. If these activities are open to the public, advertised, and not customer-specific, they are considered training rather than consulting. Other products, processes or services may be offered directly or indirectly, provided they do not compromise confidentiality or the objectivity or impartiality of its certification process or decisions [refer to IAF Guidance on the Application of ISO/IEC Guide 62, Issue 2, dated 4 December 2001 to ISO/IEC Guide 62:1996.]

customer: For the purposes of ISO/TS 16949, references to "customer" in this document shall be interpreted as DaimlerChrysler for organizations pursuing third-party registration to ISO/TS 16949.

initial process study: Initial process studies are short-term studies conducted to obtain early information on the performance of new or revised processes relative to internal or customer requirements. In many cases, initial process studies should be conducted at several points in the evolution of new processes (for example, at the equipment or tooling subcontractor's plant, after installation at the organization's plant). These studies should be based on variables data evaluated using control charts. See Production Part Approval Process manual.

parts per million quality metrics (ppm): Parts per million is a method of stating the performance of a process in terms of actual nonconforming material. Parts per million data can be used to prioritize corrective actions. Definition of nonconforming units varies with customer (for example, all sorted, only those found to be wrong, all in box).

site: Includes vehicle assembly plants

General Motors (GM)

---

active part: An active part is one currently being supplied to the customer for original equipment or service applications. The part remains active until tooling scrap authorization is given by the appropriate customer activity. For parts with no customer-owned tooling or situations where multiple parts are made from the same tool, written confirmation from the customer purchasing activity is required to deactivate a part.

Note: For bulk material, "active part" refers to the bulk material contracted, not the parts that are subsequently produced from that material.

aftermarket part: Replacement parts not procured or released by OEM for service part applications, which may or may not be produced to original equipment specifications.

---

continued

General Motors (GM)

consulting: For the purposes of TS16949:2002, consulting is the provision of training, documentation development, or assistance with implementation of quality systems to a specific customer. If these activities are open to the public, advertised, and not customer-specific, they are considered training rather than consulting. Other products, processes or services may be offered directly or indirectly, provided they do not compromise confidentiality or the objectivity or impartiality of its certification process or decisions (refer to IAF Guidance on the Application of ISO/IEC Guide 62, Issue 2, dated December, 2001.)]

customer: References to "customer" in ISO/TS 16949:2002 and this document shall be interpreted as the procuring division of General Motors for suppliers pursuing third-party registration to ISO/TS 16949:2002 to satisfy General Motors' sourcing requirements third-party quality system assessment registration.

ergonomics: Ergonomics is the evaluation of the design of a product or process to assure compatibility with the capabilities of human beings. Analysis of motion refers to capabilities of people with respect to tasks (for example, lifting, twisting, reaching) to prevent or relieve problems of strain, stress, excessive fatigue, and so on. Factors involved include anatomical dimensions of the worker, placement of products to be worked upon, placement of buttons/switches, physical loads imposed on the worker, and environmental effects such as noise, vibration, lighting, and space.

initial process study: Initial process studies are short-term studies conducted to obtain early information on the performance of new or revised processes relative to internal or customer requirements. In many cases, preliminary studies should be conducted at several points in the evolution of new processes (for example, at the equipment or tooling subcontractor's plant, after installation at the supplier's plant). These studies should be based on as many measures as possible. When utilizing X-Bar and R charts, at least 25 subgroups (minimum of four pieces per subgroup) are required to obtain sufficient data for decision making. When this amount of data is not available, control charts should be started with whatever data are available. See Production Part Approval Process manual.

parts per million (ppm): Parts per million is a method of stating the performance of a process in terms of actual nonconforming material. Parts per million data can be used to prioritize corrective actions. Definition of defective units varies with customer (for example, all sorted, only those found to be wrong, all in box).

organization: Organizations are defined as providers of: a) production materials, b) production or service parts, or c) heat-treating, plating, painting or other finishing services, directly to General Motors or other customers subscribing to this document.

Note: In QS-9000, these providers are typically referred to as suppliers to DaimlerChrysler, Ford, and General Motors; however, for the purpose of this document they are defined as the "organization" or "supply organization." TS 16949:2002.

service parts: Replacement parts manufactured to OEM specifications that are procured or released by the OEM for service part application.

suppliers: Suppliers (previously called subcontractors in QS-9000) are defined as providers of production materials, or production or service parts, directly to an organization provider of General Motors or other customers subscribing to this document. Also included are providers of heat-treating, painting, plating, or other finishing services.

value-added production processes: Activities or operations for which a customer would be willing to pay, if given the option. See also *ISO/TS 16949:2002,* second edition (March 2002), definition of "manufacturing" 3.1.6, "site" 3.1.11, and "remote location" 3.1.10.

continued

Ford Motor Company

active part: An active part is one currently being supplied to the customer for original equipment or service applications. The part remains active until tooling scrap authorization is given by the appropriate customer activity. For parts with no customer-owned tooling or situations where multiple parts are made from the same tool, written confirmation from Ford Engineering and the buyer is required to deactivate a part.

aftermarket parts: Replacement parts not procured or released by Ford Motor Company for service part applications, which may or may not be produced to original equipment specifications.

capacity verification: A verification methodology to demonstrate that an organization can meet the capacity planning volume requirements as defined in the purchasing request for quote (RFQ).

consulting: For the purpose of ISO/TS 16949:2002 and supporting documents, consulting is the provision of training, documentation development, or assistance with implementation of quality systems to a specific customer. If these activities are open to the public, advertised, and not customer-specific, they are considered training rather than consulting. Other products, processes, or services may be offered directly or indirectly, provided they do not compromise confidentiality or the objectivity or impartiality of its certification process or decisions [refer to IAF Guidance on the Application of ISO/IEC Guide 62, issued December 4, 2001].

customer: For the purposes of ISO/TS 16949:2002, references to "customer" are interpreted as the entity, for example, Ford Motor Company, which is both purchasing and receiving product from the organization complying with ISO/TS 16949:2002.

ergonomics: Ergonomics is the evaluation of the design of a product or process to assure compatibility with the capabilities of human beings. Analysis of motion refers to capabilities of people with respect to tasks (for example, lifting, twisting, reaching) to prevent or relieve problems of strain, stress, excessive fatigue, and so on. Factors involved include anatomical dimensions of the worker, placement of products to be worked upon, placement of buttons/switches, physical loads imposed on the worker, and environmental effects such as noise, vibration, lighting, and space.

Ford Motor Company: The names "Ford Motor Company" or "Ford" refer to the corporate entity comprising all brands under Ford Motor Company.

Ford Engineering: Ford Motor Company Product Development Engineering, including program and nonprogram engineering organizations.

initial process study: Initial process studies are conducted to obtain early information on the performance of new or revised processes relative to internal or customer requirements. In many cases, initial process studies should be conducted at several points in the evolution of new processes (for example, at the equipment or tooling subcontractor's plant, and after installation at the organization's plant). These studies should be based on variables data evaluated using statistically valid methods.

organization: Facility adding manufacturing value to production materials: providers of production or service parts, or heat-treating, plating, painting or other finishing services, directly to Ford Motor Company.

Note 1: For the purposes of registration under ISO/TS 16949:2002, the "organization" is the entity normally referred to by Ford as the "supplier." Ford Motor Company will continue to use that term when negotiating with the organization.

continued

continued

Ford Motor Company

Note 2: To avoid additional confusion, although the term "supplier" is used by ISO/TS 16949:2002 to indicate "subcontractor," Ford Motor Company will continue to use the term "subcontractor" in its normal usage.

Note 3: "Full Service Suppliers" also provide engineering services. Program-specific Engineering Statement of Work defines engineering responsibilities.

Note 4: Sequencing warehouses and other facilities not adding *manufacturing* value to the product are not eligible for stand-alone registration to ISO/TS 16949:2002.

part per million (ppm) quality metrics: A method of stating the performance of a process in terms of actual nonconforming material. Part per million data can be used to prioritize corrective actions.

process approach: A method to measure and improve organizational performance in terms of customer metrics and specifications.

shall: A mandatory requirement.

should: Indicates a mandatory requirement with some flexibility allowed in compliance methodology. Organizations choosing other approaches to satisfy a "should" must be able to show that their approach meets the intent of ISO/TS 16949:2002.

SIM: Supplier improvement metrics—supplier performance measurements available through https://fsn.ford.com/ or FSP (Ford Supplier Portal).

Site: An organization's individual manufacturing location that has material/part input and part output.

Note: Includes assemblers and vehicle assembly plants.

SREA: supplier request for engineering approval, per AIAG PPAP.

STA: Supplier technical assistance—Ford Motor Company's team dedicated to assist in the development of supplier processes.

subcontractor: Provider of production materials, or production or service parts, directly to an organization complying with ISO/TS16949:2002. Also included are providers of heat treating, painting, plating, or other finishing services to organizations.

value-added production processes: Manufacturing activities or operations for which a customer would be willing to pay, if given the option.

final customer: Owner of the vehicle sold through commercial or private transaction.

global 8-D process: A disciplined process that addresses problem solving in a methodical and analytical method, addressing root causes to eliminate the source(s) of the concern.

ISO/TS 16949–RELATED REQUIREMENTS FOR DAIMLERCHRYSLER

Tooling Management *(ISO/TS 16949 cl. 7.5.1.5)*

Tooling management is not required of warehouses or distributors.

Production part approvals, tooling records, purchase orders, and amendments shall be maintained for the length of time that the part (or family of parts) is active for production and service requirements plus one calendar year unless otherwise specified by DaimlerChrysler. [Note: All DaimlerChrysler purchase orders/amendments are included in this requirement. Organization purchase orders/amendments for DaimlerChrysler-owned tooling are included in this requirement.]

Quality performance records (for example, control charts, inspection and test results) shall be retained for one calendar year after the year in which they were created.

Records of internal quality system audits and management review shall be retained for three years. Retention periods longer than those specified previously may be specified by an organization in their procedures. The organization shall eventually dispose of records.

These requirements do not supersede any regulatory requirements. All specified retention periods shall be considered "minimums."

Special Characteristics Not Identified with Symbols *(ISO/TS 16949 cl. 3.1.12, 7.2.1.1, 7.3.1.1, 7.3.2.3, 7.3.3.1)*

Those product or process characteristics chosen by DaimlerChrysler or the organization that affect fit, form, function, or appearance that are not identified with a symbol.

Design Changes *(ISO/TS 16949 cl. 7.3.7)*

All design changes, including those proposed by subcontractors, shall have written DaimlerChrysler approval, or waiver of such approval, prior to production implementation. See ISO/TS 16949 cl. 7.3.7 and the Production Part Approval Process manual.

For proprietary designs, impact on form, fit, function, performance, and/or durability shall be determined with DaimlerChrysler so that all effects can be properly evaluated.

Production Part Approval Process (*ISO/TS 16949 cl. 7.3.6.3*)

The organization shall comply with the DaimlerChrysler, Ford, and GM Production Part Approval Process manual to comply with ISO/TS 16949, cl. 7.3.6.3. (Does not apply to vehicle assembly plants that use the pilot vehicle process.) The organization shall require PPAP from its suppliers.

Certification Body/Registrar Notification

An organization shall notify its certification body/registrar in writing within five working days when DaimlerChrysler places the site in the "needs improvement" category. Being in this category is a violation of 8.2.1.1 of ISO/TS 16949.

Supplier Quality Management System Development (*ISO/TS 16949 cl. 7.4.1.2*)

DaimlerChrysler will accept registration to QS-9000 in lieu of ISO 9001:2000 until July 1, 2004.

Third-Party Registration Requirements

All production and service part organizations supplying to DaimlerChrysler shall be third-party registered to ISO/TS 16949 second edition by July 4, 2004.

Product Creation Process

DaimlerChrysler has a documented method of product assurance planning (PAP). This method, combined with the team's dedication and knowledge, is the tool used throughout the product creation process to consistently develop and produce products that will satisfy the customer. All team members, including organizations, shall participate in producing products using DaimlerChrysler's PAP method. On occasions when DaimlerChrysler's PAP method is not required, products shall be developed according to the advanced product quality planning (APQP) process. The applicable version of PAP shall be used.

Special Characteristics Not Identified with Symbols (*ISO/TS 16949 cl. 3.1.12, 7.2.1.1, 7.3.1.1, 7.3.2.3, 7.3.3.1*)

Those product or process characteristics chosen by DaimlerChrysler or the organization that affect fit, form, function, or appearance that are not identified with a symbol. Suppliers (if applicable) should be knowledgeable of the following standards: PS-9336<H>, PS-10125<T>, and AS-10119<A>.

Special Characteristics Identified with Symbols (the Shield <S>; also <E>; the Diamond <D>)

The shield identifies special characteristics that require special due diligence since the consequence of a likely assembly or manufacturing variation may cause a nonconformance to safety and regulatory product requirements. Suppliers (if applicable) shall be knowledgeable of the following standards: PF-Safety<S>, PF-Emissions<E>. <S> designates product safety/regulatory requirements. <E> designates government-regulated vehicle emissions requirements.

The diamond identifies characteristics of a component, material, assembly, or vehicle assembly operation that are designated by DaimlerChrysler as key to the function and customer acceptance of the finished product. Diamonds also highlight important characteristics on fixtures and gauging procedures during design verification, product validation, or revalidation. The symbol <D> identifies key but nonsafety/nonregulatory product characteristics or processes that may be susceptible to manufacturing variation and require additional controls to assure conformance to specifications and customer satisfaction. A diamond <D> requires that a process control plan be developed for that characteristic. [It also requires the use of statistical process control (SPC) or 100 percent inspection unless otherwise agreed to by the DaimlerChrysler Commodity Specialist.] Presence of a diamond does not affect the significance of a shield(s) on the same document. For further detail, organizations shall refer to PS-7300.

Annual Layout

To ensure continuing conformance to all DaimlerChrysler requirements, a complete annual layout inspection, including all subcomponents, shall be required for all parts.

Design Verification (DV) and Production Validation (PV)

Design verifications are tests, inspections, and procedures that must be accomplished to verify design intent before production starts. Production validations are tests validating the production tooling, methods, and processes used to manufacture a component. Refer to PF-8500 and to the DaimlerChrysler Product Assurance Testing manual. Design verification and production validation must be satisfactorily completed before process sign-off (PSO) can be completed. Note: Per PF 8500, production validation must be performed at least once every model year (unless waived in writing by DaimlerChrysler).

Continuing Conformance

Continuing conformance inspection/tests shall be performed during the model year to assure production items or products continue to meet specified requirements and tolerances. Refer to PF-8500 and to the DaimlerChrysler Product Assurance Testing manual (unless waived in writing by DaimlerChrysler).

Internal Quality Audits

The organization shall conduct an internal quality audit at least once per year.

Corrective-Action Plan

A written corrective-action plan following the "DaimlerChrysler Seven-Step Corrective-Action Process" or the "five-why" format shall be submitted to the DaimlerChrysler supplier quality specialist, as requested, for those issues not already included in the online PRISM system.

PRISM

An organization shall have at least two individuals at each of their locations who have completed all DaimlerChrylser Corporation PRISM training. These individuals shall regularly access the system. The organization shall incorporate DCC procedure PSFD0270 into its quality system to the degree necessary to effectively respond to all PRISM issues.

Appearance Masters

Appearance masters for color, gloss, and texture shall be approved by DaimlerChrysler's design office.

Packaging, Shipping, and Labeling

Organizations shall be familiar and comply with DaimlerChrysler packaging, shipping, and labeling instructions.

Process Approval

A systematic and sequential review of the organization's process shall be completed through a PSO performed by the product team. The purpose is to verify the organization's process readiness and to assure understanding of complete program requirements, prior to a PPAP submittal.

A DaimlerChrysler-led PSO shall be performed for parts that have a high or medium initial risk evaluation as identified by the product team. Low-risk parts shall have an organization-led PSO to establish production readiness. Parts that have been out of production for 12 months or more shall have an organization-led PSO unless otherwise determined by the product team. PSO should be completed prior to providing sign-off level parts to DaimlerChrysler. The PSO shall be completed prior to S1 build. PSO shall be completely approved prior to a PPAP submission.

Control Plans

Control plans are required for prototype, prelaunch, and production phases. A DaimlerChrysler representative's signature is not required on control plans, unless specifically requested by the buyer or quality specialist.

"Forever" Requirements—Extended Enterprise

The role of the organization in the Extended Enterprise network: The organization shall proactively communicate with DaimlerChrysler regarding changes that may impact product quality. Specifically, notification to the supplier quality manager and purchasing agent shall be completed verbally with written follow-up before any of the following can be implemented at the organization's location or any supplier location:

- Proposed material changes
- Proposed process changes

- Proposed manufacturing location changes

The organization shall notify the supplier quality manager and purchasing agent when they become aware of:

- Supplier issues

- Potential supply or capacity issues

Electronic Communication

The organization shall establish a connection for electronic communication with DaimlerChrysler through the Extended Enterprise Network (EEN). Instructions for creating an EEN connection are available in the First Time Users section of the Extended Enterprise Network home page (http://extranet.daimlerchrysler.com). Assistance is available by calling the DaimlerChrysler Help Desk at 1-586-274-6000, press 0, and then 2 (or in the United States only at 1-800-332-9978, press 0, then 2). Note that EEN has replaced SPIN (Supply Partner Information Network).

ISO/TS 16949–RELATED REQUIREMENTS FOR GENERAL MOTORS

Tooling Management

The requirements for tooling management (7.5.1.5) may not be applicable to warehouses or distributors at remote sites.

Records Retention

Production part approvals, tooling records, purchase orders, and amendments shall be maintained for the length of time that the part (or family of parts) is active for production and service requirements plus one calendar year unless otherwise specified by the customer. [Note: All customer purchase orders/amendments are included in this requirement.]

Organization purchase orders/amendments for customer-owned tooling are included in this requirement.

Quality performance records (for example, control charts, inspection and test results) shall be retained for one calendar year after the year in which they were created.

Records of internal quality system audits and management review shall be retained for three years.

Retention periods longer than those specified previously may be specified by an organization in its procedures. The organization shall eventually dispose of records.

These requirements do not supersede any regulatory requirements. All specified retention periods shall be considered "minimums."

Electronic Communication *(Reference cl. 7.2.3.1)*

Note: Examples of such systems for suppliers to GM's North American Operations are:

1. Requirement planning

2. Shipping schedules

Shipment Notification System *(Reference cl. 7.2.3.1)*

Note: Examples of such systems for suppliers to GM's North American Operations are: 1) the ANSI ASC X12 856 transaction set, or 2) the EDIFACT DESADV message. For EDI assistance, contact 01-810-947-5566. For EDIFACT assistance, and confirmation of the required implementation date for a supplier, contact 01-248-265-9907.

Special Characteristics

The supplier shall use GM Key Characteristic Designation System definitions and symbols to comply with ISO/TS 16949:2002 special characteristics requirements (for example, cl. 7.2.1.1).

Design Changes

All design changes, including those proposed by suppliers, shall have written customer approval, or waiver of such approval, prior to production implementation. (See cl. 7.3.7 and 7.1.4. See also the Production Part Approval Process manual.)

For proprietary designs, impact on form, fit, function, performance, and/or durability shall be determined with the customer so that all effects can be properly evaluated.

Official Language Version

The English language version of ISO/TS 16949:2002 or QS-9000, third edition and related reference documents shall be the official version for purposes of third-party registration. Sanctioned translations shall:

- Be for reference only

- Reference the English language as the official version

- Not contain ISO 9001:2000 text verbatim

- Include GM in the copyright statement

Any other language translations are not authorized.

Part Approval Process

The supplier shall comply with the Chrysler/Ford/GM Production Part Approval Process manual to comply with cl. 7.3.6.3 (PPAP-Vehicle Assembly Centers Assembly Plants) Unless otherwise specified by the customer, PPAP requirements for vehicle assembly centers shall be taken from a specified production run of saleable pilot vehicles.

Customer Satisfaction

Trends in quality system performance and customer satisfaction (see cl. 5.2, 5.6.1.1, 7.4.3.2, and 8.2.1.1) should be compared to those of competitors, or appropriate benchmarks, and reviewed by top management.

Internal Auditor Qualifications

Internal auditors should be qualified as recommended in ISO 19011 as a minimum.

Supplier Quality Management System Development (cl. 7.4.1.2)

Registration to QS-9000:1998, (QS-9000, third edition) shall be accepted as an alternative to registration to ISO 9001:2000.

Third-Party Registration Requirements

All production and service part suppliers to GM, including GM Holdens, shall be third-party registered to ISO/TS 16949:2002, including the requirements in this document, by an IATF-recognized certification body using the automotive registration scheme, *Automotive Certification Scheme for ISO/TS 16949:2002, Rules for achieving IATF recognition, First Edition for ISO/TS 16949:2002*, March, 2002. In the alternative, organizations to which certification applies may satisfy GM third-party registration requirements by obtaining certification to ISO/TS 16949:1999 by an IATF-recognized certification body in accordance with the appropriate and current "rules" for certification until December 15, 2003, or to QS-9000:1998 by an automotive registration scheme recognized by GM until December 14, 2006. Such certification shall include the requirements in this document, or in the case of QS-9000: 1998, the General Motors–Specific Requirements.

General Procedures and Other Requirements

The GM publications listed below contain additional requirements or guidelines that shall be met, if applicable, by GM supply organizations. For General Motors Europe (GME), the publications listed below contain requirements that shall be met, with the following exceptions:

- GM 1407, GM 1689, GM 1724, GM 1730, TIR 15-300/GM 1731, GM 1737, and GM 1797.

- Specific questions on the content of these publications should be directed to the appropriate contact at the GM procuring division. (Information on the latest revision dates for these publications and ordering information can be obtained by calling Boise Cascade Office Products at 1-800-421-7676 or 1-586-758-5400.)

- GM supply organizations shall verify annually that they are using the latest version of these documents.

Other Procedures and Requirements

- *Pre-Production/Pilot Material Shipping Procedures* (GM 1407)

- *Supplier Submission of Match Check Material* (GM 1689)

- *Shipping Parts Identification Label Standard* (GM 1724)

- *Component Verification & Traceability Procedure* (GM 1730)

- *Traceability Identifier Equipment* (TIR 15-300) (GM 1731)

- *Specifications for Part and Component Bar Codes ECV/VCVS* (GM 1737)

- *Supplier Quality Processes and Measurements Procedure* (GM 1746)

- *Continuous Improvement Procedure* (GM 1747)

- *GP-10 Evaluation and Accreditation Test Facilities* (GM 1796/A; see also ISO/TS 16949:2002, cl. 7.6.3)

- *Shipping and Delivery Performance Requirements* (GM 1797)

- *Key Characteristics Designation System (KCDS)* (GM 1805 QN)

- *GP-11 General Procedure for Pre-Prototype and Prototype Material* (GM 1820)

- *C4 Technology Program, GM—Supplier C4 Information* (GM 1825)

- *GP-12 Early Production Containment Procedure* (GM 1920)

Run at Rate Procedure *(GM 1960)*

Required for all new parts; physical verification that the production process is capable of producing quality products at quoted rates.

ISO/TS 16949:2002 Applicability

ISO/TS 16949:2002 in conjunction with the specific requirements applies to all applicable contracted GM supply organizations utilizing ISO/TS 16949 to satisfy GM third-party certification requirements for quality system assessment. [Note: QS-9000:1998 (third edition) expires December 14, 2006, and QS-9000-certified supply organizations are strongly urged to upgrade to ISO/TS 16949:2002.]

UPC Labeling for Commercial Service Applications

GM Service Parts Operations (SPO) requires use of UPC labeling for certain commercial applications rather than AIAG labeling. Contact your SPO buyer for instructions.

Layout Inspection and Functional Test

Unless specified otherwise by a GM procuring division, there is no customer-established frequency for layout inspection after receiving production part approval. Reference is made to ISO/TS 16949:2002, cl. 8.2.4.1.

Customer Signature on Control Plan

GM does not provide waivers to suppliers for control plan approval because GM's signatures on the control plan are not required.

GM Holdens–Specific Requirements

The following additional documents are required for suppliers to GM Holdens in Australia:

- *Pre-Production/Pilot Material GP4 Supplement* (SGP04), February, 1996

- *Breakpoint Identification & Procedure* (SPB01), February, 1996

Certification Body Notification and Certification Status—"New Business Hold—Quality"

The organization shall notify its certification body within five business days after being placed in GM New Business Hold—Quality. The status of "New Business Hold—Quality" shall be a violation of clause 8.2.1.1 Customer satisfaction—Supplemental.

The certification of the organization shall be placed on immediate probation* by the certification body of record upon receiving notice of GM "New Business Hold—Quality."

1. In the event of certification probation as a result of an organization receiving notice of GM "New Business Hold—Quality," the organization shall complete a corrective-action plan. The supplier shall submit the corrective-action plan to the certification body of record and to the affected customer(s) within 10 business days of the date of the letter of notification of probation. The corrective-action plan of the organization shall be consistent with the affected customer(s) requirements including correction steps, responsibilities, timing information, and key metrics to identify effectiveness of the action plan.

2. Before any probation can be lifted, the certification body of record will conduct an on-site assessment of appropriate length to verify effective implementation of all corrective actions.

---

*See Annex 4, *Automotive Certification Scheme for ISO/TS 16949:2002, Rules for achieving IATF recognition, first edition for ISO/TS 16949:2002*, March 2002.

3. If probation is not lifted within four months of its issuance, the certification body of record shall revoke the ISO/TS 16949 certificate of the organization. Exceptions to this revocation shall be justified in writing by the certification body based upon its on-site review of the organization's corrective-action plan effectiveness and agreement obtained from the affected GM customer(s).

Management Review

Management review of quality system performance (cl. 5.6.1.1) at a minimum shall be conducted at planned intervals, but not less than annually.

ISO/TS 16949–RELATED REQUIREMENTS FOR FORD MOTOR COMPANY

Scope of Quality Manual *(ISO/TS 16949:2002 cl. 4.2.2)*

While it is technically feasible to register only one part of an organization's facility (one product line or area) to ISO/TS 16949, this type of limited scope is not permitted for the demonstration of capable quality systems in Q1 2002.

For Q1 2002, the entire facility (producing automotive products) must be registered.

Different customer specifics may apply to each product line, but all automotive manufacturing lines must meet the requirements of ISO/TS 16949:2002.

Control of Documents *(ISO/TS 16949:2002 cl. 4.2.3)*

All quality system documents (policies, procedures, and work instructions, and so on) in the organization shall be reviewed for adequacy at least annually. Evidence of these reviews shall be made available upon request.

Where the organization uses Ford documents/instructions or other documents of external origin, the organization ensures that the appropriate revision level is used—this is either the most current version available from https://fsn.ford.com or FSP (Ford Supplier Portal), or as specified by Ford Motor Company. [Note: Engineering standards may be obtained from Information Handling Services at 1-800-716-3447 or Autoweb Communications Inc. at 616 396-0880.]

If any standards are not available through the aforementioned sources, organizations should contact Ford Engineering, or for organizations with Ford Intranet access, http://www.rlis.ford.com/cgi-bin/standards/iliaccess.pl may provide a more complete inventory.

Engineering Specifications *(ISO/TS 16949:2002 cl. 4.2.3.1, 7.3.5)*

Heat-treating specification. Organizations and subcontractors providing heat-treated product and heat-treating services shall demonstrate compliance to Ford Motor Company Manufacturing Standard W-HTX. All heat-treating processes shall be assessed annually against Ford Heat Treat System Survey Guidelines available on https://web.bli.ford.com.

The supplier shall maintain at the supplier site the survey reports and other evidence of compliance to W-HTX and make them available to STA upon request. Ford or supplier heat-treat assessments or compliance to W-HTX does not relieve the supplier of full responsibility for the quality of supplied product.

To reduce the risk of embrittlement, heat-treated steel components shall conform to the requirements of Ford Engineering Material Specification WSS-M99A3-A.

Control of Records *(ISO/TS 16949:2002 cl. 4.2.4)*

Production part approvals, tooling records, purchase orders, and amendments shall be maintained for the length of time that the part (or family of parts) is active for production and service requirements plus one calendar year unless otherwise specified by Ford Motor Company. [Note: All Ford Motor Company purchase orders/amendments are included in this requirement. Organization purchase orders/amendments for Ford-owned tooling are also included in this requirement.]

Production inspection and test records (for example, control charts, inspection and test results) shall be retained for one calendar year after the year in which they were created.

Records of inspection shall be maintained for each inspection or test performed, unless waived in writing by STA. The actual test result (variable or attribute) should be recorded. Simple pass/fail records of inspection are not acceptable for variable measurements.

Records of internal quality system audits and management review shall be retained for three years.

Retention periods longer than those specified previously may be specified by an organization in its procedures.

Specified retention requirements may be revised at the direction of Ford Motor Company Office of General Counsel.

These requirements do not supersede any regulatory requirements.

Customer Focus *(ISO/TS 16949:2002 cl. 5.2, 8.2.4, 8.5.1)*

The organization shall demonstrate enhanced customer satisfaction by meeting the continuous improvement requirements of Q1 2002, as demonstrated in the organization's quality operating system (QOS).

The organization shall use the QOS Assessment in the development of its QOS—the QOS Assessment is available on https://web.bli.ford.com.

Customer Representative *(ISO/TS 16949:2002 cl. 5.5.2.1)*

The organization's customer representative may be the joint quality engineer as defined by STA.

The organization shall notify Ford Motor Company STA within 10 working days of any changes to senior management responsible for quality or company ownership.

Management Review *(ISO/TS 16949:2002 cl. 5.6, 5.1)*

The organization management shall hold monthly QOS performance meetings as specified in the Q1 2002 Manufacturing Site Assessment, available on https://web.bli.ford.com/. The results of these QOS reviews shall be integral to the senior management reviews. [Note: The frequency of the manufacturing site assessments is specified by the Q1 2002 requirements, available on https://web.bli.ford.com/; Also, the management review need not be held as one meeting, but may be a series of meetings, covering each of the metrics monthly.]

Management Review Input *(ISO/TS 16949:2002 cl. 5.6.2)*

Management review input must also include the Q1 2002 Manufacturing Site Assessment results.

Training *(ISO/TS 16949:2002 cl. 6.2.2.2, 6.2.2.3, 6.2.2.4)*

The organization shall ensure that only trained and qualified personnel are involved in all aspects of the manufacture or design (as appropriate) of Ford Motor Company parts. The training shall include the appropriate Ford systems.

Ford training opportunities are available through Ford Supplier Learning Institute at https://web.fsli.ford.com.

Records of training shall be traceable to the revision of the source training material (for example, policy, procedure, work instruction). These records are to be maintained for three years from the date of the training.

Provision of Resources *(ISO/TS 16949:2002 cl. 6.2.2.2, 6.3.1, 6.2.2, 6.2.2.1)*

When considering a request for quote, the organization must account for and be able to apply all necessary resources (trained personnel and equipment) to complete the purchase requirements to Ford's satisfaction.

Plant, Facility, and Equipment Planning (ISO/TS 16949:2002 cl. 6.3.1, 7.3.3.2, 5.1.1)

Manufacturing flow. The organization shall have evidence of lean manufacturing implementation plans as defined in the link below and in the Q1 2002 Manufacturing Site Assessment. Information on Ford lean manufacturing principles is available through https://web.tcm.ford.com.

Contingency Plans *(ISO/TS 16949:2002 cl 6.3.2)*

The organization shall notify the Ford receiving plant, the buyer, and the STA engineer within 24 hours of organization production interruption. The nature of the problem shall be communicated to Ford and immediate actions taken to assure supply of product to Ford. [Note: Production interruption is defined as an inability to meet the Ford-specified production capacity volume.]

Cleanliness of Premises *(ISO/TS 16949:2002 cl. 6.4.2)*

Product cleanliness. (Part dunnage is included in this requirement.)

Planning of Product Realization *(ISO/TS 16949:2002 cl. 7.1, 7.3.1,4.2.1d, 7.3.4.1, 5.4.1, 5.4.2)*

Appropriate to the supplier's responsibilities, the organization shall meet the requirements of the Quality and Reliability Statement of Work (available on https://web.bli.ford.com).

The organization shall report APQP status including, at a minimum, the elements specified in the APQP Reporting Guidelines and forms—available on https://web.bli.ford.com.

When the organization is also sourced with the production of prototypes, effective use should be made of data from prototype fabrication to plan the production process.

Specific requirements and supporting data, percent inspection points that satisfy tolerance (PIST) and percent indices that are process capable (PIPC) may be required by STA to support prototype vehicle evaluations. PIPC is the number of characteristics that are process capable, divided by the total number of characteristics being checked, multiplied by 100. On the other hand, PIST is the number of conforming inspection checks divided by the total number of checks made, multiplied by 100].

Acceptance Criteria *(ISO/TS 16949:2002 cl. 7.1.2)*

The acceptance level of zero defects refers only to the sample, not the entire population.

Customer-Related Processes *(ISO/TS 16949:2002 cl. 7.2.1)*

Ford requires all manufacturing sites to be registered to ISO 14001 by July 1, 2003, and report all materials per WSS-M99P9999-A1, as noted in PPAP, Ford-Specific Instructions.

These requirements are detailed on https://fsn.ford.com (environmental) or Ford-Supplier Portal (FSP).

Review of Requirements Related to the Product—Supplemental *(ISO/TS 16949:2002 cl. 7.2.2.1)*

The customer authorization for waiving formal review may be obtained from the buyer, and when appropriate, Ford Engineering.

Manufacturing Feasibility *(ISO/TS 16949:2002 cl. 7.2.2.2)*

Manufacturing feasibility reviews, for example, APQP CD-ROM appendix II, shall include all supplier and Ford Engineering organizations, as appropriate.

Product volume change requests from Ford Motor Company increasing volume by 20 percent or more over the previously verified volume capability shall require full volume feasibility studies. (APQP or capacity verification may be required.)

Customer Communication—Supplemental *(ISO/TS 16949:2002 cl. 7.2.3.1)*

Assistance in C3P or legacy data system compatibility with Ford CAD systems is available through https://web.c3p.ford.com/cgi-bin/admin/ load_page.cgi.

Multidisciplinary Approach *(ISO/TS 16949:2002 cl. 7.3.1.1, 7.3.3.2)*

FMEA and Control Plan Approvals. Ford Engineering approval is required for all inverted delta part control plans and FMEAs by part submission warrant (PSW) submission. STA approval of control plans and process FMEAs is also required by PSW submission for all inverted-delta parts where the site is designated by Ford to be PPAP level 2 through 5. Approval of revisions to these documents after initial acceptance is also required. Ford reserves the right to require approval of FMEA and/or control plans for any part from any supplier.

FMEAs. The organization shall prepare documented process FMEAs for all the Ford parts it manufactures. Where the organization is responsible for design, the organization shall prepare documented design FMEAs for all Ford parts it designs. FMEAs may be written for families of parts, where typically the only difference in the parts is dimensional, not form, application, or function. However, in all cases, use of family process FMEAs shall be approved by STA and use of family design FMEAs shall be approved by Ford Engineering. Suppliers are to provide copies of FMEA documents to Ford Motor Company upon request. Suppliers shall comply with the Ford FMEA Handbook requirements (see https://fsn.ford.com/ keyinfo—subsection FMEA or FSP). Suppliers complying with the Ford FMEA Handbook will meet the FMEA and related requirements of the Q1 2002 Manufacturing Site Assessment.

Control Plans. All Ford Motor Company parts shall have control plans [or dynamic control plans (DCP) if required by Powertrain]. See https://web.bli.ford.com/ Q1 2002 site assessment, ISO/TS 16949:2002 Annex A, and AIAG APQP for control plan requirements, and APQP CD-ROM appendix II for DCP information. Design and process controls shall focus on prevention rather than detection and correction. Repaired and/or reworked product shall be reinspected in accordance with the control plan and/or documented procedure.

Material Analysis—Heat-Treated Parts

Prior to release of metal from an identified mill heat, a sample from at least one coil or bundle of wire, rod, strip, or sheet steel shall be analyzed and tested to determine its conformance to specifications for chemical composition and quenched hardness. A sample from each additional coil or bundle in the heat shall be tested for either chemical composition or quenched hardness. The results shall be documented and referenced to the steel supplier's mill heat number. This requirement applies to both purchased material and material produced by the organization. [Note: External material test facilities used shall meet the requirements specified in section 4.36 of this document *(Laboratory Requirements)*].

Material Analysis—Non-Heat-Treated Parts

The identification of each coil or bundle of wire, rod, strip, or sheet steel shall be visually checked to determine that the mill heat number agrees with the steel supplier's mill analysis document and applicable specifications. Each coil or bundle shall be tested for hardness and other applicable physical properties.

Lot Traceability

Lot traceability shall be maintained.

Supplier Notification of Control Item Requirements

When data from control charts and engineering specification (ES) tests indicate a high degree of capability, the organization may request a revision to the testing and inspection requirements for control item parts. Ford Engineering and STA approval of a revised control plan will authorize the revision. Approval shall be obtained prior to implementing the change. The same approach shall be used to replace finished product inspection/testing with upstream controls. The organization shall submit requests for approval via the Supplier Request for Engineering Approval (SREA) per AIAG PPAP. Ford Powertrain requires use of the SREA to initiate all requests for approval of process and design changes; see https://web.bli.ford.com/ for the Powertrain SREA requirements.

Special Characteristics *(ISO/TS 16949:2002 cl. 7.3.2.3, 7.2.1.1)*

Symbols. The organization is to contact Ford Engineering to obtain concurrence for the use of Ford Motor Company special characteristics symbols defined in the glossary of this document. For internal use, the organization may develop its own special characteristics symbols.

Ford-Designated Special Characteristics. Critical characteristic (∇) Parts Ford designated Control Item Parts are selected products identified by Ford Engineering, concurred by Ford Manufacturing, and identified on drawings and specifications with an inverted delta (∇) preceding the part and/or material number. Control item products have critical characteristics that may affect safe vehicle operation and/or compliance with government regulations. Unique symbols identifying safety and regulatory characteristics on components designed by other companies (for example, Mazda) are equivalent to the inverted delta (∇) symbol. Examples are the Mazda "A" and "AR" symbols or special fastener base part numbers beginning with "W9", which are to be treated as inverted delta. Critical characteristics for fasteners may be designated by methods defined in Ford Engineering Fastener Specifications available through Ford Global Materials and Fastener Standards, or the specification providers listed in 4.2 of this document.

Other Special Characteristics. Significant, high-impact, operator safety and pass-through characteristics. [Note: The definitions of the special characteristics are provided in the Ford FMEA characteristics module, available through https://web.keyinfo.ford.com/northamerica/manuals/secured/docs/FMEA-Handbook/Special.pdf.]

Design and Development Review *(ISO/TS 16949:2002 cl. 7.3.4, 7.3.1, 7.3.6.1)*

The organization shall use Ford Product Development System (FPDS) (unless approved otherwise in writing by Ford Engineering) when reviewing product design and development stages. Information on FPDS is available through FSN or FSP on https://fsn.ford.com/pd.frames.html.

Product Development

For inverted-delta (∇) parts, full-service suppliers shall include Ford Engineering and Ford Assembly/Manufacturing in FPDS milestone design reviews, as appropriate.

Where feasible, full-service suppliers shall include Ford Engineering and Ford Assembly and/or Manufacturing in design reviews for all Ford parts.

Design and Development Verification *(ISO/TS 16949:2002 cl. 7.3.5)*

The organization shall perform design verification to show conformance with the appropriate Ford vehicle design specification(s) (VDS) and system design specification(s) (SDS). Verification methods shall be recorded with the test results. [Note: SDSs are a compilation of performance metrics for a system or subsystem. Performance metrics are measurable characteristics derived from customer expectations.]

VDSs and SDSs are available from Ford Engineering.

Prototype Program *(ISO/TS 16949:2002 cl. 7.3.6.2)*

The organization is responsible for the quality of the parts it produces and for any subcontracted services, including subcontractors specified by Ford Motor Company. This applies to all phases of product development, including prototypes. Individual statements of work may specify alternate responsibilities.

The organization shall request Ford Motor Company confirmation of the need for a prototype program control plan.

Product Approval Process *(ISO/TS 16949:2002 cl. 7.3.6.3,)*

PPAP. The organization shall comply with the AIAG Production Part Approval Process manual. The organization is responsible for managing PPAP for all tiers of subcontractors per the Q1 2002 requirements. Subcontractors are to meet all requirements of PPAP. Subcontractor PSWs (unless waived in writing by STA) are to be submitted to Ford, as part of the organization PPAP submission. Consistent with Q1 2002 Manufacturing Site Assessment Expectations, section 4 (PPAP and run-at-rate review), all design changes, including those proposed by subcontractors, shall have written approval per PPAP prior to production implementation. Per PPAP, all design change requests shall be made via Worldwide Engineering Release System (WERS), unless the organization or subcontractor does not have access to WERS. Process change requests and design requests without WERS shall be managed using the SREA form 1638 per PPAP Ford-specific requirements.

All proposed design and process changes, including supplier proprietary designs, must be submitted to Ford for approval and to obtain concurrence on effect on part fit, form, function, finish, and/or durability prior to implementation.

Additionally, full-service supplier status does not relieve the organization of the SREA requirement, unless approved in writing by the responsible design activity and STA. The organization shall obtain Ford approval for *all* process changes for inverted-delta (∇) parts or emission components per the PPAP SREA process (no waivers apply). Full PSW approval by STA will not be granted if the part is under WERS alert. Only when the alert has been cleared can full STA approval be given.

"Run-at-Rate." When specified by Ford, PPAP PSW "run-at-rate" requirements are met by demonstrating "Production verification," Phase 2 of phased PPAP implementation. Contact STA for the phased PPAP methodology.

Regulations *(ISO/TS 16949:2002 cl. 7.4.1.1)*

Applicable regulations shall include international requirements for export vehicles as specified by Ford Motor Company, for example, plastic part marking (E-4 drafting standard—available on https://fsn.ford.com/ key-info); WSS-M99P9999-A1 and European End of Life of Vehicle (ELV)—both available on https://fsn.ford.com/ environmental or FSP. Material reporting requirements for ELV are specified by WSS-M99P9999-A1.

Subcontractor Development *(ISO/TS 16949:2002 cl. 7.4.1.2)*

"Goal of supplier conformity with [ISO/TS 16949:2002]" may be met by either of the following:

- Subcontractors to achieve accredited third-party certification to either ISO/TS 16949:2002, or the current version of ISO 9000.

- Successful biannual assessments of the subcontractor by an STA-approved second-party auditor. Details of subcontractor development assessments acceptable to Ford are available on https://web.bli.ford.com/ under "QS-9000/ISO/TS 16949 requirements and authorizations." Ford or supplier second-party assessment or third-party certification of subcontractors does not relieve the organization of full responsibility for the quality of supplied product from the subcontractor.

Although all subcontractors must be assessed per this section, subcontractor improvement efforts shall focus on those subcontractors with the highest impact. Upon request, the organization shall make available to Ford a list of its subcontractors. The subcontractor list shall be updated at least twice annually.

Customer-Approved Sources *(ISO/TS 16949:2002 cl. 7.4.1.3)*

When required by the contract with Ford, subcontractor approval shall be obtained from the Ford Motor Company buyer, and concurred by STA.

Incoming Product Quality *(ISO/TS 16949:2002 cl. 7.4.3.1)*

The organization shall have incoming quality measures and shall use those measures as key indicators of subcontractor quality management, unless waived in writing by STA. Any incoming quality inspection shall be commensurate with the risk and quality impact of each subcontractor. Refer to the Q1 2002 Manufacturing Site Assessment requirements. [Note: "measures" include chemical, dimensional, certifications, and electrical measurements. The organization may add other parameters as appropriate. Also, the functional approval requirement on the PPAP PSW form provides a mechanism to validate incoming subcontractor product functionality prior to acceptance.]

Scheduling Subcontractors *(ISO/TS 16949:2002 cl. 7.4.3.2)*

In support of Ford's expectation of 100 percent on-time delivery, the organization shall also require 100 percent on-time delivery from subcontractors.

In-house premium freight expenses related to subcontractor late deliveries should be monitored and shall be minimized.

Job (Work) Instructions *(ISO/TS 16949:2002 cl. 7.5.1.2)*

Operators shall use the most current work instructions, unless otherwise authorized in writing.

Verification of Job Set-ups *(ISO/TS 16949:2002 cl. 7.5.1.3)*

Set-up verification requirements include manual tooling exchanges. Records of all job set-up verifications shall be maintained for one year.

Preventive Maintenance *(ISO/TS cl. 7.5.1.4)*

The organization shall have a documented system for preventive maintenance. This shall include a timely review of planned maintenance activities and a documented action plan to address any backlog. Action plans are to be included in the management review process. Records of maintenance are to be maintained for one year. [Note: Predictive maintenance should be used wherever possible, be based on appropriate statistical techniques, and consider cost of quality prior to implementation].

Identification and Traceability, Preservation, Storage, and Inventory *(ISO/TS 16949:2002 cl. 7.5.3, 7.5.4, 7.5.5, 7.5.5.1)*

The organization shall meet all logistics requirements as specified by material planning and logistics (MP&L). MP&L requirements are available on the Web page https://web.fsli.ford.com/mpl/index.html. Key requirements are: compliance to Material Management Operation Guideline (MMOG), Odette (Volvo requirements), or MS-9000, as specified by regional requirements, including:

- Annual certification

- Adherence to Ford delivery rating requirements

- Part identification and tracking

- Lot traceability through shipping (lot traceability shall include subcontracted components of an assembly/module that are associated with compliance to any FMVSS requirement)

- Prevention of damage or deterioration

- Maintenance of returnable dunnage

- Use of Ford packaging requirements form 1121R (and maintenance of packaging screens P1 and DAIA in MS3 and CMMS3), available through https://web.fsli.ford.com/mpl/index.html.

In all cases, if unsure of the MP&L requirements, contact the delivery analyst for the supplier site. The analyst contact information is available through SIM. [Note: physical part identification is not required unless indicated on the design record. The inverted delta symbol (∇) shall precede the Ford Motor Company part number in accordance with the Packaging Guidelines for Production Parts and Shipping Parts/Identification Label Standard, both available through Ford Supplier Network MP&L page https://web.fsli.ford.com/mpl/index.html.

Measurement Systems Analysis *(ISO/TS 16949:2002 cl. 7.6.1)*

All gages used for checking Ford components/parts per the control plan shall have a gage R&R performed in accordance with the methods described by the latest AIAG Measurement Systems Analysis Manual (MSA) to determine measurement capability.

Any measurement equipment not meeting the specifications stipulated in the MSA must be approved by STA. [Note: measurement system capability analysis may be conducted on families of equipment, providing it is essentially the same equipment (type, make, model) and is being used in essentially the same environment (temperature, humidity, range, method of measurement, and so on). Use of such family MSA studies must be approved by STA. Variable gage studies should utilize 10 parts, three operators, and three trials. Attribute gage studies should utilize 50 parts, three operators, three trials.

Effective attribute gage study samples include parts within specification and parts outside specification for each criterion being measured and within the expected range of manufacturing variability.

Laboratory Requirements *(ISO/TS 16949:2002 cl. 7.6.3, 7.6.3.2)*

Commercial/independent laboratory facilities shall be approved by the organization prior to use. The acceptance criteria should be based on the latest ISO/IEC 17025 (or national equivalent), shall be documented, and shall be approved in writing by STA.

Statistical Tools and Concepts *(ISO/TS 16949:2002 cl. 8.1.1, 8.1.2)*

The organization shall use the latest edition of the following references as appropriate:

- AIAG's SPC for manufacturing process controls

- AIAG's MSA for measurement equipment management

- VDA volume 4, part 1 *Quality Assurance prior to Serial Application*

Initial Process Studies

The choice of the capability index used for initial process studies—C_{pk} (predictive), or P_{pk} (historical)—shall be based solely on the nature of the process data collected. (See AIAG PPAP and SPC manuals). It is recommend that both indices be determined for stable processes. When used together, the indices assist in the determination of sources of variation.

Customer Satisfaction *(ISO/TS 16949:2002 cl. 8.2.1.1, 5.2)*

Certification body/registrar notification. The organization shall notify its certification body/registrar of record in writing within five working days if Ford Motor Company places the site on Q1 revocation. This notification of the registrar will constitute a "customer claim" as defined by the ISO/TS 16949:2002 rules. This step will place the organization's ISO/TS 16949:2002 certification on probation. Both Ford Motor Company and the registrar must agree with the organization's plan and actions to reinstate the certification within 90 days, or as agreed in writing between Ford and the registrar, otherwise the certificate will be cancelled (rescinded). [Note: Reinstatement of Q1 2002 from revocation requires at least six months of acceptable performance. If the registrar and STA agree that the organization has successfully implemented corrective and preventive actions, addressing all the issues that led to the revocation, the ISO/TS 16949 probation may be lifted. However, the site may still be under Q1 2002 revocation, accumulating the required six months of acceptable performance data. If either the registrar or STA cannot accept the site performance to plan as sufficient to lift the probation, then probation may be extended with approval from STA. The organization shall monitor performance and customer satisfaction metrics (as defined by Q1 2002) and updates to Ford requirements on Ford

Supplier Network (on https://fsn.ford.com/ or FSP). It is strongly recommended that the organization review its performance status on SIM at least weekly. (Some information is updated daily on SIM). At least twice per year, the organization shall communicate customer satisfaction metrics to all employees who affect the quality of Ford Motor Company parts.]

Internal Quality Audits *(ISO/TS 16949:2002 cl. 8.2.2)*

If the third-party ISO/TS 16949:2002 registrar finds and writes any major nonconformance against the organization during a regular surveillance audit, the organization shall, prior to the subsequent third-party audit, determine the root cause of the major nonconformance and implement corrective actions where the issue was discovered and implement preventive actions in all other areas using similar processes. Preventive action shall be cascaded by implementing the corrective actions (as appropriate) in related areas of the organization, not only in the area where the nonconformance was written. The internal audits shall review all documentation of the organization at least annually for adequacy and compliance (including, but not limited to, policies, procedures, and work instructions).

Internal auditors at the organization shall have been trained as an ISO/TS 16949:2002 internal auditor using an auditor training course, which covers the following:

- An initial assessment of the understanding and ability to utilize:

  - The technical specification ISO/TS 16949:2002

  - Related core tools

  - Applicable customer-specific requirements

  - The automotive process approach to auditing [including customer-oriented processes (COPs), support, and management).

- Training and testing to understand and apply:

  - The technical specification ISO/TS 16949:2002

  - Related core tools

  - Applicable customer-specific requirements

  - The automotive process approach to auditing (including COPs, support, and management)

- Practice sessions equivalent to one audit per day in:

  - Case study audits.

- Auditing role plays/simulations.

- On-site audits, conducted by a trainer who meets the requirements for ISO/TS 16949:2002 CB/Registrar Auditor Certification and Upgrade Training as specified in Annex 2 of the "Rules for achieving IATF recognition." [Note 1: Equivalent internal auditor experience is acceptable in place of the third-party experience stated in Annex 2. Note 2: The trainer is not required to be a certified third-party auditor or to be a certified trainer in ISO/TS 16949:2002. The trainer needs to have the background qualifications required of a certified ISO/TS 16949:2002 third-party auditor. In addition, the auditor must have conducted at least five internal ISO/TS 16949:2002 audits during a period of 24 months under the supervision of an auditor trained as specified in the requirements, covering all elements of the standard and all processes directly impacting Ford part quality at least once over the five or more audits.]

Monitoring and Measurement of Manufacturing Processes (ISO/TS 16949:2002 cl. 8.2.3.1, 7.1.2, 7.5, 7.5.2)

Tables A and B of the special requirements document detail the requirements for the qualification of product characteristics, and process and product monitoring. All process controls shall have a goal of reduction of variability, using Six Sigma or other appropriate methods. The Statistical Process Control manual provides additional guidance where tool wear impacts variability. All process metrics are to be traceable to Ford requirements.

Table A—Qualification of All Product Characteristics. Suppliers shall select the appropriate methods (for example, AIAG MSA, SPC) to control all dimensions and other characteristics of their products. For characteristics not controlled with SPC, but requiring control, one or more of the following methods should be selected:

- Product qualification for attributes characteristics using the appropriate tables

- Product audits performed on a regular basis

- Periodic layout and laboratory tests

Table B—Ongoing Process and Product Monitoring. The information gathered from the process shall be used to make disposition on product produced by a process for which SPC is in use. After process stability has been demonstrated and capability has been calculated, the most recent point on the control chart and the historical process capability indices (Cpk/Cp) may be used to determine appropriate actions.

Monitoring and Measurement of Product (ISO/TS 16949:2002 cl. 8.2.4, 8.3.4)

Engineering Specification (ES) Test Performance Requirements. The goal of ES testing is to confirm that the design intent has been met. ES test failure shall be cause for the organization to stop production shipments immediately and take containment actions. The organization shall immediately notify Ford Engineering, STA, and the using Ford Motor Company facility of test failure, suspension of shipments, and identification of any suspect lots shipped. After the root cause(s) of ES test failure are determined, corrected, and verified, the organization may resume shipments. Suspect product shall not be shipped without sorting or reworking to eliminate the cause of failure. These ES requirements apply equally to subcontractors. Product validation engineering specification testing frequency requirements shall be clearly noted in the control plan and process failure mode and effects analysis (PFMEA). Any revisions to these frequencies require Ford Engineering approval and STA concurrence.

Ford reserves the right to require the use of an independent third-party inspector to ensure that only compliant product is shipped to Ford facilities.

Layout Inspection and Functional Testing *(ISO/TS 16949:2002 cl. 8.2.4.1)*

A layout inspection and functional verification (to all engineering material and performance requirements) shall be performed annually. The measurements shall be documented on the Production Part Approval—Dimensional Results form CFG-1003 or equivalent. Reference AIAG PPAP Manual.

Appearance Items *(ISO/TS 16949:2002 cl. 8.2.4.2)*

Where the manufacturing process(es) or environment could affect the craftsmanship of the product, the organization shall implement processes and measures such as Ford Global Craftsmanship. These processes and measures shall be implemented into the control plan and APQP reporting. Appearance approval requirements are specified in PPAP, Ford customer-specific requirements. Further details on global craftsmanship may be found at http://www.globalcraftsmanship.ford.com.

Control of Nonconforming Product *(ISO/TS 16949:2002 cl. 8.3, 8.5.2, 8.5.3)*

The organization shall have processes and systems in place to prevent shipping of nonconforming product to any Ford Motor Company facility. Any nonconforming product or process output shall be analyzed using the Global 8-D methodology to ensure root cause correction and problem prevention, unless an alternate methodology is approved in writing by STA.

Customer Concerns

Organizations shall respond to quality rejects (QRs) with a Global 8-D that includes an immediate containment measure, and the results of root cause analysis within five business days or as specified by the receiving plant. In all cases, containment must be implemented immediately or as specified by the receiving plants.

A full 8-D study is required within 10 business days or as specified by the receiving plant or STA.

Returned Product Test/Analysis

The organization shall have a documented system for internal notification, analysis, and communication of all Ford receiving plant returns. The organization shall communicate the results of analysis to the responsible Ford and organization work groups.

Ford receiving plant PPM shall be communicated to all organization plant team members. The organization shall develop a system to monitor Ford receiving plant concerns. The organization shall also implement corrective actions to prevent future Ford plant concerns. Returned product test results are to be included in the monthly QOS report as part of the management review.

Customer Waiver *(ISO/TS 16949:2002 cl. 8.3.4)*

Ford Motor Company authorization of product differing from Ford specifications is managed by WERS, limited to the quantity or time period approved in the WERS alert. Information on WERS is available through https://fsn.ford.com/ or FSP, followed by a search on "WERS."

The WERS help desk can also provide information on WERS. Please call 1-313-845-2972 or request help via e-mail: hwers@ford.com. Ford approval is required before the use or implementation of a nonconforming or changed process. Such process change authorization is obtained through the SREA process specified in PPAP or the Powertrain SREA process available on https://web.bli.ford.com/. Contact STA to determine which SREA process is to be used.

Ford may specify other formats of approval (available through STA or Ford Engineering). [Note: Although process change approval may be obtained through the SREA process, the part must still meet all PPAP requirements prior to shipping any parts from the changed process].

REFERENCES

DaimlerChrysler (Chrysler Group). 2003. "Customer-Specific Requirements for Use with ISO/TS 16949," 2nd ed. (January 7).

Ford Motor Company. 2002. "Customer-Specific Requirements for Use with ISO/TS 16949:2002." (December).

GM. 2002. "GM Customer-Specific Requirements for Use with ISO/TS 16949." (September).

SELECTED BIBLIOGRAPHY

Automotive Certification Scheme for ISO/TS 16949:2002—Rules for achieving IATF recognition.

DaimlerChrysler Blue Dot Manuals. *PSO,* 4th ed. Product Assurance Testing

DaimlerChrysler, Ford Motor Company, General Motors. 1998. *Quality System Requirements (QS-9000),* 3rd ed. (March).

———. 1999. *Production Part Approval Process (PPAP),* 3rd ed. (September).

———. 1992. *Statistical Process Control (SPC),* 1st ed.

———. 1994. *Advanced Product Quality Planning (APQP) and Control Plan* (June).

———. 2002. *Measurement Systems Analysis (MSA),* 3rd ed. (March).

———. 2001. *Potential Failure Mode and Effects Analysis (FMEA),* 3rd ed. (April).

———. 1998. *Quality System Requirements, QS-9000, Semiconductor Supplement,* 2nd ed. (December).

Ford Motor Company. *Advanced Product Quality Planning Reporting Guidelines,* available through FSN or FSP (Ford Supplier Portal) https://web.bli.ford.com.

———. *FMEA Handbook,* available on https://fsn.ford.com/keyinfo—(subsection FMEA) or FSP (Ford Supplier Portal).

Ford Quality and Reliability Statement of Work (FQRSOW), available on https://web.bli.ford.com.

International Accreditation Forum. 2001. *Guidance on the Application of ISO/IEC Guide* 62, no. 2 (December).

IATF. 2002. *Guidance to ISO/TS 16949:2002,* AIAG edition.

———. *Automotive certification scheme for ISO/TS 16949:2002. Rules for Achieving IATF Recognition,* 1st ed. for ISO/TS 16949:2002 (March).

MMOG (Material Management Operation Guideline), available through AIAG http://www.aiag.org.

MS-9000 (Materials Management System Requirements), available through Material Planning and Logistics, https://web.fsli.ford.com/mpl/index.html on FSN or FSP (Ford Supplier Portal)

Note: The latest copies of QS-9000, PPAP, APQP, SPC, MSA, and other related manuals are available from AIAG at 01-248-358-3003 and http://www.aiag.org, and Carwin Continuous (UK) at 44-1708-861333.

5

Transition from
ISO 9001:1994 to
ISO 9001:2000 and QS-9000
to ISO/TS 16949

As mentioned before, the new standards are a continuum in the path of the continual improvement process. Therefore, it makes sense to expect that the transition from ISO 9001:1994 to ISO 9001:2000 and QS-9000 to ISO/TS 16949 is expedient and as painless as possible.

To understand the process of transition, the primary requirement is that your organization must recognize the need to transition from ISO 9001/2/3:1994 to ISO 9001:2000 and from QS to ISO/TS. The second requirement is that your organization must understand the basic differences between the two standards. The third and final requirement is that your organization must have the knowledge of how a registrar will conduct the transition assessments. So far we have discussed both of these in the introduction and chapters 1 and 2. The following information will help you understand the third requirement.

Although the transition deadline was December 2003, there are many organizations that are not even close to meeting the requirements (see p. 11 for the latest statistics). Now that the deadline has passed it is up to your organization to choose how many assessment visits you want to complete the transition in. It will only cost you more if you require unscheduled visits or additional assessment time. The thing to remember throughout is that you will be surprised at how many of the new standard's requirements you will already meet—perhaps as many as 30 percent. However, there is still much work that needs to be done for the complete transition. Let us examine the transition process procedurally.

1. *Understand new and changed requirements.* When you are planning a trip, you must know your starting point and ultimate destination to decide on the most efficient and effective route. Similarly, you need to understand the new and changed ISO 9001:2000 requirements before plotting your transition path.

Start by ordering the ISO 9000:2000, ISO 9001:2000, and ISO 9004:2000 family of standards. Copies can be purchased from several sources including ASQ, the SEEMS organization, the ISO organization, and others. Before opening the *ISO 9001:2000 Requirements* standard, review the quality concepts described in the *ISO 9000:2000 Fundamentals and vocabulary* standard. If you are unsure of any of the terms, look up their definitions in section 3 of ISO 9000:2000. When you examine ISO 9001:2000, pay particular attention to the process approach described in its introduction. The process model illustrates the clause linkage based on the PDC(S)A approach.

Refer to Annex B in the new ISO 9001 standard to see the clause relationship between ISO 9001:2000 and ISO 9001:1994. Now you are ready to begin reading through the requirements to understand the differences between these two standards.

On the other hand, the ISO 9004:2000 standard provides guidance on performance improvements beyond the basic requirements of ISO 9001:2000. In fact, the items covered in ISO 9004:2000 are not audited and therefore are not part of the certification process. They are there to help you by providing ease of reference. These requirements are shown in ISO 9004:2000 as boxed text. Since ISO 9004:2000 uses the same clause structure as ISO 9001:2000, it can be used to gain a better understanding of the requirements by seeing possible practices. Remember, however, that for registration purposes your system will be evaluated against ISO 9001:2000, not ISO 9004:2000.

2. *Determine scope and permissible exclusions.* ISO 9001:2000 is intended to be generic and applicable to all organizations, regardless of type, size, and product category. However, not all requirements in the new standard will be relevant to all organizations. Under certain circumstances, an organization may exclude some specific requirements. For example, if there is no design in the organization, the elements pertaining to design will not be applicable.

Clause 1.2, Application in ISO 9001:2000 states that requirements can be excluded only if they are limited to clause 7, Product realization. Exclusions are acceptable only if they do not affect the organization's ability or responsibility to provide product that meets customer and applicable regulatory requirements. If you find your organization cannot apply a product realization requirement, you must define and justify the exclusion in the quality manual. In addition, any publicly available documents such as registration certificates and marketing materials should be carefully phrased to avoid confusing or misleading customers and end users regarding the scope of registration.

Part of defining the scope of your system is deciding on the products and sites to include for registration purposes. A clear description of the scope is of increased importance since certificates cannot be issued for ISO 9002 or ISO 9003 after the transition period, which ended in December 2003.

Another consideration is that any outsourced processes must be identified and controlled. If a product realization process is outsourced to an external organization, that is not adequate justification for excluding the process from your QMS. Refer to clause 4.1, General requirements, in ISO 9001:2000 for the specific outsourcing requirement. See clause 1.2 for some limited guidance.

Starting with the quality manual (this could vary from being a creative one page to a very large document), you need to look at what is best for your business. Companies must avoid creating overburdensome documentation, as this is not the intent of the standard. You might even decide to define some processes and not document them due to their simplicity, and rely instead on the skills, training, and experience of the people performing the work. This may and will cause some auditors to fully review their auditing techniques, as some will find difficulty with this approach.

The use of electronic media may be a good way forward, especially for organizations starting this venture for the first time. Business mapping or process mapping (process flowcharting) will help identify product realization processes and will enable the organization to clearly identify what documentation is critical in the application of their QMS.

Naturally, the extent of documentation and applicability of more creative forms of documentation will vary with organization size, activity type, process complexity, and personnel competence. While documents can be in any form or media, they must be maintained and controlled. For further guidance on quality manuals, procedures, and instructions, see chapter 7 and CD-ROM appendixes VII through XII.

3. *Adopt the process approach.* A "process" is a system of activities that uses resources to transform inputs into outputs. The "process approach" promoted by ISO 9001:2000 systematically identifies and manages these processes and their interaction within a QMS. As mentioned earlier, the *process model* illustrates the linkage of ISO 9001:2000 clauses (4–8) based on the PDCA approach. This PDCA methodology can be applied to all processes.

In the plan step, you establish the objectives and processes necessary to deliver results in accordance with customer requirements and organization policies. These processes are implemented in the do step. Then you monitor and measure the processes in the check step and report the results. In the act step, actions are taken to continually improve process performance.

An advantage of the process approach is the ongoing control it provides over the linkage between individual processes within a system of processes, as well as their combination and interaction. According to clause 4.2.2 in ISO 9001:2000, the quality manual must describe the interaction of the processes within the QMS.

4. *Revise your quality manual and procedures.* Most companies will already have documentation in place that addresses the requirements of the new standard. The documentation for a compliant QMS must include the quality policy, quality objectives, quality manual, required procedures, and other documents deemed necessary for its effective planning, operation, and control.

Documentation required is defined in clause 4.2.1 of the standard. Companies must have a documented quality manual that defines the scope of their QMS, including details of, and justification for, any exclusion. In addition, it must describe the interaction between key processes and include or reference the procedures. Organizations registered to ISO 9001:1994 along with a specific industry scheme (QS-9000 for automotive, TL 9000 for telecommunications, or AS9100 for aerospace) may find that many of the new ISO 9001:2000 requirements are already being practiced within their current system.

What the standard does not say is how all this should be documented and there now lies the golden opportunity to be creative in the preparation of the QMS. In our CD-ROM appendixes we provide three distinct ways of producing quality manuals and more than 40 completed procedures.

5. *Focus on an expanded top management role.* ISO 9000:2000 defines top management as the person or group of people who direct and control an organization at the highest level. Top management leadership, commitment, and active involvement are essential for an effective QMS, and successful registration. Every subclause in clause 5, Management responsibility, begins with the phrase "Top management shall." Top management must provide evidence of their commitment to the development and implementation of the QMS, as well as the continual improvement of its effectiveness.

Management must focus on meeting customer requirements and establishing the quality policy and objectives. Responsibilities must be defined and communicated within the organization. The system must be planned and the results reviewed at planned intervals. Review these duties with top management and explain the expected benefits for the organization. You need them as willing and active participants in the transition effort.

6. *Establish measurable quality objectives.* When you drive down the road, you can glance at the indicators on the dashboard to see how your car is performing. In a similar fashion, your organization needs to identify the key quality measures for evaluating the performance of your QMS.

To start the process, use the quality policy statement as the framework for establishing your process and product goals. Then set specific, measurable targets on the path to attaining these goals. The product objectives will be largely determined by your product specifications. Focus your attention on the process objectives and the methods you will use to measure process performance. These objectives must be established at the relevant functions and levels within your organization. See clause 5.4.1 on quality objectives for the requirements.

Provide the necessary resources to collect the product and process data. Analyze the data (as called for by clause 8.4) and use the facts for more effective decision making. If your desired results are not being achieved, identify the actions necessary to make it happen. ISO 9001:2000 requires an effective system, in other words, a system that is carrying out activities according to planned arrangements and achieving planned results. An efficient system is certainly desirable, but not required by the standard. Efficiency relates to the resources used to achieve the desired results. Keep this in mind as you set objectives.

7. *Prepare your transition plan.* We began this discussion by talking about planning a trip. To know your starting point, you should assess your current system against the requirements of the new standard (your destination). This gap analysis will identify any missing documentation and practices.

Knowing the needed deliverables, you can determine the appropriate activities and assignments to enhance your current system for conformity to ISO 9001:2000. Develop the transition schedule in consultation with your registrar. Depending on your system status and business needs, you may decide to make the transition quickly by having your entire system assessed during your next scheduled surveillance visit. Or, you can stage the transition over several surveillance visits to minimize its impact and cost. Your registrar will develop an assessment plan with you to meet the desired timing for your registration to the ISO 9001:2000 standard. You must maintain conformity to the ISO 9001:1994 standard during the transition period to keep your current certificate in place. A key consideration is to maintain the currently required procedures during the transition. You can't drop these procedures until the transition is completed, even if ISO 9001:2000 doesn't require them.

Clause 5.4.2 of ISO 9001:2000 requires planning any system changes and maintaining the integrity of the system during the changes. Switching to the ISO 9001:2000 standard is a significant change for your system and its planning may be the subject of an audit. Have your planning evidence ready. Registrars want to see objective evidence of effective system operation before conducting an audit. You will need to collect records as evidence that your system is complying with planned arrangements, meeting requirements, and effectively achieving the planned results.

8. *Inform your organization of changes and plans.* It is important to keep everyone within the scope of your QMS informed of your plans and progress. Clause 5.5.3 of ISO 9001:2000 requires that internal communication channels be established to share information about the effectiveness of your QMS. Top management will rely on internal communications to convey the importance of meeting customer requirements. The organization must also make employees aware of the relevance and importance of their activities and how they contribute to achieving the quality objectives.

Providing this information will allow everyone to help improve performance and meet the established objectives for their areas. Management should actively encourage feedback and communications from people within the organization.

9. *Update your internal audit program.* Clause 8.2.2, Internal audit, requires an organization to consider the process status and importance when planning an audit program. Since the QMS will be revised to comply with ISO 9001:2000, your internal audit schedule should focus on the areas of new and changed practices. In addition, the internal audit procedure must be updated to comply with the requirements of clause 8.2.2. Don't overlook training your internal auditors on ISO 9001:2000. The auditors need to understand how the new clause structure and requirements will affect their audit plans. Instead of auditing by clause, the organization may decide to audit by functional areas to evaluate the effectiveness of functional interfaces with various processes. Auditors should consider the new audit trails and expected evidence for conformity to ISO 9001:2000. For example, to audit to the requirements on quality objectives requires consideration of clause 5.4.1, Quality objectives, as well as related clauses that refer to quality objectives (4.2.1.a, 5.1.c, 5.3.c, 5.4.2.a, 5.6.1, 6.2.2.d, 7.1.a, and 8.5.1). Use of an electronic version of the standard will help auditors identify important cross-references.

The Registrar Accreditation Board (RAB) has approved ISO 9001:2000 transition training courses for certified auditors. You should consider this same training for your internal auditors. You can see a list of approved training courses at: http://www.rabnet.com/content/ISO9k2/ApprovedCourses.htm. Internal audits should be conducted against your modified system to determine the degree of conformity and to identify actions for your transition plan. Ensure that the system is ready and objective evidence is available before the registrar arrives for the assessment.

10. *Identify areas for continual improvement.* According to clause 8.5.1, the organization must continually improve the effectiveness of the QMS through the use of the quality policy, quality objectives, audit results, analysis of data, corrective and preventive actions, and management review.

Management should continually seek to improve process effectiveness rather than wait for problems to reveal opportunities for improvement. When a problem does occur, the cause must be determined and a corrective action taken to prevent its recurrence. The new standard emphasizes planning for the system, its resources, its processes, and the measurements necessary to evaluate performance. Part of the planning is to anticipate what might go wrong and try to prevent the occurrence of these potential problems. Even when processes are producing compliant products, the processes could be more efficient and effective. The aim of a continual improvement program is to increase the odds of satisfying customers by identifying areas needing improvement. After setting improvement objectives, the organization searches for possible solutions, selects and implements the appropriate one, and evaluates results to confirm objectives are met.

The documented quality policy statement must include a commitment to continual improvement. To ensure this focus, the management representative must report to top management on the need for any improvements. In fact, recommendations for improvement must be one of the management review inputs and any actions or decisions regarding improvements must be recorded.

DOCUMENTATION

The new standard only requires three core documents and six procedures. The new standard allows a great deal of flexibility in what a procedure is. You can consider the following as alternatives to procedures:

- A well-designed form

- Flowcharts

- Physical process flow

- A video

- Instructions on the work area wall

- Many others . . . do what works best for you

The Transition Assessment Process

The registrar's auditors will work with you to decide the appropriate number of visits. (Remember, transition was to be completed by December 3, 2003. However, since many of the organizations (see p. 11) have not fulfilled this requirement, the registrar that you will choose will work with you in the months before the assessment to develop an assessment plan detailing the areas of your business that will be looked at. This plan will also show which areas of ISO 9001/2:1994 will be assessed as the main part of the assessment, as well as the areas of ISO 9001:2000 that will be addressed within those parts of your business. This gives you the time to focus on these areas to ensure you are up to scratch.

The assessment will take place to ISO 9001/2:1994, but the assessor will be assessing your level of conformance to the additional requirements of ISO 9001:2000 at the same time. *All* nonconformities to both ISO 9001/2:1994 and to ISO 9001:2000 will be raised in the assessment report. This will help you identify where you need to do more work before the next assessment to maintain your conformance to ISO 9001/2:1994 and to meet the requirements of ISO 9001:2000.

At the end of the assessment, the assessor will leave you an assessment summary sheet (a matrix) to show which areas of the new standard you are already in conformance with. It will indicate areas "covered" or "partially covered."

As part of the assessment, the organization must recognize that there are two possible steps in pursuing registration. They are:

1. *One-step upgrade.* Generally this step tries to pack all of the above into one assessment visit. This will require a lot more work on your part before the assessment, but will get the transition over and done with, and allow you to focus on continual improvement.

2. *Gap analysis.* At any time, you can ask your registrar's representative to conduct a gap analysis, which is like a trial-run assessment. It will help you to identify areas where you will need to improve to meet the requirements. There will be a charge for this service based on the additional assessment days required. You will need to close down nonconformities against both the ISO 9001/2:1994 and ISO 9001:2000 standards. After all areas of ISO 9001:2000 have been covered, and all nonconformities closed down, recommendation for registration to ISO 9001:2000 will be given by the assessor. Assessment reports will be reviewed by a member of your selected registrar's staff, independent of the assessment, and a decision taken. If successful, your ISO 9001:2000 certificate will be issued. This gap analysis may also be conducted by your own internal auditors.

TRANSITION FROM QS-9000 TO ISO/TS 16949

In the previous section we addressed the concerns and issues of the transition process for the basic ISO standard. In this section we address the issues and concerns for ISO/TS 16949.

We have selected 13 items of concern as they apply to the automotive industry and addressed some of the transition activities that are necessary for compliance. These activities are shown in Table 5.1.

Table 5.1   The transition from QS-9000 to ISO/TS 16949.

Change	What This Means in the Automotive Industry
Identify and communicate stakeholder (customer) requirements	*Your organization* shall establish a procedure to identify and communicate customer (internal and external) needs and requirements.
Document quality objectives	*Your organization* shall define, document, and communicate quality objectives for all products, processes, and activities.
Assess and plan for training to develop organizational competence	*Your organization* shall establish a procedure to control the education, training, and qualification of personnel necessary to achieve the organization's quality objectives.
Preserve information, data, and knowledge	*Your organization* shall establish a procedure to control, access, and protect information, data, and knowledge (corrective and preventive action database).
Ensure infrastructure is in place to ensure quality	*Your organization* shall define, document, implement, maintain, and evaluate the infrastructure (buildings, workspace, equipment, hardware, software, tools, services, etc.) to satisfy *your organization's* needs, functions, and services.
Ensure work environment promotes quality	*Your organization* shall define, document, implement, maintain, and evaluate the human (job enrichment, empowerment, reward, recognition, career planning) and physical aspects of the work environment to ensure quality.
Include all processes that affect quality within scope	*Your organization* shall identify and include in the quality system all processes necessary to meet customer (internal and external) requirements. Exclusions shall be supported by documented rationale that the excluded process will not result in a risk to quality (all activities).
Measure effectiveness of all process within scope	*Your organization* shall design processes such that they monitor desired capability and incorporate feedback as a basis for continual improvement of product and process.

continued

continued

Change	What This Means in the Automotive Industry
Include service of product by agents (dealers)	*Your organization* shall document provisions for the types and extent of servicing provided including servicing responsibilities, planning of service activities (including activities performed by the dealer), service tools and products, technical support, training and competence of service personnel, and so on.
Conduct internal audits of product and process measures	*Your organization* shall audit measures to control product and process performance at appropriate intervals to ensure continuing acceptability of measures.
Inspect and test servicing software and hardware	*Your organization* shall check test software and hardware prior to release for servicing and recheck at prescribed intervals thereafter.
Ensure continual improvement	*Your organization* shall set objectives and evaluate performance for customer satisfaction and process measures. The objectives shall be based on competitive or comparative information and reviewed periodically for adequacy.
Ensure effective, disciplined corrective and preventive action process is used	*Your organization* shall define and document a structured corrective- and preventive-action process (disciplined problem solving) for identifying and eliminating product nonconformities, defects, or other undesirable situations identified by customers or customer or process measures (QOS, corrective and preventive action database).

Methodology used may be QOS.

There are 12 transition steps to accomplish these tasks. They are:

Step 1: Define the User Groups Affected by the Transition

- Areas of the organization not currently under the ISO/TS 16949 standard

- Areas of the organization currently compliant to the ISO/TS 16949 standard

- Areas of the organization currently compliant to other standards that will be affected such as:

  - QS-9000

  - Tooling and Equipment (T&E) Supplement

  - ISO 14001

Step 2: Consult with the Registrar

The following should be considered during discussions with the registrar:

- Timing required of your organization to upgrade to the revised standard

- The possibility of the upgrade coinciding with an existing planned surveillance audit

Step 3: Develop the Project Schedule

- Use basic project management techniques.

- Define key milestones.

- Assign responsibilities, identify resource needs.

Step 4: Identify Changes in ISO/TS 16949

- This course serves as a basis for identifying the changes

- This information may need to be disseminated to other personnel throughout the organization as appropriate

Step 5: Perform a Gap Analysis

A gap analysis is normally one of the first tasks of implementation. It takes requirements from the standard and breaks them down into audit-style questions to ask. A gap analysis is performed to:

- Identify the ISO/TS 16949 requirements applicable to your company.

- Identify current policies, procedures, and practices that could satisfy the ISO/TS 16949 requirements.

- Identify gaps between what the organization currently does, and what it must do to satisfy the ISO/TS 16949 quality system requirements.

Step 6: Create the Process Map

Develop a flowchart to map out major organization activities, from order to customer delivery.

- This flowchart will be used to identify all of the major quality-related activities of the organization.

- It can also assist in the organization of resources required for the implementation.

Step 7: Redesign the System to the Process Management Approach

If the current QMS is not geared to the process approach as required by ISO/TS 16949, then:

- Appropriate personnel must be trained in the approach.

- The system must be redesigned to use the approach.

Step 8: Revise Current Processes and Procedures

- Evaluate in more detail current procedures, instructions, and activities that could be used to address the requirements, as identified during the gap analysis.

- If current procedures exist, verify that they satisfy the requirements and that they accurately reflect current practices.

- Flowchart/map all current processes that are not already documented, then compare the activities as performed against the requirements.

- Where no activities are performed to address a specified requirement, or where activities must be modified, determine the best way to meet the requirement, considering the needs of the organization and its customers.

- Update the project milestone chart as additional actions are identified.

Step 9: Conduct Training

Some of the key training areas include:

- Revised processes/procedures

- Internal auditor training (focusing on changes between current and new standards)

- Understanding process management

- Management awareness

- General staff awareness

Step 10: Implement the Revised Quality System

- Procedures can be rolled out all at once or phased in as they are completed.

- During planning, consider that one to three months of operation of the system is required prior to a registration audit.

In this step of the transition the organization may divide the tasks in four categories. They are:

- *Prerequisites.* Train all persons involved in developing and implementing ISO/TS.

- *Phase 1.* Communications; quality system planning and process validation; document and data control (include training); process control

- *Phase 2.* Management review; design development; customer satisfaction monitoring; purchasing; corrective and preventive action; information management; nonconformance control; handling, storage, packaging, preservation, and delivery; monitoring and measurement; identification and traceability. [Note: During this phase the organization should begin the internal quality audit.]

- *Phase 3.* Control of quality records; customer-supplied property; continuous improvement; control of monitoring and measuring equipment. [Note: During this phase the organization should perform a desk audit of the quality system; hold a complete internal audit of the quality system; modify (as needed) procedures and system based on findings; and conduct a second round of internal audit (if needed).

Step 11: Conduct the Internal Audits

- Start the initial internal audits after implementation has begun.

- Ensure that the schedule of audits is aligned with implementation plans.

- Revise procedures, instructions, and so on, as needed based on audit findings.

- If possible, conduct a second series of audits.

- Conduct at least one management review prior to registration.

- Verify the adequacy and suitability of the system.

- Evaluate the need for changes in the QMS, policy, and/or objectives.

Step 12: Conduct the Registration Upgrade Audit

- Allow time for one to three months of system operation prior to any final registration upgrade audits.

- For planning purposes, allow for 30 to 45 days for corrective actions resulting from audits.

TRANSITIONAL REGISTRATION ISSUES

Generally, there are two fundamental concerns in the transitional registration process. They are: 1) the general rules that must be followed, and 2) the general time line for completion of the registration.

1. The general rules for registration in a transition phase are:

   - Organizations must use a certification body approved by the IATF.

   - The scope of certification must include all products supplied to customers subscribing to the ISO/TS 16949 standard.

   - Certification bodies will review the following documentation prior to the on-site visit:

     – Quality manual (for each site to be audited).

     – Internal audit and management review planning results (previous 12 months).

     – List of qualified auditors.

     – List of customer-specific requirements.

     – Customer complaint status.

     – Operational performance trends (previous 12 months minimum).

     – A preaudit may be conducted, but it will not be considered part of the initial certification audit.

     – The initial certification audit must be completed within three months of the document review.

– Multiple visits for the initial audit are not permitted.

– Certification body auditors are required to record all noconformities identified . . . even if corrected on the spot!

– Certificates will only be issued if there is 100 percent compliance to ISO/TS 16949 and all applicable customer-specific requirements.

– Organizations must resolve all nonconformities within 90 days of the issue date on the final report.

2. A typical time line may include these tasks:

- Gap analysis

- Develop new, more efficient process that also fills the gaps

- Develop concise procedures

- Train personnel to new processes and procedures

- Implement

- Internal audit

- Corrective actions

- Upgrade audit

6

AS9100 Aerospace Requirements

E very organization, regardless of size or sector, strives to provide a quality culture that will permeate every level of their organization. But establishing optimal working practices, which can enhance profit as well as customer satisfaction, does not happen by accident.

Today's most successful companies know the importance of having a proven QMS in place. Various QMSs have been used in the aerospace industry for many years. They have helped the industry deliver exemplary levels of product quality and operational safety. However, suppliers faced the need to maintain a different QMS for each of their large OEMs. Efforts by members of the global aerospace industry to establish a single common QMS have resulted in AS9100:2001-08 (known in this work as AS9100) and its supporting family of standards. Its use is now supported by many of the world's leading aerospace companies including Boeing, Lockheed Martin, Northrop Grumman, Rolls Royce Allison, General Electric Aircraft Engines, and NASA.

[Special note: In chapter 4 we summarized the important characteristics in common between the three major players in the automotive industry (DaimlerChrysler, General Motors, and Ford Motor Company). In this chapter we cannot do the same comparison for the aerospace industry because the players are many and there is no single or small group that sets the direction for quality. To facilitate this diversity, the Americas Aerospace Quality Group and the International Aerospace Quality Group have been designated with the responsibility for the development and implementation of the family of aerospace standards. These standards are the documents called AS9100 and EN9100 in the United States and Europe, respectively.

The two documents are exactly the same. Equivalent documents are also available in Brazil, Japan, China, and Russia].

ISO 9001:2000 is the basis of AS9100. Many aerospace companies are familiar with ISO 9001:1994, and the 20 clauses that it comprises. However, much of the new AS9100 is based on ISO 9001:2000 with specific variations. These variations address the unique industry requirements associated with specific portions of the business and they are:

1. AS9110—Applies to organizations that provide repair services

2. AS9120—Applies to organizations that warehouse, store, and distribute components and parts for the aerospace industry

3. AS9101—Quality system assessment guidelines and requirements for verifying and auditing AS9100:2001

4. AS9102—Is a product and part and approval process, and required for submittal of first article and subsequent contractual controls for products and processes

So, you need to understand the ISO 9001:2000 standard as well as what was added to make AS9100.

ISO 9001:2000 has as its core the principle of process management and the PDC(S)A cycle. The single most significant change to ISO 9001 is the movement away from a procedure-based approach to management (stating how you control your activities), to a process-based approach (understanding what you do). This shift enables organizations to link business objectives with business effectiveness more directly. The revitalized standard focuses not only on the familiar clauses of the previous ISO 9000 series, but extends them to view the organization as a series of interacting processes—the very processes that produce the products and services customers buy. It emphasizes much more and directly the concept of continual improvement of the QMS by examining and reviewing:

- Who are the customers?

- What are the customer's requirements?

- What is the product realization input?

- What is the product realization output?

- Is management responsibility evident?

- Is measurement, analysis, and improvement appropriate and applicable?

- Is resource management appropriate and applicable?

- Is customer satisfaction tracked through appropriate and applicable feedback methods?

Just like in any other certification scheme, the certificate of registration is a sign of acceptability that helps you demonstrate your organization's quality standards to discriminating customers. Registration to AS9100 is associated with the following benefits:

- Demonstration of operation to globally recognized aerospace quality standards

- Improved product and process quality

- Additional confidence for global sourcing

- Reassignment of supplier resources to quality improvement

- Common quality system approach in the supply chain for supplier/subcontractor development and consistency

- Potential reduction in variation of quality and increase in efficiency

- Potential reduction in second-party system audits

- Common language to improve understanding of quality requirements

- Compliance with a system supported by regulatory bodies

- Excellent levels of traceability throughout the supply chain

However, in the aerospace industry, even though registration is not mandatory, compliance is. For example, GE and Boeing not only require compliance, but they also have their own professional body of auditors to determine supplier's compliance.

DEVELOPMENT OF AS9100

AS9100 is a QMS standard originally based on ISO 9001:1994 and now based on ISO 9001:2000. Furthermore, the requirements of AS9100:1999 are brought into the AS9100:2001 version. Thus, *contentwise,* it is not significantly different than adding AS9100:1999 requirements to ISO 9001:2000. The key difference between ISO 9001:2000 and AS9100 is that

AS9100 contains supplements to ISO 9001:2000 to satisfy industry, internal, government, and regulatory requirements. Specifically, the AS9100:2001 contains more than 70 unique requirements applicable to the aerospace sector and further extends 18 ISO 9001 requirements. These additional requirements address civil and military aviation and aerospace needs.

Specific AS9100:2001 clauses relate requirements for:

- Configuration management
- Reliability
- Maintainability
- Safety
- Special processes
- Validation and verification process at design stages
- Approve and review subcontractor/supplier
- Verification of purchases
- Lifecycle costs based on design
- Product documentation (key characteristic identification and variability reduction)
- Product/process changes are controlled
- Control of software and *componentry* to automate aided processes
- Control of work performed outside of premises/organization
- Added internal audit requirements
- First article inspection ("first piece inspection" controls)
- Review and effective disposition of nonconformity

AS9100 was developed by representatives from the aerospace industry in the Americas, Europe, and Asia. It is published in the Americas by the Society of Automotive Engineers (SAE). Of course, the new AS9100 replaces the previous version AS9000. AS9100 is the first of a family of standards that reflect the specific concerns of the aerospace business.

To begin the process of conforming to AS9100, an organization must begin with at least the following nine steps. They are:

1. Purchase the standard. ·

2. Review support literature and software.

3. Assemble a team.

4. Consider training.

5. Review consultancy options.

6. Develop the organization's QMS.

7. Implement the organization's QMS.

8. Choose a registrar.

9. Gain registration.

These nine steps in implementing an AS9100-based QMS are important and essential in the process of achieving registration. The key step to registration, however, is a registration assessment, during which your entire AS9100 management system will be assessed.

SUMMARY OF ADDITIONS

The developers of AS9100 added elements to the basic ISO 9001:2000 standard to:

- Ensure that quality in the aerospace industry is maintained at the highest level, in part due to the criticality of the use of the final product.

- Focus on the management of key characteristics of products if they are identified.

- Recognize the requirements set by regulatory bodies, and ensure that records are kept and activities are conducted to help meet these requirements, ultimately aiming to reduce government oversight of aerospace manufacturers and suppliers.

- Recognize the complex nature of the final products and the need to ensure complete confidence in every component of the final product.

- Recognize the use of subcontract organizations within a process, and ensure this is effectively managed.

AS9100—AN EXPLANATION OF THE ADDITIONAL REQUIREMENTS

The following pages detail clause by clause the core concepts that have been included in AS9100, over and above ISO 9001:2000.

Clause 4—Quality management system

Documentation: Aims to make this more specific to the aerospace industry and helps to meet the regulatory requirements set by bodies such as the FAA. Specifically in:

- *Clause 4.2.1—General.* A requirement is added as section (f) to denote that the regulatory authorities have access to the QMS. [Note: By applying to be registered to AS9100, a company is also giving authority for OEMs and regulatory authorities to accompany the registrar on assessments to undertake oversight activities at any time—this is not normal practice for companies registered only to ISO 9001. Regulatory authorities within the aerospace industry have legal right of access at any time. Therefore, a registered company is saying "we are registered, therefore, we are good all the time, come look for yourself."]

- *Clause 4.2.2(b).* An added requirement emphasizes the need for the relationship between the ISO requirements and procedures to be clearly shown.

- *Clause 4.2.3(g).* Emphasis on coordinated effort between documented changes and regulatory requirements is required.

- *Clause 4.2.4—Control of records.* A requirement that focuses on the method of controlling, and the availability of the documents to customers and regulatory authorities.

- *Clause 4.3—Configuration management.* An element unique to the aerospace industry, this requires strict control of drawings of parts and aircraft, and includes the identification and control of manufacturing specifications, external customer documents, and quality records.

Clause 5—Management responsibility

This gives stronger weight and importance to the role of the management system representative, ensuring that he or she has authority to make changes when appropriate. Without support from senior management the role of the representative is toothless. Specifically in:

- *Clause 5.5.2—Management representative.* A requirement is added as section (d) to resolve matters pertaining to quality.

The reader will notice that there is no requirement for a quality manager.

Clause 6—Resource management

- *Clause 6.4—Work environment.* Recognizes the need for strong emphasis on cleanliness and precision required in the manufacture of aerospace parts.

Clause 7—Product realization

- *Clause 7.1—Planning of product realization.* A requirement is added as section (e) to places emphasis on the long term and lifecycle of a product including support and maintenance. Aerospace parts usually have a long lifecycle, and require traceability from specification to disposal. Design has to consider the user.

- *Clause 7.2.2—Review of requirements related to the product.* A requirement is added as section (d) to highlight the issue of risk. Because of the nature of this industry, emphasis is placed on the subject of risk evaluation, for example, where new technology is implemented or where demands are set for short delivery time of product/services. As there are a number of activities that can impact risk, this subject should be given special attention.

- *Clause 7.3.1—Design and development planning.* Basic require- ments are more robust due to the importance and cost of investment often required. The additional requirements also focus on the key characteristics of products, as this is where they are identified and where the people, tasks, and equipment need to be identified to ensure that the key characteristics are effectively managed throughout the process. Specifically, in 7.3.1 (a): The development stages must be determined with respect to the organization, task sequence, mandatory steps, significant changes, and method of configuration control. In section (c) of the same clause, the standard emphasizes the need for structuring the design and the analysis of each of the elements of that design. Furthermore, the same clause and section makes a point that it is a mandatory requirement that the tasks of different designs must be defined according to specified safety and functional objectives in relation to customer and/or regulatory requirements.

- *Clause 7.3.3—Design and development outputs.* A requirement is added as section (e) to identify key characteristics and all pertinent data required by design or contract to allow the product to be identified. Key characteristics are: critical, significant, high impact, and operator-safety items that need special consideration in design and process.

- *Clause 7.3.4—Design and development review.* A requirement is added as item (c) to authorize progression to the next stage.

- *Clause 7.3.5—Design and development verification.* A note is added to clarify the design and development verification activities.

- *Clause 7.3.6—Design and development validation.* A note is added to clarify the design and development validation.

- *Clause 7.3.6.1* This clause is added to make sure that all documentation is complete and meets the specification requirements for all identified operational conditions.

- *Clause 7.3.6.2* This clause is added to make sure that when design, verification, and validation tests are necessary, appropriate documentation is planned, controlled, reviewed, and documented. Five specific conditions are identified: 1) test plans, 2) test procedures, 3) correct configuration, 4) requirements must be observed, and 5) acceptance criteria are met.

- *Clause 7.3.7—Control of design and development changes.* An additional statement is added to this clause to clarify the organization's change control process. According to this clause, the organization must provide the customer or the regulatory body approval of changes.

- *Clause 7.4.1—Purchasing process.* Additional requirements are added to the ISO base to recognize the regulatory requirements in the area of supplier control. The aim is to ensure that bona fide parts are used, and that there is accountability and responsibility in all activities. Includes increased role of verification of product as it is delivered, as this is when the company assumes responsibility for supplied parts. It must be emphasized here that these additional requirements are industry practices for DoD, NASA, and commercial product.

- *Clause 7.4.2—Purchasing information.* A number of specific and important requirements are added through the addition of items (d–j) that specifically address the product to be purchased and how it is to be delivered. This is because of the extensive length of the supply chain and the importance of every level controlling the performance of their suppliers.

- *Clause 7.5.1—Control of production and service provision.* Additional requirements to recognize where and how key characteristics are identified and effectively documented through traceability and control.

- *Clause 7.5.1.1* addresses the specific requirements for production documentation.

- *Clause 7.5.1.2* addresses the specific requirements for control of production process changes.

- *Clause 7.5.1.3* This clause addresses the specific requirements for control of production equipment, tools, and numerical control machine programs.

- *Clause 7.5.1.4* This clause addresses the specific requirements for control of work transferred, on a temporary basis, outside the organization's facilities.

- *Clause 7.5.1.5* This clause addresses specific requirements for control of service operations.

- *Clause 7.5.2—Validation of processes for production and service provision.* This clause emphasizes the importance of special process. Not only does it define it, but it also clarifies it by adding a note under item (a) requiring the defined criteria to be set prior to use. Furthermore, under (c) the standard requires that control of the significant operations and parameters of special processes must use specific methods and procedures as applicable.

- *Clause 7.5.3—Identification and traceability.* There are additional requirements that define identification and traceability. Specifically, this clause requires the organization to maintain the identification of the configuration of the product in order to identify any differences between the actual configuration and the agreed configuration, as well as provide adequate documentation throughout product life.

- *Clause 7.5.4—Customer property.* A clarification of intellectual property is given through a note.

- *Clause 7.5.5—Preservation of product.* Additional requirements are added in this clause defining preservation in much more detail than the ISO standard.

- *Clause 7.6—Control of monitoring and measuring devices.* The emphasis on calibration was reduced in ISO 9001:2000, but it has been reemphasized in AS9100, as it is deemed to be key in the aerospace industry. Specifically, clause 7.6 clarifies the monitoring and measuring devices through a note and adds stronger language for maintaining a register of monitoring and measuring devices and defines the process for their calibration. It also adds item (f) to a list of specific requirements that addresses the issue of recall when required. (Readers are encouraged to see ISO0012-1 to help in the development of their own system.)

Clause 8—Measurement, analysis and improvement

- *Clause 8.1—General.* A note for clarification is added. Fundamentally, the note focuses on a better definition for gathering information and trend analysis for long-term benefit in the aerospace industry, and the need to analyze product at all phases from design to end use. It clarifies the statistical techniques and the support activities via appropriate record keeping and documentation.

- *Clause 8.2.2—Internal audit.* Additional requirements are added for detailed tools and techniques to support audit of the QMS requirements.

- *Clause 8.2.3—Monitoring and measuring of processes.* Additional requirements are identified for process nonconformity.

- *Clause 8.2.4—Monitoring and measuring of product.* Additional requirements are added for key characteristics. Specifically, they have to be identified, monitored, and controlled. If sampling and inspection are used, then they have to be statistically valid and have to confirm to the specific requirements. It also provides for the control of product released prior to confirmation of conformance.

- *Clause 8.2.4.1* The entire clause focuses on inspection documentation. Specifically, it identifies areas that should be included, such as: a) criteria for acceptance, b) where sequence testing is performed, c) a record of measurement system, and d) type of measurement instruments.

- *Clause 8.2.4.2* The entire clause deals with first article of inspection (FAI). It specifies that the system must provide a process for the inspection, verification, and documentation of the first production run with appropriate documentation. It is also interesting to note that this clause also suggests the use of AS9102 for guidance in performing first article of inspection.

- *Clause 8.3—Control of nonconforming product.* This clause recognizes the need and practice in the aerospace industry for a more robust process for disposition and identification of nonconforming product. Overall, it recognizes the need to prevent nonconforming product from getting into the industry, and allowing customers to know if a part has been reworked at any time. In essence, it has specific requirements that limit the organization's authority to disposition nonconforming material.

- *Clause 8.5.2— Corrective action.* Item (f) is added in this clause and it requires the need to involve the supplier when it is determined that they are the root cause of the problem.

PREPARATION FOR REGISTRATION

When the organization is ready to pursue registration, certain things must be ready. Some of the most important items are:

- Establish the *commitment by management* to pursue certification not just because the customer or a regulatory body requires it but because you believe that the certification is going to improve the overall effectiveness of the organization.

- Understand *process approach.* Be prepared to view the process in a holistic approach rather than evaluate it in a piecemeal approach.

- *Assemble a team* that is cross-functional and multidisciplinary.

- *Consider training* for all employees as appropriate and applicable.

- *Develop documentation* that reflects your organization through a quality manual, procedures, and instructions.

- *Communicate implementation* to all levels of the organization.

- Focus on *continual improvement* as well as *effectiveness* of what is being done in the entire organization.

- *Conduct gap analysis* to identify the shortcomings and areas for potential improvements.

- *Collect data and review* the system for appropriate improvements.

- *Choose a registrar* that has your interest in mind and, above all, is approved by the international aerospace quality group (IAQG), if the organization expects the industry to recognize the registration.

- *Gain registration* and proclaim it with pride.

- Provide *summary and evaluation of the process* for future reference.

- *Create AS9100 checklist.*

The industry has a checklist (AS9101) that is mandatory for registrars, and it includes a scoring methodology. Strictly speaking there is no need to worry about a checklist. However, if an organization wants to go beyond the requirements, a checklist of its own may be helpful. Therefore, the AS9100 checklist is a fairly significant addition to the management systems assessment process, and is the major difference companies will see during an assessment. At the initial assessment or upgrade assessment the checklist is completed in full. The score will be made public through the IAQG/ American Aerospace Quality Group (AAQG) database. At each continuing assessment visit, the assessor completes the checklist for only those activities covered during the assessment, and the total score is updated. At each reassessment by strategic review, the checklist is consolidated and the score submitted to the database. This score is an evaluation of effectiveness of the QMS. (This scoring methodology was added to provide a clear and consistent assessment of an organization's ability and performance, and to provide a benchmark against which continual improvement can be measured. The reader may want to reference the AS9101(A) Quality System Assessment for a reference checklist or appendix VI on the CD-ROM.)

Gaining Registration

The route to registration is the same as that for ISO and ISO/TS. Specifically, there are seven steps in gaining registration to AS9100. They are:

1. You will be asked to complete a company profile. The registrar's representative will do everything he or she can to help you do this. [Note: This item presupposes that the organization has done some work to identify potential registrars.]

2. Based on the profile, the registrar will forward a proposal for delivery of assessment services.

3. At this point you submit a formal application to the chosen registrar.

4. Your principal contact with the registrar throughout the registration process and beyond will be appointed. They will have knowledge concerning the nature of your business and will offer support whilst you develop your system.

5. An optional preassessment can be undertaken to review your QMS and to establish your readiness for initial assessment.

6. The formal assessment of your system is entirely objective, checking that you do what you say you do and that your system meets the requirements of the standard. The AS9101 checklist is completed and a score calculated. You will be informed of the recommendation before the assessment team leaves your premises.

7. The initial assessment report is independently reviewed, the formal registration decision taken, and, if successful, your certificate of registration is issued. Then you can begin to advertise your success and promote your registration with the registrar. Your registrar will periodically visit you to ensure that your system continues to meet the requirements of the standard. The AS9101 checklist is updated and the score is revised.

REFERENCE

SAE. The Engineering Society for Advancing Mobility, Land, Sea, Air, and Space. 2002. *Aerospace Standard (AS9100 Rev. A)*. Warrendale, PA: SAE.

7

Documentation

For anyone to begin discussion on documentation, he or she must have an understanding of "system thinking" process. Obviously, since we are talking about quality as it relates to ISO, one must be aware of the "quality system." A quality system is the set of policies and procedures that present the way an organization performs its process. The quality system assures that a quality program exists and is followed, so that the quality of the product or service is delivered to the customer without problems or nonconformances. This quality system generally is based on four levels, each one relating to each other in a hierarchical manner. The levels are:

- *Level 1—Quality manual.* Overview of the company and its products and services; agreement to comply with applicable ISO 9001 requirements; system scope; exclusions; organization and responsibilities; sequence and interaction of processes; documented procedures. Often, this level of documentation makes references to Level 2 documents.

- *Level 2—Procedures.* Describes the quality processes and inter-departmental controls that address the ISO 9001 requirements; may be in ISO 9001 order or process order; references lower-level documentation. ISO 9001 mandates six specific procedures.

- *Level 3—Instructions.* Explains details of specific tasks or activities; the how of performing a specific task. This level may include quality plans, work instructions, drawings, flowcharts, workmanship standards, product specifications, machine manuals, and so on.

- *Level 4—Forms, tags, labels, and other documents.* Documents that prompt the recording of evidence (per levels 1, 2, and 3 documentation) of compliance to requirements. Records may be mandatory or implied for each ISO 9001 clause.

These four levels make up the documentation of the organization. Obviously, it is organization-dependent, and to generate the appropriate and applicable documentation an organization must understand the process and the customer. To begin with, a process is an entity that may be individually independent or made up of a combination of the following: manpower, machine, method, material, measurement, and environment. The goal of the process is to transform inputs to outputs. The goal, of course, in any organization is to make money; however, to make money one must satisfy the customer. To satisfy the customer, one must deliver consistent, repeatable, and predictable quality products and or services. It is this delivery of quality products or services that drives documentation.

Generally speaking, the documentation is in a hierarchical format. The hierarchy shows the level of detail and explains the policy and procedures not only to those who are doing the task but to someone who is about to do the task. Traditionally speaking, there are four levels of documentation. A fifth tier is sometimes added but is optional (see Table 7.1).

In each case, the documentation for each level or tier (both terms are used interchangeably) covers specific information. For example: The quality manual covers the policy and direction of the organization and those of the individual departments. A policy is a visionary statement that becomes a guide for action in the organization. The procedures contain the *why, where, who, what* and the *flow* or *direction* of the process. The instructions describe the *how* of the task to be done. The records confirm a quality event; a form is an empty template where the verification of a quality event will be reported. A record is a filled-out form. A tag is a variation of a form. The guideline is a reference document—usually nonaudible—clarifying either a procedure and/or instruction.

Table 7.1 Levels of documentation.

Quality Manual	Tier 1	Level 1
Procedures	Tier 2	Level 2
Instructions	Tier 3	Level 3
Forms, records, tags, and so on	Tier 4	Level 4
Guidelines (optional)	Tier 5	Level 5

In the last couple of years the trend seems to be that major corporations are focusing on three levels of formal documentation. That is, the quality manual, a combination of procedures and instructions, and records. Very few are using guidelines, and if they do, it seems most of them recognize them as an addendum to their procedures.

QUALITY MANUAL

The quality manual is the highest level of documentation. It is a mandatory item of any quality system. The content of the quality manual should include:

- Organizational quality policy
- Proper authorization
- Issuing date
- The organization's principles and objectives
- A short description of the customers and/or suppliers
- Organizational structure
- Overview of the functions of the organization's executives
- Description of each functional area
- Related documentation and/or references
- Distribution list
- Document change and control
- Copyright statement (optional)

For samples of quality manuals see the CD-ROM.

PROCEDURES

The second level of documentation. Procedures are very fundamental to any quality system for they provide the flow and specific information about individual processes. Procedures are one of the most important parts of the quality system. A procedure document must accurately reflect the operation or function it is describing, who is responsible, and any records that flow from these activities. The content of the procedures should include:

- *Purpose.* Why is this procedure performed?

- *Inputs.* What comes into the process? Which inputs need to be measured?

- *Outputs.* What are the outputs? What needs to be measured?

- *Acceptance criteria.* How are tests, standards, or tolerance limits selected?

- *Responsibility.* Who is responsible to initiate, perform, and monitor?

- *Procedure step.* How is the process performed?

- *Audit requirements.* What is the frequency, who performs it, what happens with the results?

- *Resources.* What process(es) is (are) required to do the procedure?

- *Training.* What training is required for operators of the task?

- *Approval authority.* Who approves and authorizes the procedure?

To do an appropriate procedure, one must: a) determine the requirements, b) perform needs analysis, c) define documentation effort, d) develop and refine documentation—usually through a process flow diagram, and e) control the documentation. Typical procedures using process flowcharts may be found on the CD-ROM. [Good sources for explaining the usage of process mapping (process flow diagram) are Stamatis (1997), Brassard and Ritter (1994), and Brassard et al. (2002).]

WORK INSTRUCTION

The third level of documentation. A work instruction is the detailed procedure for a task. Another way of thinking about it is to think of instructions as a step-by-step approach to doing a specific task. To develop an appropriate instruction, follow these steps:

- Start with the most important step and continue to develop.

- Follow the correct order.

- Begin with an active verb (for example, place, drive, hold, and so on).

- It may be presented as a flowchart.

- It may be posted as a job aid.

- It may be available through electronic devices. (It is imperative that all instructions must be available to operators performing the task or the process. It is for this reason that all instructions must be current.)

RECORDS

The fourth level of documentation. Records are the proof that a quality event has taken place and that it is effective. A record is typically the result of a task, audit, inspection, test, or review. As a consequence, all quality records fall into the following categories:

- Process control results

- Inspection and test results

- Audit results

- Training records

- Product and process review

- Logs and service calls

RETRIEVAL AND RETENTION

All records must be retrievable when needed, maintained safely, legible, and readily identifiable. Furthermore, the quality system should provide a method for:

- Indicating retention times

- Removing and disposing of documentation that is outdated

PRODUCTION

In today's world, documentation may be of two types, and both are acceptable. (In some cases there is a dual system—in other words, both are used and/or a combination of the two.) The first is the electronic type, and the second is the hard copy. With the electronic system, the main advantage is that controlling of all the documentation is very easy and the updates or modifications to any portion of the documentation are fast, efficient, and thorough. On the other hand, a major concern of the electronic type is that everyone must know how to access the files and how to locate the information. The reader should recognize that individuals may or may not know how to access the electronic file(s). What is important is that the individual must know a source to help him or her on the job to get access to the required documentation as it relates to his or her particular task.

With the hard copy, the documents must be maintained in a master file by the document administrator. They should be attractive for ease of readability and usefulness.

Regardless of what documentation type is used, all documentation should have headers or footers with some basic information regarding the specific document. Generic information usually includes the following:

- Title

- Element

- Document number

- Version date or number

- Effective date

- Revision date

- Authorized signature

- Page

DOCUMENT CONTROL

Document control helps to assure that employees and suppliers have the necessary paperwork to do their job. The question of what constitutes document control is not easy to answer. It depends on the organization and the documents needed for verification of a particular task. To help define document control we can look at ISO 9004 17.3, which provides some basic guidelines.

Perhaps the most important issues of document control are the issues of document administration and document change process. In document administration some of the issues that are addressed are:

- Original content or changes.

- Review and approve content.

- Publish document.

- Keep track of person, location, and ownership of the document.

- Security of the document.

- Distribute changes.

- Replace document after a practical number of changes.

On the other hand, in the document change process some of the issues that are addressed are:

- Identify the required change(s).

- Write the change(s).

- Approve the change(s).

- Distribute the change(s).

- Include the "new" documentation.

- Remove the "old" documentation.

THE BASICS OF HOW TO PREPARE DOCUMENTATION

When visualizing a company manual, most people think of a big, fat book crammed full of small type and complex charts. They usually identify such company manuals with giant corporations. Sadly, they are usually correct.

Practically every large corporation today has a company manual of some sort. Many have a whole series of manuals covering every aspect of their operations broken down by department and, still further, to individual job functions. Entire departments are devoted to continually analyzing systems and procedures with the objective of eliminating wasteful steps, simplifying methods, and improving communications and controls.

At what point does a company achieve the level of development where an operations manual is needed? It's never too soon if it is a company that intends to grow and stay in business. But contrary to the big, fat manuals we visualize for large corporations, the smaller company can get along with a manual that is proportioned to its relative size and complexity. In the CD-ROM of this book we provide four distinct manuals to demonstrate the options an organization may have in developing its own manual.

Some companies are in more complicated businesses than others. This alone may force a relatively small company to produce a manual that is considerably larger than might be indicated by mere size alone.

The answer to the question, "What is a company manual?" then is quite simple. It is a written study of the philosophy, systems, procedures, techniques, and concepts under which a given business is operating—set forth in such a manner and style as to be easily referenced and fully understood. Of course, since we are discussing quality in this book, the focus is on a quality manual. However, the reader should notice that the mechanics of any manual are the same. The focus of the content will differ.

This definition sometimes may create the illusion that a company manual may not be needed. This of course may be true if the business is small. However, generally, the few businesses that may have little reason for a company manual are those that either depend on an individual's personal skill or are so straightforward as to be obvious to practically anyone. Businesses of the former type are usually difficult to transfer and might include small businesses in such specialties as shoe repair, radio and TV service, auto mechanics, electrical installation and repair, plumbing, commercial art, photography and, of course, most of the degreed professions.

This is not to imply that all of these categories are impossible to transfer. As going businesses, even doctors' offices and practices are often sold. The same holds true with accounting practices and others. The relevant factor is that a medical practice must be sold to a doctor and a shoe repair business must be sold to a qualified shoemaker. In either case, the continuity of the business depends upon the skills and knowledge of the individual rather than the incidental systems and procedures under which the business functions.

As with any rule, there are exceptions. There is today at least one chain of shoe repair shops that operates under quite unique systems and procedures. Without a doubt their operation should be manualized. The same holds true with any other specialty business that is operating under a unique concept that can, and might, be duplicated in several locations.

In the realm of particularly straightforward businesses that are so obvious as to preclude the need for a manual might be included, with qualifications, such businesses as: manufacturer's representative, lawn trimming, house painting, refuse removal, package delivery, and other businesses that deal with a single, uncomplicated product or a relatively unskilled service.

By way of qualification, we would have to eliminate from the category of "may not need a company manual" any business for which the owners have plans to branch out. This might include opening company branch operations or appointing franchisees, licensees, agents, or representatives.

By contrast, in both automotive and aerospace and in fact any business that pursues ISO 9000 certification, a company manual is a must.

TYPES OF MANUALS

Depending upon objectives and planned utilization, there are a wide variety of types of company manuals. These are:

1. *Internal manuals.* Those needed for personnel and departments to clarify and control work "flow." Within the scope of internal manuals are:

    a. *Administrative.*

      • Manuals codifying overall company policies and objectives

      • Those explaining the functions and procedures of specific departments

      • Those setting forth personnel policies and company benefits

    b. *Technical.* Comprises manuals that spell out technical working procedures as, for example:

      • Research and development

      • Manufacturing techniques

      • Installation procedures

      • Servicing

    c. *Systems and procedures.* Breaks down a specific task or a series of tasks into sequential steps or operations. Generally used for:

      • Data processing

      • Product assembly

      • Paperwork flow and disposition

    d. *Marketing.* These are manuals that develop the company's concepts regarding:

      • Public image to be projected

      • Introduction of new products

      • Methods for evaluating relative market position and opportunities

      • Selling philosophy and procedures

2. *External manuals.* These comprise manuals that go outside the organization. For example:

   a. Manuals that go to customers to help them assemble, install, use, and maintain the company's products

   b. Manuals that go to affiliates such as:

      • Affiliated or associated companies

      • Jobbers and distributors

      • Outside service organizations and installers

      • Representatives

      • Retailers to help them sell the line

      • Franchisees and licensees

   c. Manuals that instruct outside consulting organizations on how to handle the company's graphics with regard to style and trademark usage and other pertinent policies:

      • Advertising agencies

      • Public relations counselors

      • Industrial film producers

      • Printers and signage suppliers

Manuals can be done in an unlimited variety of shapes and sizes depending upon the complexity of the business, individuals to whom directed, anticipated frequency of changes and additions, security considerations, and overall purpose.

Let's take a look at these one at a time:

1. *Complexity of the business.* To a great degree would dictate the size of the manual in terms of overall bulk. This is determined by the number of subjects to be covered, how many departments have to be explained, the number of systems and procedures, and their interlocking relationships that must be detailed. When a business reaches the degree of complexity that might cause its manual to become unwieldly, it is advisable to break it up into separate books: that is, personnel procedures; purchasing manual; sales manual; accounting and administration manual; manager's guide; forms and systems manual; installation manual; manufacturing quality manual; and so on.

2. *Individuals to whom directed.* If the person who is supposed to use the manual is expected to carry it around in his or her pocket, then without

a doubt it should be pocket-sized. This means length, width, bulk, and weight, for you can rest assured that if you exceed any one of these dimensions, the manual, which you nurtured so carefully and in which you invested so much time, effort, and money, will be left behind in the car, office, or home at the critical moment for which you so carefully planned its use.

A manual directed to typists and secretaries explaining the company's policies regarding letter format, filing systems, interoffice communications, and telephone policy need not, and probably should not, contain scads of nonrelevant information about purchasing procedures or how to handle marketing problems. On the other hand, the office manager who is doubling as personnel manager should certainly be provided with manuals covering all of the functions, systems, procedures, and job titles encompassed by his or her responsibilities. Since portability is not a consideration in this case, size and bulk are not important factors.

3. *Anticipated frequency of changes and additions.* Is the major point that dictates the method of binding to be used. Obviously, any permanent type of binding makes it difficult (if not impossible) to make changes, additions, and deletions. For this reason, although there are several disadvantages, most companies use loose-leaf binders that are available in a variety of sizes and capacities. (Each of these items is discussed separately later in this section and in appendix XII on the CD-ROM.)

If frequent revisions are expected, a page numbering and indexing system should be incorporated that permits the user to know whether his or her manual is up to date. A subsequent section will suggest and detail various methods that have been used successfully.

Anticipated frequency of changes might also influence the choice of copy preparation method, reproduction process, and quantity of manuals to be run. If substantial changes are expected, reproduction quality typing would probably be used rather than considerably more expensive printer's type. Electronic word processing is particularly applicable to manual preparation because it permits text editing and correcting without necessitating the complete typing of each draft. After completion, the magnetically recorded text (magnetic card, tape, rigid or floppy disc, or CD) may be permanently retained for future updating and repeated use. If changes are inevitable, it would be poor judgment to reproduce more manuals than are immediately needed. [Note: Each of these items will be discussed separately later in this section.]

4. *Security considerations.* This is a most difficult subject to discuss since there is no doubt that any competitor would love to gain possession of your company operations manual—especially if you have a reputation for running a smooth, profitable, well-organized operation. The other party

you must be concerned with is the ambitious, highly motivated employee who might borrow your manual for purposes of going into competition with you. Of course, any size manual can be appropriated; however, if the various departmental and functional sections are bound separately and are distributed on a "need-to-know" basis, the chance of someone walking off with the whole store is somewhat lessened. Actually, the principal means of protecting yourself against unauthorized use of your materials by an employee or former employee is through a properly drafted restrictive covenant and trade secrets clause in a valid employment agreement. [Note: It must be noted here that even with a computerized manual, there is no guarantee that an employee may not walk off with a manual. This is why in the case of a quality manual we talk about "document control." We want to make sure that only authorized individuals have access to the manual (for use and changes).]

5. *Overall purpose.* A company operations manual can serve many purposes and should, therefore, be designed accordingly. Primarily, it will be used as a reference source when there is a question as to the proper procedure or policy that might affect a given transaction. For this reason, it must be divided, subdivided, and indexed for ease in finding the answers to specific questions.

Company manuals are also used as planning guides. For this reason, there must be a smooth and logical flow of information so that top management can be sure that new programs and procedures blend well without upsetting ongoing activities. All of the checks and balances built into the systems must be focused upon so they are not ignored or weakened when instituting changes.

Company manuals are also used as textbooks in the training of new employees and in retraining old employees for new or added responsibilities. Further, they are used extensively in the training of franchisees, licensees, agents, dealers, and independent representatives. It is important, therefore, that in addition to excellence of content, the overall impression projected by a company's manual is one of efficiency and solidity. No one wants to be associated with a company whose direction seems confused and whose substance appears questionable.

In the case of a quality manual, the purpose should be stated early in the manual, and the content is dependent upon the standard that the organization follows and how that standard fits in the organization.

6. *Problems of small and medium-sized business.* The vital details of a complex business are often carried around in the head of a single person. He or she can't take a day off without worry. Heirs, investors, employees, and creditors are always at risk. He or she feels they don't have the manpower

or time to develop a company manual, and paying for outside assistance is difficult because of more "pressing" needs. Regardless, a company manual for the smaller business is as important as having adequate "key man" life insurance and is far less costly. A continuing business can support heirs forever while life insurance pays off and is finished. With this manual, any businessman can reasonably produce an operations manual. By delegating, the details can be done by others with the "key man" tying it all together.

While a quality manual is a mandatory item for any organization that pursues ISO, AS, and ISO/TS, other manuals are optional. Figure 7.1 may prove helpful in defining the need for any manual.

The second question regarding the manual has to do with extensiveness. How extensive a manual do we need? Assuming you've already determined

---

Does My Company Need an Operations Manual?

If your answer to any one of these questions is "yes," then chances are your company should have at least a modest operations manual. If there are two or more "yes" answers, there is no doubt about it, you need one.

1. Does management wish to accelerate the current rate of growth? ☐ Yes ☐ No

2. At the current rate of growth, or at a desired accelerated rate of growth, would the number of employees requiring training rise proportionately? ☐ Yes ☐ No

3. Do you now have branch operations (includes company-owned branches, franchisees, licensees, agents, independent representatives) or do you contemplate having such branch operations in the foreseeable future? ☐ Yes ☐ No

4. If any executive, key employee, or group of employees were to leave the company or unexpectedly become unavailable, would the loss of such personnel's knowledge make the uninterrupted continuation of the business difficult? ☐ Yes ☐ No

5. Is it the owner's desire that the business continue without interruption after his or her retirement or demise? ☐ Yes ☐ No

Figure 7.1   Operations manual questionnaire.

you need a manual (remember it is mandatory to have a quality manual; this exercise is for other company manuals that you may consider), a rating totaling 10 or more indicates you need more than just a minimum, basic manual (10 to 12 typed pages explaining systems and procedures). If your total is 15 to 20, you probably need a manual detailing the functions of each department. A total of 20 to 25 indicates the addition of separate job descriptions and responsibilities. A rating greater than 25 indicates that a full manual is needed, probably requiring separate volumes for each department an each major function (see Figure 7.2).

PLANNING AND SCHEDULING PROCEDURES

Once the decision to produce a company manual has been made, it is wise for management to see that a careful job of *delegating, planning,* and *scheduling* is done before any work is actually begun. It is most important that these be given thoughtful consideration since the quality of the finished product will depend heavily upon the skills of the coordinator and how well the initial planning has been done.

Delegating

A large company will usually have a systems and procedures department, which, naturally, is charged with the responsibility of developing and revising systems and procedures, as well as their implementation and manualization. Smaller companies, which do not have such departments, must delegate the work to individuals or groups who are competent to analyze what is going on and present it in readable, understandable language. In many cases there is at least one person in the company who has the broad perspective and ability to quarterback the job. He or she will be an individual who thinks logically, is inquisitive, and who expresses himself or herself well in writing. If no such individual is available, or if he or she cannot be relieved from other duties, then it may be necessary to seek outside assistance.

The type of talent needed is generally found at one of several different types of management consultants. If the company's activities are financially or commercially oriented, then the assistance of one of the larger accounting firms might be solicited—they often have management consulting groups available for various types of assignments. (Obviously, outside consultants are not mandatory to develop any kind of manual and/or procedures. Their services are always optional.)

1. Through attrition, turnover, growth, or other reasons we must hire and train at least five new employees a month.

Never	Sometimes	Frequently	Always
(0 points)	(5 points)	(10 points)	(25 points)

2. We open branches (includes company-owned branches, franchisees, licensees, agents, independent representatives), or are planning to open branches, at the rate of at least two a year.

Never	Sometimes	Frequently	Always
(0 points)	(5 points)	(10 points)	(25 points)

3. Due to changing technology, new products, mergers, acquisitions, or other major business changes, we must introduce our procedures and concepts to groups of new associates or employees.

Never	Sometimes	Frequently	Always
(0 points)	(5 points)	(10 points)	(25 points)

4. Our gross volume is:

   a. Under $1 million . . . . (0 points)

   b. $1 to $5 million . . . . (5 points)

   c. $5 to $10 million . . . . (10 points)

   d. $10 to $25 million . . . . (15 points)

   e. $25 to $50 million . . . . (20 points)

   f. Over $50 million . . . . (25 points)

Figure 7.2   Determining the need for a company manual.

If the major activity of the company is marketing, then any number of marketing specialists might be considered as possible sources of assistance. These might include: the company's advertising or public relations agency, sales and marketing consulting organizations, or freelance marketing consultants.

When manufacturing, construction, or other technical activities play an important role, it might be wise to investigate the many engineering firms or engineering job shops that may have suitable personnel to assign to the project of researching and writing your manual.

If branch expansion through franchising or licensing is, or is planned to be, important in the future of the company, then the best source for talent is probably a franchise marketing consulting organization.

Any or all of the aforementioned, as well as any of the reputable management consulting firms, may have the person or persons needed to accumulate information and be responsible for writing the manual, no matter what the company's main activity might be. In most cases it will be found that a generalist with wide business experience and good graphic communications skills will do the best job.

In the case of a quality manual or quality procedures, generally there is a synergistic effort to develop them between the quality department, operations, and management.

Planning

The first step in planning the company manual is to agree upon objectives. What is the purpose of this particular manual? What should it accomplish? To whom and for whom should it be directed? How will it be used and what format should it have? (See sidebar.)

After everyone involved in the decision-making process has agreed upon the objectives, and they have been committed to writing in the form of a brief statement of objectives, the next step is to prepare a broad outline

---

PURPOSE AND SCOPE OF PROPOSED COMPANY MANUAL

The purpose of the proposed company manual is to provide a working tool for all departments and employees of the company. It shall contain all current operating systems and procedures with separate volumes for line and staff personnel. The manual shall be so designed that it may be easily revised and separated by department. Further, it shall be designed to be broken out by job category wherever possible. The style and format shall permit usage as a working reference guide and as a training textbook for new employees and others being retrained or upgraded.

of the major topics to be covered. This step is relatively simple and merely requires the application of logic to the problems that have been defined and objectives that have been spelled out. In your planning, bear in mind that it is always good to do a bit of merchandising of the manual and public relations for the company by providing prospective readers with a certain amount of background information and reasons why, as well as how to. Based on the statement of objectives on the previous page, below is a typical broad outline of a proposed company manual.

Typical Broad Outline of Company Manual

    I. Introduction

        A. Brief company history

        B. Company philosophy

        C. How to use and update this manual

   II. Organization of Company

        A. Explanation of chain of command

        B. Table of organization

  III. Operating Policies

  IV. Personnel Policies

   V. Purchasing Policies

  VI. Housekeeping and Maintenance

 VII. Supplies and Inventory

VIII. Forms, Systems, and Filing Procedures

  IX. Departments and Functions

        A. Accounting and administration

        B. Advertising and public relations

        C. Sales and marketing

        D. Purchasing

        E. Estimating

        F. Manufacturing

    G. Customer service

    H. Maintenance

    I. Office services

    J. Personnel

    K. Engineering

    L. Research and development

    M. Quality control

    N. Safety

    O. Order processing

    P. Legal

    Q. Data processing

    R. Word processing

 X. Procedures for Making Changes in Systems, Forms, and Manual

    A. General policy

    B. Employee suggestions

    C. Development

    D. Approval

    E. Implementation and distribution

XI. Detailed Index

After the broad outline has been thoroughly reviewed and accepted by all of the concerned executives, the next step is to expand and detail the outline. To accomplish this, one of two techniques may be employed. The first technique is for the person who is coordinating the project to conduct interviews with executives and key personnel in each department. During these interviews, his or her objective is to extract enough information to gain a general understanding of the functions of each department and its interlocking relationships with other departments. This should provide enough knowledge to expand the broad outline into the fully detailed outline. The alternate technique that might be employed is to assign each departmental manager the task of detailing the outline for his or her department. In all cases, he or she should be given a general format to follow so there is a certain amount of uniformity and cohesiveness to the submissions from each department. Additionally, each manager should be given a due date by which time he or she is expected to have completed and submitted their outline.

In Figure 7.3 we suggest a form that might be used for guiding department managers in preparing their detailed outlines. After receiving the completed outlines from the department managers, the coordinator will create the fully detailed outline by editing the outlines and arranging everything into a logical sequence and format for management's approval prior to proceeding with the first draft.

The following is a guide to the general content and format of your department's manual outline. Do not confine yourself to this if you feel another approach might be better. Expand your outline to any degree you deem necessary to cover all systems, procedures, functions, objectives, and activities. Since other parts of the company manual will depend upon timely completion of this portion, please adhere strictly to the following schedule. Many thanks for your help.

   I. Primary Departmental Function

      A, B, C, etc. for secondary functions

  II. Table of Organization

 III. Job Titles, Descriptions, Functions, and Responsibilities

      A, B, C, etc.

 IV. Forms Instituted, Negotiated, and Disposition

      A, B, C, etc.

  V. Departmental Systems and Procedures

      A, B, C, etc.

 VI. Departmental Files and Retention Schedule

      A, B, C, etc.

VII. Interdepartmental Flow and Relationships

      A, B, C, etc.

Please complete and submit before _____

Figure 7.3   Suggested manual outline.

Of special interest here is the fact that in pursuing a quality manual and/or procedures, the direction of the content is already predetermined by the standard that it is to be followed. This makes the planning much easier and less time-consuming than if one had to start without any guideline.

Scheduling

In any project as complex and involving as many people as developing a company manual, establishing and adhering to a schedule is of paramount importance. Not only is it necessary for obtaining the input when it is needed, but proper establishment of a segmented schedule exposes all of the many pieces that must fit together while focusing on the sequential steps that are necessary.

Many parts of the project can be undertaken simultaneously, while others will have to wait for preceding portions to be completed. For this reason, the type of scheduling we have found to be most efficient is a modification of the "PERT" system. PERT is the acronym for "Program Evaluation and Review Technique," which was developed early in the Space Age as a system for scheduling and supervising highly complex missile development programs. (The reader may want to review the process of PERT in Stamatis 1998.) Since then, the term has come into general use to define a system of diagramming the steps of any relatively complex program. Parallel and interconnecting lines are used to indicate the sequential flow of actions as well as the steps that may be performed concurrently or parallel. For each step, a box is utilized to set forth the activity or "milestone" and the estimated time for its accomplishment.

Finally, after the steps have all been diagrammed, and the connecting and parallel lines have been drawn, we can identify the "critical path." This is done by following the line from start to finish that allows for completion of all steps that cannot be completed before preceding steps are done. In essence then, the critical path, indicated by a heavier line, is the shortest time in which the project can be expected to be completed if all schedules are maintained.

Especially in the development of the quality manual and procedures rather than the more technical methodology of PERT, it is common to use the Gantt chart. Its advantage is simplicity and straightforward time line requirements. However, because some organizations are quite complex, the following discussion about PERT may be helpful.

What Do We Learn from the PERT Chart?

First, of course, we see a graphic representation of the many steps it takes to produce a company manual, and the projected time for completing each step. The heavier lines and arrowheads used to illustrate the "critical path" place into sharp focus the shortest possible time projected for completion of the project. If thoughtfully developed and properly executed, a PERT chart is an extremely valuable management tool. But, frankly, the person who prepares the PERT chart can, either deliberately or unintentionally, distort the scheduling and time estimates. This may cause the completion time to appear grossly exaggerated or unrealistically short.

It is management's responsibility to study the PERT chart to be certain that no steps have been overlooked and that time estimates are realistic. If the critical path indicates a completion date that is too far distant for planned need, then it may be necessary to follow one of these courses: 1) assign additional manpower to the project; 2) establish more stringent completion priorities to eliminate time losses built into projections; or 3) revise company planning to make the projected later, but realistic, completion date more acceptable.

How to Use the PERT Chart

When PERT charts are used in complex engineering or construction projects, computers are often employed to monitor progress for the purpose of spotlighting delays before they become critical. For preparing a company manual, no such expensive nor sophisticated an approach is needed.

During the course of the project, however, the coordinator, as well as management, will use the PERT chart in very much the same way—to monitor progress and spotlight delays. When several actions can, and should, be done simultaneously, the PERT chart will serve as a continuing reminder of this situation. When one step must be completed before another step can be started, the PERT chart will prevent oversights that may cause subsequent delays.

It is a good idea to mount a copy of the PERT chart on cardboard and hang it on a wall near the coordinator's desk. In this way he or she can mark off steps as they are completed and see exactly what action or actions must be completed next. By checking against vacation and travel schedules, he or she can make sure the individuals he or she must interview, and from whom he or she must obtain approvals, are available when he or she is planning to see them—or adjust their plans accordingly to prevent loss of time and momentum.

OBTAINING AND ORGANIZING INPUT

For purposes of this section, it is assumed that one person has been charged with the responsibility of gathering, organizing, and transcribing all of the input needed to produce the company manual. For illustrative purposes, it is further assumed that this person has limited knowledge of the company's business and must gain all of his or her information through interviews, observation, and deduction.

Preparing for Interviews

Before conducting even the first interview with an executive of the company, as the project coordinator you should familiarize yourself with the company's business and standing in its community and industry. If the company is publicly owned and issues an annual report, obtain copies for the past three to five years. Reading these will not only provide an insight as to the image the company strives to project and the graphic style that management prefers, but will also reveal the company's financial progress. [Note: Do not underestimate the power of the internal intranet in your organization. Most of this information should be available to you.]

Try to obtain a Dun and Bradstreet report on the company, since this may reveal pertinent background information and problems that may not otherwise surface. If the company has "gone public" in the last five years, ask for a copy of the prospectus. This is a booklet, prepared under strict government rules, that provides an uncolored exposé of the company, its business, and its principals. A prospectus may generally be obtained through a stockbroker, if unavailable from the company. You might also obtain a copy of the company's most recent 10-K form. This is a more detailed annual report that each publicly owned company must submit annually to the Security and Exchange Commission. Ask the company treasurer for a copy.

Ask for and study advertising literature, product specification sheets, price lists, packaging, guarantee policies, existing manuals, forms, directives, bulletins, employee benefit pamphlets, help-wanted advertising, press releases, customer complaints, customer testimonials . . . and any other scrap that may enrich your knowledge and perspective of the company.

Find out who the principal competitors are and get copies of their financial reports for comparison. If possible, obtain copies of competitive sales literature, catalogs, guarantee policies, and any other bits and scraps that may help fill in your knowledge of the company's industry.

As you go through the procedure of rapidly learning the company's business, you may open avenues of study that will lead you to the research section of the public library and to pertinent trade associations and government agencies. Be sure you exercise good judgment and diplomacy in all of your research activities so you do not open any hornets' nests that may backfire on you or the company.

When you feel you have a pretty good grasp of the company's business, you are ready to start interviewing. It might be a good idea, at this time, to prepare a general outline of the line of questioning you wish to pursue. At the end of this section we provide a set of questions as a guide to preparing a list of questions to start and keep the interview moving. The list of questions should begin with questions that refer to the chief executive and work their way down from that level. [Note: Of course, depending upon the size and the nature of its business, a company may have many more or far fewer executive titles to interview. You may have to combine the questions indicated for several titles and ask them of just one executive. Or, you may find it necessary to work up questions for many additional titles; that is, sales manager, advertising manager, facilities manager, manager of research and development, operations manager, controller, house counsel, data processing manager, word processing manager, and on and on.] Interviews with lower-echelon personnel may also be indicated, but in each case be sure that permission is obtained from the direct supervisor of the person to be interviewed.

In any case, the questions presented at the end of this section can be used as a guide to the nature and quality of the information you will need. Remember, the interview should not necessarily ride on these particular questions. They are merely suggested as being appropriate to start interviews and to be used as prods if the interview slows down. The very best interviews occur when the subject becomes talkative and wanders into completely unanticipated areas. If the conversation becomes completely nonpertinent, the interviewer can always steer the subject back by timely insertion of a pointed question.

Interview Techniques

The good interviewer, although fully prepared and well organized, approaches the interview with an open mind. Even though he or she has prepared an outline and a list of questions, that person does not confine the interview to preconceived ideas. Without losing control of the interview, you can, and should, allow the interviewee to give as much detailed information as possible. As with any other type of encounter between individuals, it is necessary to break the ice before plunging in. This can be done by starting with general conversation—the weather or recent sport events are always good openers. Avoid politics and any other nonpertinent conversation that may in any way be controversial.

After you have established rapport, it is usually a good practice to start at the beginning, the time the person you are interviewing first joined the company. Lead him or her into telling you about his or her progress with the company and the depth of his or her experience in various departments, functions, and activities. Explore his or her relevant experience with other companies and his or her pertinent educational background. Then, of course, lead him or her into their current responsibilities and activities with the company.

Try to avoid asking questions that can be answered with simply a "yes," a "no," or another one-word answer. In other words, ask questions related to "how," "where," "when," and "why."

During interviews, it is necessary to make extensive notes so you can recall details at a future date. To be effective at this you will have to develop your own system of shorthand so conversation can proceed at a normal pace while you do not miss important items that should be noted.

Proper use of a tape recorder is highly recommended. However, it is a poor practice to rely solely on this medium, since the job of listening through recordings of lengthy interviews to retrieve small portions of them is most time-consuming. Having a typist transcribe such recordings is also a laborious job that will require the expenditure of much time and effort to separate the gems from the rocks.

The recommended procedure is to tape-record interviews while simultaneously writing notes, along with pertinent tape counter index numbers, on all important matters that develop. This will help you find sections of the tape you may want to review while your notes will serve as a backup in the event the recording is less than perfect, or comes up blank, as sometimes happens.

When a tape recorder is employed, it is a poor practice to use it surreptitiously. Always tell your subject that the interview is being recorded and, in fact, place the microphone, and even the tape recorder, in full view. At the beginning of the interview this may cause a bit of stage fright and tension, but if the "warm-up" conversation is properly handled, this will quickly pass and a relaxed interview will follow. Incidentally, by having the recorder in full view there is a much better chance you will notice, and be able to correct, a malfunction or ended tape before missing the entire interview.

While allowing the interviewee to broaden the anticipated scope of the interview, be sure you have obtained the information you will need to write the manual. For instance:

- Be sure the interviewee has detailed the full "table of organization" of his or her department and has explained how he or she thinks it fits into the overall company structure.

- Have the interviewee provide two sets of all forms handled by his or her department. Then ask the interviewee to explain the need for and use of every form employed by or passing through his or her department. Find out who has the responsibility of initiating each form and learn who receives which parts and how they are passed along. Also, find out how each form is acted upon, filed, and eventually disposed of.

- Dig into departmental budgets, how they are developed, who approves them, and how they are controlled during budget periods.

- Note the various job titles and enumerate pertinent job responsibilities. Try to gain an understanding of the flow and control of work within the department and between it and other departments.

- Investigate the checks and balances built into the systems and procedures and, if they are lacking, make appropriate notes without getting into any controversy with the interviewee.

Since you will not have had the benefit of exposure to other departments and activities, the early interviews may seem to be more confusing than later interviews. As the interview program develops, pieces and parts will fit together and an overall picture will emerge. At times it may be necessary to go back to the subjects of earlier interviews to ask further questions that developed during later interviews. [Note: It is not necessary, nor is it desirable, for the interviewer to appear to be a brilliant, overpowering conversationalist. At all times he or she should defer to his or her subject. The overall attitude should be one of seeking and needing the interviewee's most valued help in preparing the company manual].

It is most important that a bit of salesmanship be used to convince each interviewee that the manual is important for the company, for him or her, and for every other employee. Do not allow yourself to come across as the person whose objective it is to upset or change things. All you want to do is record everything exactly the way it is done. If the subject wishes to suggest improvements in any of the systems, procedures, and techniques, by all means encourage him or her to give you the benefit of his or her ideas. Do not try to "kick holes" in his or her ideas but try to understand his or her reasons for offering his or her thoughts.

You will find that every department and every individual has certain tasks that recur regularly. Often individuals do not even realize the cyclical nature of these tasks; therefore, it is necessary for the interviewer to actually ferret out and record recurring activities whether they recur daily, monthly, quarterly, semiannually, or annually. As the manual develops, this will form the basis for valuable departmental and individual task schedules.

Physical Organization of Input

From the very beginning of your research, you will be accumulating a massive amount of paper. Unless a system for categorizing this material is utilized from the outset, it will not be long before you are virtually swamped in paper.

Assuming you will not be using a computer or word processing system for this phase of the work, it is recommended that a file drawer, preferably legal size, be set up with hanging file folders. Use one hanging folder for each department and others for financial information, promotional literature, competitive information, and general background.

Within each hanging file folder, use tab-cut manila file folders to further separate and classify the materials it contains. The tabs of these file folders might be given such titles as, "Departmental Forms," "Interview Notes," "Department Suggestions and Contributions," and so on. If a computer is used, then try to have separate file for each of the categories just mentioned.

Organizing your paperwork as it develops will save countless hours of shuffling papers later on. Further, it will greatly simplify the preparation of the detailed outline and the subsequent writing of the manual.

Suggested Questions for Department Heads and Executives

These questions are presented merely as ideas as to the types of questions you might ask in order to get interviews started and keep them moving. Many may have already been answered during your preliminary research and still others may come to mind as the interview progresses. Adjust accordingly.

Questions for the Chief Executive Officer

1. Can you give me a brief summary of the history of the company, its founders, and the steps it went through to arrive at its current status?

2. What goals or objectives do you envision for the company regarding dollar volume, expansion, other activities, new products, staff, and so on?

3. What is the company's relative position in its industry and what is the trend?

4. What would you consider the company's major strengths?

5. What are its most vulnerable points?

6. Can you give me the company's philosophy of doing business?

7. If there is no formal table of organization, can you give me a sketch of one as you see it?

8. Is there anything in the company's unannounced planning I should know about that might materially affect the project of preparing the company manual?

9. Does the company hire executives from outside the company or does it develop its own from within?

10. Explain the company's procedures for hiring top executives.

11. Broadly describe the company's employee benefit program.

12. Are there any forms used in your office? If yes, please give me two sets and explain their use.

13. What reports do you receive? Who prepares them? How are they forwarded to you? Do they provide you with the information you need to do your job as you see it?

14. As an overall project, what would you like to see accomplished through the production of the company manual?

15. What part do you play in the establishment and control of corporate budgets and what, if any, is your involvement in departmental budgets?

16. How does "quality" fit in your title and what exactly do you do to make sure that the rest of the organization is on board with your thinking?

17. Do you have a quality policy? Vision statement? Business plan? How was the quality policy developed? How was the vision developed? How are these items communicated? How do you make sure that they are communicated?

18. What are your organization's quality objectives?

Questions for the Chief Financial Officer

1. If a formal table of organization does not exist, can you give me your idea as to the chain of command operating under your jurisdiction?

2. What is the system of controls over purchasing with reference to integrity and being assured that purchasing is at best terms and prices available?

3. For purposes of estimating prices at which goods or services are sold, who establishes departmental cost figures and how are targeted profit margins determined?

4. Is there a cost control system, and how is it administered'?

5. How are departmental budgets established and monitored?

6. What is company policy regarding travel and entertainment expenses and how are they monitored?

7. How do you monitor "premium freight?"

8. How do you monitor "scrap," "rework," and "cost of quality?"

9. How are unauthorized or double payments of vendor invoices prevented'?

10. What is company policy regarding extending credit? What collection procedures are used? How are delinquent accounts handled? Is there a "credit hold" system operating and how does that work'?

11. How are "short" shipments detected, reported, and handled with reference to paying suppliers' invoices? How is possible collusion between truckers and receiving clerks controlled?

12. How do you control demurrage?

13. How does the company's system of inventory control operate?

14. If the company's records are maintained by computer, what controls are there to detect major errors or fraud of various types? What system secures the company's customer list and other secrets that may be available through access to the computer system?

15. What systems and controls are in effect that prevent or detect employee theft of cash, supplies, tools, and so on, or collusion of employees with others for the same purpose?

16. Are the company's excess funds kept in bank accounts or are they invested in short-term securities? Who controls these funds? If invested, what are the criteria for such investments?

17. How are the future financial needs of the company determined?

18. Who is charged with negotiating short-term financing? Long-term? Briefly describe the procedures followed.

19. Who signs company checks? (In the case of larger companies where checks are signed by machine, determine how this is controlled.)

20. How are cancelled checks balanced against bank statements and what system is used, if any, to detect unauthorized payments or boosting of amounts?

21. What is company policy toward employees who are detected accepting bribes or converting company funds or property? Exactly how is this policy implemented?

22. When working on departmental procedures, with whom shall I speak regarding:

    a. Accounts payable

    b. Accounts receivable

    c. General accounting and/or data processing

    d. Insurance

    e. Petty cash system

    f. Cost of quality

23. In your opinion, what are the weak points in the company's system of financial controls?

24. What are your recommendations for curing such weaknesses?

Questions for the Director of Marketing

1. If a formal table of organization does not exist, can you give me your idea as to the chain of command operating under your jurisdiction?

2. To whom exactly does the company sell its products or services?

3. What media are used in the company's promotional efforts and how much is spent in each of these?

4. Who establishes promotional budgets and how?

5. Does the company have its own sales organization? How large a staff?

6. If the company does not have a sales organization, how are products and services sold and distributed?

7. How are new products or services introduced?

8. Are market research and analysis techniques used? How are they used and for what purpose?

9. Is information feedback from sales personnel encouraged? How is it used?

10. How is the sales staff compensated and what is the rationale behind such method?

11. How are broad marketing objectives determined and implemented?

12. How are salesmen's expenses authorized, monitored, and controlled?

12. How are the time and activities of field sales personnel controlled and assessed?

13. Who works with outside marketing consultants, public relations agencies, and advertising agencies? How are these organizations selected and evaluated?

14. With whom shall I speak to learn more about:

    a. Sales procedures

    b. Hiring and training of sales personnel

    c. Promotional programs and systems

    d. Liaison between outside consultants and company

    e. Planning, budgeting, and administering of sales conventions, seminars, and sales meetings

    f. Selection of dealers and/or distributors

15. What, in your opinion, are the company's major strengths in marketing?

16. What are its weaknesses and your recommendations for improvements?

Questions for the Director of Personnel

1. If a formal table of organization does not exist, can you give me your idea as to the chain of command operating under your jurisdiction?

2. Is there now a formal set of personnel policies?

3. If not, what policies are there and how are they enforced?

4. What fringe benefits, including mandatory government and union benefits, do employees have? How are employees apprised of these benefits?

5. Is there now a brochure or other means for welcoming new employees and explaining essential company policies?

6. If not, how is this function handled?

7. How are prospective new employees located, evaluated, hired, and trained for:

   a. Factory

   b. Office

   c. Middle management

   d. Executives

8. What is company policy and system regarding internal advancement?

9. Does the company have a system of wage administration and how does it operate? Is there a system for periodic employee review and evaluation? What role do department managers play?

10. How are personnel records maintained? Who is responsible for maintaining them? Who has access to personnel records?

11. What is company policy regarding:

    a. Employees with garnishments on their wages

    b. Giving references for former employees

    c. Checking references and educational claims of prospective new employees

    d. Employing people who have an arrest record

e. Employing people who have a prison record

f. Employing people who have physical disabilities or health problems

g. Employing people who have worked for competitors

h. Employing people who are over 40 . . . over 50 . . . over 55 . . . over 60

i. Equal Employment Opportunity (EEO)? Is there an approved Affirmative Action Manual—or diversity policy? (Obtain a copy from the affirmative action officer.) If there is no affirmative action program or diversity program, should there be one?

12. Is there now any type of manual or set of procedures used by the personnel department as a guide for:

a. Preparing "help-wanted" ads

b. Performing executive searches

c. Evaluating resumes

d. Interviewing prospective employees

13. Does the company use employment agencies? Does the company pay the fees?

14. Who makes decisions to discharge an employee?

15. Explain the full procedure for discharging employees.

16. Does the company have an "exit interview" policy? If yes, who conducts it? What are the objectives? If no, why not? (Perhaps it should be incorporated into departmental procedures.) Are "outplacement" services utilized?

17. How much are departmental managers involved in the hiring process? How is this operative?

18. Does the company have a work enrichment program? How does it operate?

19. Does the company have a retirement program? Give details.

20. What is the system for keeping record of employee work hours (for payroll), authorized and unauthorized days off, and so on?

21. Does the company give awards for:

    a. Outstanding service

    b. Suggestions

    c. Anniversaries of employment

    d. Retirement

    e. Safety

22. Who determines the budget for such awards and how are they administered? If these are tied to company functions, such as banquets, luncheons, picnics, and so on, who plans and administers them? Explain the entire process.

23. Obtain copies of all departmental forms and ask for an explanation of use and disposition.

24. What is the policy on using temporary employees? Who determines need? Who purchases such services? How is continuation of need monitored?

25. If there are periodic company social functions, what are they, when do they occur, and how are they planned? By whom are they administered?

26. Who establishes and controls budgets?

27. What are the company's greatest strengths in its personnel practices?

28. What are the company's greatest weaknesses in its personnel practices and what are your recommendations for improvement?

29. How are training needs identified?

30. Is training evaluated for effectiveness? How?

Questions for the Office Manager

1. If a formal table of organization does not exist, can you give me your idea as to the chain of command operating under your jurisdiction?

2. How is office work assigned to typists, stenographers, and other clerical employees?

3. How are requests for clerical help from various departments handled?

4. How are requisitions for supplies handled?

5. Explain the various filing systems under your control. Who has access to them for filing? For retrieval? What is retention policy pertinent to the various types of documents that are filed?

6. Is there a system for indicating that documents have been removed from files? Explain its operation and implementation.

7. Does each department maintain its own filing system? If yes, are they in any way centrally controlled?

8. By what process is it determined that office employees are working to capacity?

9. Are there any formally written procedures for various jobs and responsibilities, such as:

   a. Handling of outgoing and incoming mail

   b. Distribution of interoffice correspondence

   c. Establishment of letter format style

   d. Handling of specific forms and communications

   e. Reception of visitors

   f. Telephone and switchboard techniques

   g. Making travel arrangements

   h. Others

10. If there are written procedures for the above, get copies. If such procedures are unwritten, obtain full explanations.

11. Is there a system of "cross-training" of employees? How does it operate?

12. Who specifies, and how is purchasing done on:

    a. Office equipment

    b. Office supplies

    c. Office furniture

    d. Office accessories

13. Who controls the institution and design of new forms? (Obtain copies of all forms and explanations of uses.)

14. Are there fluctuations in the volume of work during the year? Do these recur on a predictable cycle?

15. What is company policy, or practice, with regard to size of staff? Is sufficient staff maintained for minimum or maximum needs?

16. If staffing is for maximum needs, what do excess people do during slack periods?

17. If staffing is for minimum needs, how are overloads and rush jobs handled during peak periods?

18. How are working time and time off of employees recorded and reported for purposes of payroll and personnel records?

19. What jobs and procedures do you feel should be separately manualized? (Obtain the necessary information.)

20. What improvements would you suggest in:

    a. Record keeping

    b. Forms, systems, and controls

    c. Manpower utilization

    d. Employee recognition

    e. Equipment and machinery replacement and/or acquisition

    f. Work hours

    g. Vacation, sick leave, and optional time-off policies

Questions for the Quality Manager

1. If a formal table of organization does not exist, can you give me your idea as to the chain of command operating under your jurisdiction?

2. How do you get your authority and responsibility?

3. How is "quality" work assigned? Evaluated?

4. How are requests regarding quality methodologies from various departments handled?

5. How are customer complaints handled?

6. Explain the various quality initiatives under your control. Are they effective? Are there procedures for these initiatives? Who has access to them? For retrieval? What is retention policy pertinent to the various types of quality documents that are filed?

7. Is there a system for indicating that documents have been removed from files? Explain its operation and implementation.

8. How are quality training needs identified? How is training defined for these needs? Is the training monitored for effectiveness?

9. Is customer feedback analyzed?

10. How are customer's requirements defined?

Questions for the Purchasing Manager

1. If a formal table of organization does not exist, can you give me your idea as to the chain of command operating under your jurisdiction?

2. To whom do you report?

3. How do requisitions for purchasing reach your department? What forms are used? Who authorizes the various types and sizes of purchases?

4. How do you select suppliers? Is there a formal process? How is the process approved?

5. Who draws up specifications and by what process are they approved?

6. Are bids required on all purchases or only on purchases over a specified amount? How many bids are required?

7. Is there a system for qualifying (or disqualifying) bidders? Explain how it operates.

8. Who makes final purchase decisions? Are there any rules that are followed?

9. Get copies of all purchasing department forms and a complete explanation of how they are used.

10. What is company policy pertaining to purchasing personnel having lunch with vendors? Accepting gifts? Being entertained by suppliers/vendors?

11. Are there any types of purchases that can be made by other departments without going through purchasing department? If yes, describe nature of such purchases and explain why they are handled as they are.

12. Is there a procedure for checking quality and count of commodities and merchandise purchased? Explain how it works.

13. What is the system for approving vendor invoices prior to payment?

14. Do you know of any communication problems between purchasing and other departments? Explain.

15. Is there any friction between purchasing and other departments? If yes, how would you solve such problems?

16. How would you improve the entire purchasing procedure of the company, if you feel it could be improved?

Questions for the Production Manager

1. If a formal table of organization does not exist, can you give me your idea as to the chain of command operating under your jurisdiction?

2. To whom do you report?

3. With reference to manufacturing, *how* are decisions made regarding:

    a. When specific products are to be produced

    b. Quantity to be produced

    c. Raw materials that will be needed

    d. Deployment of manpower and production facilities

4. How are manufacturing decisions implemented?

5. What is your policy for scrap, rework, inspection, and quarantine?

6. Do you use teams in your work environment? Empowerment? Problem solving analysis?

7. Is there a production control system? How does it operate?

8. Is there a cost control system? How does it operate and how are results communicated to personnel charged with estimating and pricing?

9. Is there a quality assurance/control system? How does it operate?

10. Explain the decision process in acquiring new production machinery.

11. Who is in charge of plant layout and what procedures are employed?

12. What part do you play, if any, in new product development?

13. Are you given specific budgets under which you must operate? How are they determined? How do they work out in practice?

14. Are you kept informed as to company objectives? What do you do to conform production capability to company objectives?

15. How are new production employees hired? How are fluctuations in work load handled? How are promotions awarded?

16. Is there an aggressive plant safety program? How is it promoted and administered? Who is in charge of it?

17. What is the procedure for taking care of employees who are injured on the job? How and to whom are injuries reported?

18. How is employee work time recorded and transmitted to payroll department?

19. What is the system for:

    a. Scheduling vacations

    b. Reporting absences

    c. Reporting tardiness

20. Obtain copies of all forms used in production department with full explanation of:

    a. Who institutes

    b. Who authorizes

    c. How they are used

    d. Distribution of parts

    e. Retention policy

21. Are there any weaknesses in liaison between production and other departments? Explain.

22. Do you have any suggestions for overall improvement of the company's production systems?

Questions for the Manager of Corporate Development

1. If a formal table of organization does not exist, can you give me an idea as to the chain of command operating under your jurisdiction?

2. To whom do you report?

3. What is the substance of your directive and authority?

4. By what means does the company plan to grow [Note: The means of corporate growth that are given here may very well determine the nature and ultimate use of the company manual]:

    a. New markets for existing products or services

    b. Introduction of new products

    c. Additional productive capacity to meet demand of new products

    d. Establishment of additional locations or branches

    e. Establishment of franchises, licensees, distribution centers, dealers, and so on

    f. Acquisition of other businesses

5. How do the growth objectives of the company relate to the business strategy of the organization?

6. Explain the decision process as related to the adaptation of any of the aforementioned means of growth.

7. Are there now any manuals, written policies, or literature pertaining to franchising, licensing, site location, company acquisition, and so on?

8. Obtain copies of all forms used by the department. Ask for explanation of use.

9. Do you have any suggestions that might improve the department or the relations and liaison between your department and others?

10. How do you keep abreast of competitors?

11. How do you make sure your development is current and competitive?

MAKING ORDER OUT OF CHAOS

No matter how methodical you are in categorizing, classifying, and filing the materials accumulated during the information gathering phase, you'll be up to your hip bone in paper. Your mind will be spinning with new concepts and misconcepts. You will understand the basic business of the company but the details of how and why things are done as they are will not have fallen into a meaningful pattern and cohesive sequence.

You'll have been exposed to a wealth of knowledge and experience that took years to accumulate. How could you possibly be expected to fully understand and coherently verbalize all of this information? Still, you have the task of making order out of chaos by putting this mass of input into a viable company manual. What is the next logical step?

Going back to the broad outline that was approved by management before you started interviewing and gathering information. You should have a skeleton upon which you can now add sinews, muscles, and ligaments. The meat, fat, and epidermis come later.

Reviewing the "Typical Broad Outline of Company Manual," you will quickly see how the input you've gathered builds upon the skeleton. The answers to the questions you asked the chief executive officer allow you to expand a good portion of the introduction section. For example:

I. Introduction to Company Manual for Xerikia Corporation

    A. Company History

        a. Founded 1914 as Xerikia Company

        b. Original business making seats

        c. Founders Diomidis and George Stamatis (brothers)

        d. Charalambos was salesman—Timothy was mechanic

        e. George died 1934—business sold to Stephen Stamatis.

    B. Company Philosophy

        a. To grow on a solid foundation within industries it knows best.

        b. Give customers full value by making top-quality products and selling direct at reasonable prices.

        c. Keep abreast of new technology and methods.

        d. Progress of company has been, and will continue to be, a team effort.

e. Shareholders are entitled to a fair return on investment and every employee has responsibility to assure continuation of profitability.

f. Excellence of workmanship and company loyalty is expected but company rewards those who perform exceptionally.

g. Company believes in equal opportunity for all.

h. Management shall observe "open-door" policy toward all employees.

i. All who deal with company are entitled to a fair profit but are expected to meet or exceed specifications and remain competitive. The company shall strive to develop and maintain continuing relationships with suppliers.

C. How to Use and Update This Manual (material not obtained from chief executive)

a. Explain department breakdown structure of manual.

b. Explain page numbering system.

c. Detail the updating system:

i. How to suggest changes and revisions

ii. Who is authorized to make revisions

iii. How revisions are prepared and reproduced

At this point the facilitator or the coordinator responsible may send a letter to the department heads that participated in the interview. A typical letter may read like the one in Figure 7.4.

Undoubtedly, you will receive a considerable amount of feedback from executives and department heads—much of it constructive, some of it quite critical. *Do not be sensitive, nor defensive.*

ANALYZING FORMS, SYSTEMS, AND FILES

While department heads are reviewing the detailed outline is a good time to organize the forms you have collected—first by department, then companywide. After forms are more or less organized into a logical flow, a detailed study and review of the pertinent data you have assembled will

Memo to: *Name of Department Head, Title*
Subject: *Company Manual*
From: *Your Name, Company Manual Coordinator*
Date: *Current Date*

Many thanks for your help with the portion of the company manual devoted to your department.

From the wealth of information you gave me, I have prepared the accompanying detailed outline. This will serve as the framework upon which I intend to write the final draft.

To make sure I have kept things in order, and have not left out or confused any important functions or activities related to your department, please review this and return it to me with your comments, criticisms, and suggestions. If you think we should discuss this personally, let me know.

To maintain our schedule, I will have to receive your comments no later than October 22nd, so please work on it as quickly as possible.

I sincerely appreciate your kind and valued assistance.

Sincerely,

Christine

Figure 7.4 Suggested transmittal memo for detailed outline.

usually provide an excellent picture of the movement of departmental activities. Also revealed will be the workings of the communications systems between departments, and the checks and balances that are built in—or, in some cases, lacking. The information thus gained should give you much of the sinew and muscle to build upon the skeleton of the detailed outline.

After assembling all of the forms used by a given department, take each form separately and, from the information you have gleaned, write up a procedure analysis. Simply, this will set forth exactly why, how, where, when, and by whom the form is used. Further, it will trace the lifecycle of the form from origination, through distribution of its parts, to final disposition. (It is a good practice at this stage to have a duplicate set.)

After the procedures analyses have been completed, it is a good idea to have each department head or his or her representative check over those pertaining to his or her department. Use the duplicate copies of the procedures analyses for this purpose. To follow through a step further, it is recommended that the parts of each form be traced through to check their functions and dispositions in the departments to which they are subsequently routed.

Those parts of forms that are routed to destinations beyond the company require no further verification. These might include: packing slips, customer invoices, purchase orders, and so on.

The way forms are handled depends, to a large degree, upon the ultimate size of the manual and whether each department is to have a separate volume. If the entire manual can conveniently fit into one binder, then it is sufficient to have a "Forms, Systems and Files" section for each department. On the other hand, if the physical size of the manual is such that separate manuals for each department are indicated, then, in addition to the "Forms, Systems, and Files" section for each department, it is recommended that a separate companywide "Forms, Systems, and Files" manual be prepared. The purpose of this separate manual is to have a single source for reviewing, evaluating, and possibly changing forms and systems after use of the operations manual has been instituted. It will also provide a means of controlling a forms coding system and may help to eliminate unnecessary forms proliferation. Additionally, and most importantly, it will provide an overall picture of the company's systems and procedures, and how they interact between individuals and departments.

When analyzing forms, systems, and filing procedures, you will have a unique opportunity to focus in on weaknesses in the company's systems. Among the problems you may uncover are:

1. Redundancy of effort by various departments and/or individuals.

2. No means of catching or correcting errors (improper checks and balances).

3. No system for keeping transactions moving through departments (possible dead-ends).

4. Unnecessary forms.

5. Poorly designed forms making extra work.

6. Antiquated forms (not being used as originally designed).

7. Separate forms that should be combined.

8. People unnecessarily receiving parts of forms (needlessly adding to paper flow).

9. No standardization of filing systems, unlimited access to files, and no method of keeping track of items taken from files.

10. Sloppy files (making it difficult to file or locate items).

11. No forms retention and disposal system. Various types of forms should be retained for differing lengths of time for legal as well as procedural reasons. Those of a highly confidential nature may require more stringent means of disposal than others.

12. Badly designed external forms (from the esthetic viewpoint) providing a poor image of the company to customers and vendors.

13. Poor intra- and interdepartment communications (causing confusion, errors, and unnecessary delays).

[Special warning: Since our primary purpose is to manualize the company's current operations, it is not recommended that you try to solve all of the problems as they are brought to light. If you are charged with the responsibility of improving forms and systems, unless you are starting from scratch, it is best to work on them after the manual is completed and in use. In this way, you can be surer you have the best operational answer to each problem and will be better able to mesh revisions into existing systems. A better way is to write up explanations of the problems that become obvious to you as they are exposed. Maintain a file of these explanations so that after the manual is operational, you can review them for action or pass them on to the party who will be responsible for the systems and forms improvement program.]

GETTING INTO THE DRAFT

Everything you have done up to now has been leading you to this step in the preparation of the manual—writing the draft. Here is where you first become concerned with presentation style.

Will writing be narrative? Terse? Technical? Will you use graphs, charts, and illustrations liberally or only where absolutely necessary? Obviously, the principal factor dictating writing style should be the audience for whom the manual, or its parts, is targeted. That portion intended for clerical and production workers should, as much as possible, avoid technical language. If graphs and charts are used in these sections, they should be clear and uncomplicated—designed to quickly clarify a point that might be more difficult to explain verbally. Here illustrations might come in handy to emphasize important points, perhaps with the judicious use of humor. For instance, you might make a strong point of discouraging the use of company phones for personal calls by illustrating an important customer fuming and fussing, becoming angry, while phones are tied up on obvious nonsense calls.

Semihumorous illustrations are also valuable for emphasizing points relative to safety, promptness, quality standards, courtesy, time wasting, unnecessary absences, wasting supplies, care of tools and equipment, and many others. (There are many commercial sources on the Internet that you should consult if there is an interest in including clip art in the manual.)

The portions of the manual that are aimed toward engineers, technicians, and degreed professionals will be the most difficult to write, unless you are educated in the specific discipline with which you are dealing. For these portions of the manual, it is recommended that you circumvent the most technical areas by leaning upon the subject-matter experts and/or concerned department heads for technical writing assistance. Use your own talent to weave these sections together into a smooth-flowing, logical presentation.

[Note: Warning! Don't be completely hoodwinked by the technicians. You will find that much of their gobbledygook is unnecessary and often is not even clear to other professionals of a like calling. In other words, except for chemical, mathematical, and scientific formulas, and technical matters of the highest order, you should be able to make sense out of the language of most of the writing, whether it be legal, financial, electronic data processing, scientific, or whatever. Before "freezing" any of the more technical sections of the manual, be sure they are read by qualified individuals, other than those providing the input or having done the actual writing. Appendix A may be helpful in identifying the level of complexity.]

With the growing use and availability of word processing machines, it is incumbent upon writers to reassess the methods they have been using to get their thoughts down on paper. Word processing equipment makes it possible, after just one keyboarding, to make corrections, insertions, deletions, transpositions, and changes of indentions, margins, and spacing without necessitating complete retyping. With all of this capability, however, each writer must deal with his or her own preferences, capabilities, and psyche.

If you are adept at machine dictating—probably the fastest way to work—then by all means, this is the way you should work. If your dictating is fairly clean, and word processing equipment is available to you, have your work keyboarded and printed out for even the first draft. If your dictating will require extensive rewrites and complete reorganization, it is probably better to first have a rough draft typed and keyed into word processing equipment only after it has been marked up for first revisions and corrections.

If machine dictating is not for you, then use the method with which you are most comfortable—writing longhand, typing, or dictating to a stenographer or to a fast typist who can rough type as fast as you can dictate. In any case, it is a good idea to have the first draft double-spaced to allow room for notes, corrections, and changes. Word processing systems, of course, have the capability of producing draft copies double-spaced and final copy single-spaced or any of several variations in between.

Many writers of manuals find that the type of writing necessary for company manuals is best done by hand on "foolscap" paper (yellow-lined). If your handwriting is legible, and you do not have too many complications with cross-outs and insertions, your typist or keyboard operator can work directly from your notes. If this is difficult, then consider the possibility of dictating your rough notes into a voice-recording machine. This allows you to give your typist or keyboard operator smooth-flowing input, often resulting in a first draft that is amazingly clean.

In summary, *work the way that best suits you.* If this doesn't conform to the skills of your typist or keyboard operator (some are poor at reading handwritten notes, others refuse to work with a voice-recording machine), then try to get someone else to do your work. One last word about voice-recording machines—do not try to work with anything but a real office dictating machine—with matching transcriber. Ordinary tape recorders, as good as they may be for general recording, are far from ideal for dictating and transcribing. A proper dictating machine permits the dictator, and the transcriber, to easily control and advance and reversal of the machine for as few or as many words as desired with no acceleration or deceleration distortion. Corrections on machines that record on magnetic tape are usually easy to insert by redictating into the spot you want to change. Another feature on most dictating machines is the capability of "indexing." This enables you to signal your typist or keyboarder, in advance, just how long the dictated portion is going to be. Also, the indexing capability can be used to indicate an insertion or correction you have dictated after the main portion has been completed. Most people who use dictating machines find they work best with a machine having a handheld microphone with thumb controls for advance, reverse, record, nonrecord, and indexing. For transcribing, a foot pedal control for advance and reverse, keeping the keyboarder's hands free, seems to work most efficiently.

When deeply immersed in writing and creating, it is often difficult to judge the product of your efforts as objectively as you should. Therefore, it is suggested that prior to allowing others to read your work, it is usually best to reread and correct after you have put your work aside for a few days. After rereading and marking corrections on the first draft, if word processing equipment will be used but the work has not yet been inputted, now is the time to do so. Whether hand typing or using word processing, prepare a clean, new draft for submission to department heads and company executives. As with any other type of creative work, the quality of the presentation will have an important bearing on the critical response it generates. For this reason, do not penalize the product of your work with a shoddy appearance.

First, be sure that the draft you are submitting is done in a workmanlike fashion . . . that words are correctly spelled; paragraphing is done properly; indentions are uniformly handled; that headlines and subheads are capitalized and underlined in a consistent manner. Have an original and at least three copies typed or duplicated, and be sure that errors on all copies are neatly corrected. Again, have the revised draft double-spaced to allow room for corrections and comments. Leave relatively wide margins for the same purpose.

It is a good practice to submit drafts in an attractive binder. This is not only for the purpose of keeping the work together, but is a form of merchandising/packaging, if you will. It gives the reader the feeling of a more finished product and it enhances the importance of the work being submitted. There are several types of loose-leaf "report" binders available at any commercial stationery store that do a very satisfactory job. If illustrations and charts are to be used, you can handle them in the draft in any one of several ways:

- When finished art is available, paste digital copies into the correct positions in the draft.

- If art has not been done yet, allow space and type in a parenthetical description of the proposed art.

- Prepare rough renditions of the proposed art and insert in the correct positions.

Basically, the more complete your draft is, the better others will be able to visualize and judge your work. You are asking too much if you expect people to use their imagination.

WRITING STYLE

The objective of the manual writer must be to present facts and ideas to readers in such fashion that they are easily and agreeably understood. In no instance should writing style overpower the substance of the subject matter. The reader's attention should be directed to *what* is being said rather than to *how* it is said. The style of manual writing should never be obtrusive. It should be guided by the objectives of the company and the needs of the readers.

Unlike writing for general audiences, each part of a company manual is directed to people engaged in similar activities. This homogeneity of readership rather simplifies the task of establishing the tone and writing style to be used. Here are a few general guidelines that, if followed, will save you hours of rewriting.

Have Direction

Don't wander, keep on track. Each chapter, each section, each paragraph, and each sentence should have a central purpose and everything in it should contribute to its development and achievement.

Keep a Balance

The relative importance of subject matter is often indicated by the amount of space devoted to it. Usually, the more important the topic, the more thoroughly it is explained. Besides the amount of space, positioning of the parts helps to strike the balance, with more important matters usually appearing at the beginning.

Strive for Clarity

If readers do not understand what is written, they cannot use it. Worse, if they get the wrong meaning out of it, it could be more harmful than getting no meaning. What may be clear to one reader may be completely incomprehensible to another. The first consideration, then, is to determine the intelligence, educational, and cultural level of the prospective audience.

Professionals and technical experts can be expected to understand terminology commonly used in their respective fields. Business executives should be able to fully comprehend language that is common to the educated. Lastly, there are those who will be using parts of the manual who are relatively uneducated and have culturally limited backgrounds. For these, the language must be simple and nontechnical without sacrificing accuracy. When it is expected that there will be a mixed readership of professionals, technicians, executives, and laymen, the writer will have a particularly difficult time in balancing his or her writing style. The specialist must be satisfied, yet the general reader must not be overwhelmed.

For the sake of clarity, it may be necessary to define certain terms that are used in the manual. However, try to avoid using too many definitions in the text because they will interrupt the flow of the subject matter and reduce clarity. If appropriate, include a "glossary of terms" either at the beginning or end of the manual.

Be sure you are saying what you mean, since nothing will confuse the reader more than incorrect use of words and phrases. As a simple illustration, consider the confusion that could be caused if the writer said, "The substance is safe near heat since it is inflammable," when he meant to say, ". . . it is noninflammable." Writing clearly depends on many factors: careful choice of words, proper sentence structure, good punctuation, and thoughtful paragraphing. Most importantly, the writer should be thoroughly familiar with the subject matter to avoid vagueness and uncertainty as to what he or she means to say.

Be Concise

Do not leave anything out, but say what you have to say in the fewest number of words possible. One way to accomplish this is to eliminate masses of detail that probably will never be read. Often, much detail can be relegated to the appendix or exhibit section of the manual.

Analyze the Lengths of Your Sentences

If they are growing too long, examine them closely for unnecessary verbiage, redundancies, and repetition. A multiplicity of abnormally short sentences may also take away from clarity and flow. Look for unnecessary repetition of words and excessive use of pronouns. Repeated use of stereotyped phrases can get to be a habit. Use the following as a guide to avoiding redundancies and use of unnecessary phrases:

1. Wherever possible, use an active verb rather than the more verbose phrase with a noun. (Table 7.2 makes one thing obvious—avoid overusing transitive verbs like *make, give, take,* and *have.* There are enough places where you *must* use them so do not use them when a more active verb does a better job with fewer words.)

2. Try to eliminate redundancies, where two words are used to accomplish something that can better be done by one (see Table 7.3).

A form of redundancy that is frequently overlooked involves the use of the phrase "and so on" or its abbreviation, "etc." [For example: Toys are made of materials such as wood, paper, plastic, etc. They make a variety of products, for example, toys, games, dolls, and etc.; When using "such as" or "for example" or "among them," indicating that there may be more has already been done without the use of the phrase "and so on" or "etc."]

3. Reduce the complexity of sentences by eliminating unnecessary phrases that have crept into business writing when the normally spoken

Table 7.2   Active verbs.

Use	Instead of
abbreviate	make an abbreviation
adjust	make an adjustment
apologize	to make an apology
assess	make an assessment
assume	make an assumption
authenticate	check the authenticity of
allow for	make an allowance for
calculate	make a calculation
calibrate	perform a calibration
call	make a call
cancel	make a cancellation of
compare	make a comparison between
categorize	make a categorization of
cease	cause a cessation of
celebrate	have a celebration
choose	make a choice
circumvent	undertake a circumvention of
claim	make a claim
classify	give classification to
commit	make a commitment
concede	make a concession
conclude	reach a conclusion
consider	take into consideration
defend	make a defense
define	draw a definition
determine	reach a determination
elaborate	make an elaboration
feel	have a feeling
greet	extend greetings to
halt	make a stop
investigate	conduct an investigation
jest	make a joke
label it	attach a label to it
misconceive	have a misconception about
notch	cut an indentation
separate	perform a separation

Table 7.3 Redundancy reduction.

Use	Instead of
secret	confidential secret
soft	soft to the touch
triangular	triangular in shape
yellow	yellow in color
February	the month of February
started	first started
mesh	mesh together
enclosed	enclosed herewith
complete	very complete
correct	most correct
giant	large giant
smallest	very smallest
essential	most essential

Table 7.4 Complexity reduction.

Use	Instead of
disregard	pay no attention to
because	due to the fact that
resulting	as a result of
quietly	without making noise
frequently	many times
if	in the event that
obviously	it is obvious that

word says it better. Table 7.4 shows a few examples. By economizing in this way, clarity and conciseness will be achieved.

Writing for Readability

Readability refers to the ease with which written matter can be read and understood. Over the years, experts in communications have devised methods by which they claim to measure readability. These involve various formulas for counting and equating word syllables and sentence lengths. The substance of these systems, however, is that the best writing, even in difficult technical subjects, is that which has been kept as simple as possible. See appendix A.

If you observe the following general rules, your writing will probably fall within the range of acceptable readability.

1. Refrain from writing long, drawn out sentences. Try to write sentences of varying lengths—neither too long nor too short. Sentences over 20 words are probably too long. If the average sentence length is less than 10 words, they are probably too short. A series of short, jerky sentences may work well in an advertisement but in text matter may be difficult to read. It is good to follow a necessarily long sentence with a short sentence.

2. Whenever you have the choice, use a common, everyday word rather than an obscure, difficult word that will not be understood by many of your readers. In all cases, however, be sure to use the word that has the precise meaning intended rather than a synonym that may be inaccurate.

3. Eliminate words that are not needed. Excessive verbiage makes reading difficult and less interesting.

4. Structure your writing carefully so every word, sentence, and paragraph contributes to overall clarity and understanding of the subject.

5. As with sentences, paragraphs should have varying lengths. Try to avoid using either several long paragraphs or several short paragraphs consecutively—mix them up. Be sure each paragraph is related to its topic sentence. Whenever a digression is necessary, start a new paragraph.

6. Use abbreviations sparingly. They often detract from readability and seem to the reader a sign of slovenliness. When using abbreviations, be sure they are familiar to the reader and that the meaning is clear.

7. Use capitalizing, underlining, and italics for emphasis sparingly. When done properly, any of these can be an effective means of stressing certain points. When used too frequently, effectiveness and readability decrease.

8. Proofread carefully to avoid any misspelled words from slipping through. Readers are quick to recognize misspellings and lose respect for the writer and his or her work. Set yourself a firm rule for treatment of numbers and stick to it throughout. For instance, you might decide to spell out all numbers under

10 when they appear in text matter and use figures for 10 and over. When decimals appear, it is probably best to use figures. When numbers appear at the beginning of sentences, it may be best to use words except when the number refers to a specific year.

9. The major purpose of punctuation is to make reading easier and better understood. Too much punctuation can be as confusing as too little. Punctuate only where needed and not to try to clarify an overly complex, long sentence. It is probably better to simplify or shorten the sentence than to try to correct it with punctuation.

COPYING AND COPYRIGHTS

Copyright laws protect the creator, or owner, from having his or her intellectual production published or reproduced without permission. Protection is automatic upon the creation of an original piece of work whether it be writing, music, art, or photography. As long as the work remains unpublished, no filings or other legal formalities need be taken. Without going into any of the legal ramifications, when a work is to be published, it is necessary to obtain a "statutory copyright" upon publication.

To secure a copyright it is necessary to reproduce an acceptable copyright notice either on the front or back of the title page and to submit two copies of the work along with a completed form and payment to the U.S. Copyright Office, in the Library of Congress, Washington, D.C. (More specific and detailed information, and forms, can be obtained by contacting the U.S. Copyright Office.)

Whether you copyright your company manual is a management decision. If it is to be in loose-leaf form, it can be copyrighted as any other bound book. Each subsequent revision should include a copyright notice, but it is not necessary to submit them separately to the Copyright Office. Instead, you can submit the complete, updated manual annually or biannually.

Although a copyright may act as a deterrent to potential plagiarists, remember, policing of infringements is the responsibility of the copyright holder. Therefore, the question must be asked, "Is copyright protection of the manual really necessary?" (Note: Once a work is published without first obtaining a statutory copyright, it is deemed to have "entered the public domain" and anyone may use it, or adapt it, in its original form or another. Once it becomes public domain, it cannot be withdrawn.)

RESEARCH OR INFRINGEMENT?

Gathering information for any piece of business writing often involves reading and extracting ideas from the works of others. This is considered legitimate research unless the writer makes verbatim or substantial and material appropriation of properly copyrighted material. The principle is that ideas themselves are not protected by copyright, while the author's expressions, or words, are protected. When you wish to extract ideas from the works of others, the way to do it is to rewrite and rearrange as much as possible. Since only the writer knows his sources of information, it is the writer's sole responsibility to avoid infringements.

One last word on infringement—remember that illustrations, photographs, graphs, charts, maps, and all other types of art may be copyrighted. This means that you cannot just clip cartoons or other illustrations from a publication and incorporate them into the company manual just because it seems appropriate. If producing original artwork is beyond your budget, or for some reason you wish to use a particular piece of copyrighted art, most publishers will gladly grant permission if you ask nicely and explain the use. At times they may request that you print a credit line. This same technique of asking for permission to reproduce can also be used when you would like to use portions of a magazine article, newspaper clippings, or an excerpt from a book.

GRAPHS, CHARTS, AND ILLUSTRATIONS

The purpose of graphs, charts, and illustrations in a company manual should never be merely decorative—they should each be used to illustrate or emphasize a given set of facts, an idea, or a message in a way that words alone cannot do satisfactorily.

Graphs

Graphs are most effective when used to show the quantitative or size proportions between related factors, especially when such proportions are difficult to visualize in stated numbers and verbal description. There are many forms of graphs, including the familiar line graph that illustrates peaks and valleys in a linear, or analog, fashion. Other forms of analog graphs include curved line graphs, which are used to illustrate changing factors, quantities, and relationships in a continuous curve rather than from point to point.

Then there are bar graphs—both horizontal and vertical—which are used to show the comparisons between two, three, or more values by the relative length or bulk of the bars. These are digital, rather than analog, because they show the quantitative relationships at fixed intervals instead of continuously as line graphs.

Bar graphs can be most interestingly designed in that the bars do not necessarily have to be bars. They can be people, shown in different sizes, stacks of coins, factory buildings, or any variety of commodities, products, or objects shown either in different sizes or in different quantities.

Pie graphs are effectively used to illustrate the relative sizes of the several parts of a whole. Although usually done in the familiar flat pie format, interest and appearance is enhanced by using a sectioned coin, wheel, food can, or some other round or cylindrical object that may be pertinent to the subject being presented. A variation of the pie graph is the "salami" graph in which a symbolic object is used with the proportionate shares shown as slices of varying thickness.

Charts

Charts are used for several purposes, among which are:

1. Sequential checklists.

2. Cross-references (typical are mileage charts showing distances between cities or multiplication tables used by children).

3. Consequential results of measurable actions or factors (work yield from specified horsepower).

4. Illustrating flow of processing (used extensively in electronic data processing as well as in many industrial and office procedures).

5. Illustrating organizational structure (most commonly, the table of organization chart). Organization charts indicate reporting channels and authority levels along with titles and responsibilities. When a large, complex corporate structure is depicted, the relationships between authority levels can be extremely difficult to chart. If not carefully done and fully cleared with top authority prior to publication, a new or revised organization chart can be very upsetting to those who may feel slighted.

6. Conversion charts (illustrating the relationship between various standards of measurement as Fahrenheit to centigrade, inches to decimals, or pounds to dollars).

Of course, there are many other uses for charts that you may discover as you are writing the manual. Be especially alert to those situations where repeated reference must be made to the information you are presenting. If a chart will save the reader time and will help prevent errors, then by all means have an appropriate chart prepared.

Illustrations

There are two basic types of illustrations that encompass the entire spectrum of single color illustration—line and continuous tone. As the designations imply, line art is made up of solid lines against clean paper, while continuous tone art has the capability of depicting all gradations of shading between the solid color and the clean paper (or white).

Photographs are, of course, continuous tone. Also continuous tone are wash drawings and any other type of art that contains a variety of flat or blending tonal qualities.

In reproducing continuous tone art, halftones, which break up the graduations of tone into a screen of dots of varying sizes, are required. Continuous tone art, unless it has been "screened" beforehand, adds somewhat to preparation expense for reproduction since it has to be photographed separately and then combined with the film of the text matter by a manual process called "stripping."

Line drawings, on the other hand, if combined with text matter in the finished or mechanical art, can be shot at the same time with no additional reproduction costs. This assumes that the line drawing appears in its finished size and position in the reproduction copy of the page or in the same size as other matter on the page so all may be shot in one reduction or enlargement.

In recent years, new techniques have been developed whereby photographs are photomechanically converted to line art. This is not done to save money, but to achieve desired artistic effects. Conversely, it is possible to achieve tonal gradations in line art by having the artist apply screened tonal overlays to the art, or by having the printer "lay" tones or "benday" tints to specified portions of the art. Even in single-color printing, the possibilities are limited only by the creativity of the artist or designer.

Of course, the latest technology in this area is the digital camera, which can provide actual pictures directly within the printed text with the aid of the computer.

Stock Photographs

There are many companies in the stock photograph business, generally concentrated in the major advertising centers throughout the country. These companies maintain extensive libraries of various types of photographs and have them categorized in such a way that they can usually offer a selection of photographs for any specification you may provide. Some of these companies charge for the search as well as for the eventual use of the photograph. Rates are often determined by proposed usage and potential circulation. Available are black-and-white photographs, color transparencies, and movie stills. Again, with the advent of the digital camera, people can generate their own pictures with ease and hardly any professional experience.

STYLE SHEETS

Some companies have them, some do not. Typically they are only a few pages and are often the "fallout" from the ISO procedure writing effort. The style sheet identifies the fonts to be used, copywritten terms to be used, unique spelling or other usage, the standard policy, procedure, and instruction formats, standard flowchart symbols, and so on. It is important to note that even though most technical writers are aware of these items, some organizations, as a matter of policy, identify them to bring standardization to the documents produced. They are usually made up as the work proceeds and document the decisions made as to the look of the documents. The reader may also read appendix XII for more information on the manual process of documentation.

ELECTRONIC DOCUMENTATION

We would not be complete in our discussion if we did not mention that in most organizations today the documents (all levels) are electronically developed (online publishing), written, and controlled. The process is very simple:

1. Create/type the information in a typical Microsoft Word file.

2. Save the file as an html file.

3. Upload into the Web file transfer protocol (FTP) client with your company's chosen software.

4. Identify the URL.

5. Send the URL to the users.

Because the process is somewhat technical, most individuals create, type, and save the information in the html file and from then on specialists complete the rest of the tasks. Obviously, the electronic approach is much easier and efficient, but above all, makes it easier to control documents. For a manual approach to documentation read appendix XII on the CD-ROM. The appendix also deals with general guidelines of preparation, reproduction, binding, pagination, revision, and master document control.

REFERENCES

Brassard, M., L. Finn, D. Ginn, and D. Ritter. 2002. *The Six Sigma Memory Jogger II*. Salem, NH: GOAL/QPC.

Brassard, M., and D. Ritter. 1994. *The Memory Jogger II*. Salem, NH: GOAL/QPC.

Stamatis, D. H. 1997. *TQM Engineering Handbook*. New York: Marcel Dekker.

———. 1998. *Advanced Quality Planning*. New York: Quality Resources.

SELECTED BIBLIOGRAPHY

Stamatis, D. H. 1996. *Documenting and Auditing for ISO 9000 and QS-9000*. Chicago: Irwin Professional Publishing.

8

The Five Basic Pillars of Quality

Quality indeed has become a very important characteristic in all industries. In the automotive and aerospace industries, the quest for quality is so great that special standards have been formed not only to track but also to improve quality. These standards as we already have mentioned are ISO 9001, QS-9000, AS9100, and ISO/TS 16949.

While the ISO 9001 standard is the core generic international quality barometer, QS-9000 is the automotive standard that combines the ISO 9001:1994 standard and additional automotive-specific criteria.

Important characteristics of QS-9000 are:

- ISO 9001:1994 requirements

- Industry-specific requirements

- Customer-specific requirements

AS9100 is the international aerospace standard that combines the ISO 9001:2000 standard with additional aerospace requirements. Important characteristics of AS9100 are:

- ISO 9001:2000 requirements

- Industry-specific requirements

On the other hand, ISO/TS 16949 is the international automotive standard that combines ISO 9001:2000 and additional automotive-specific requirements. Important characteristics of ISO/TS 16949 are:

- ISO 9001:2000 requirements

- Industry-specific requirements

To support all these standards, supplemental documents have been published to facilitate the implementation process and their effectiveness. One such document is the quality system assessment (QSA). Strictly speaking, the QSA document is not part of the five pillars of the quality system. However, it is a very important document in both QS-9000 and ISO/TS 16949. It is a manual for helping the organization reach certification. It provides a guide to the process as well as prepares the organization with some basic questions about its own QMS. It is in fact a checklist for the quality system. For most organizations this is not a new concept, as it was a document for QS-9000. Now it is also a formal document for ISO/TS 16949:2002. The QSA is used to determine conformance to the standard, and proper use of the QSA will promote consistency between activities and personnel determining QS-9000 and ISO/TS 16949:2000 conformance. It is a minimal guide. The manual is used at the time of audits. (First-, second-, or third-party auditors are to meet the requirements established by the QS-9000 Supplier Requirements Task Force as well as the IATF.) (The aerospace equivalent of the automotive QSA is the AS9101.) It is primarily used as an initial checklist of the supplier's quality system augmented by an additional checklist created after a review of the supplier's quality manual and written procedures.

In addition to the QSA document, the IATF has also published a guidance to ISO/TS 16949:2000 with the intent to help organizations with prescriptive suggestions on a per-clause basis. Important characteristics of the QSA are:

- Quality system documentation review

- A formal minimum checklist

- A formal evaluation process

For more information see AIAG (1998), QSA (2002), and IATF (2002).

Even though the QSA has been around since the introduction of the original QS-9000, nevertheless, it is not a document that allows any organization to move beyond minimum requirements. In fact, many organizations, since the introduction of ISO 9000 and QS-9000 in the automotive industry, feel intimidated by the requirement and its application. This aura of intimidation continues with the introduction of ISO/TS 16949 and AS9100. One of the reasons these standards have been viewed with much fear and intimidation is the fact that, along with the standards, there are additional materials that the organization pursuing the certification must be aware of and in compliance with.

This additional information along with the standard itself make the so-called *five-pack*. In essence, the five-pack consists of five individual publications that support the documentation process and record keeping of appropriate and applicable quality events. All of them have been produced by the International Automotive Task Force and are being distributed by the AIAG. Our focus is merely to introduce the materials rather than to discuss them in a very detailed fashion.*

It is of paramount importance to recognize that there is no official five-pack in AS9100. However, there are many similarities, some of which touch specific tools. These are:

- First article of inspection

- Key characteristic identification and variability reduction

- Risk management and mitigation

- Software quality

- Sampling plans

The following are some typical methodologies.

STATISTICAL PROCESS CONTROL

The purpose of the *statistical process control* (SPC) manual is to harmonize statistical approaches in the automotive industry. As a consequence, the manual offers a guideline and foundation for basic SPC applications. Because it offers only basic tools and gives directions only for some of the advanced tools, the manual is of limited utility. However, in its basic form, it is a powerful manual for anyone who uses statistical analysis on the job, since most of the applications are basic anyway. Considering that the majority of people do not have a good background in statistical techniques or thinking, the manual is a must read for those who want to be successful in the automotive quality arena.

---

* If the reader is interested in purchasing the five-pack either as individual volumes or as a set, he or she may contact, in the United States, the AIAG at 248-358-3003; in Europe, one may contact Carwin Continuous at 44-1708-861333.

Important characteristics of SPC are:

- Deming's profound knowledge
- Concept of variation
- Prevention versus detection
- Systems thinking
- Process control versus product control
- Process capability

These characteristics may be displayed as in Figure 8.1.

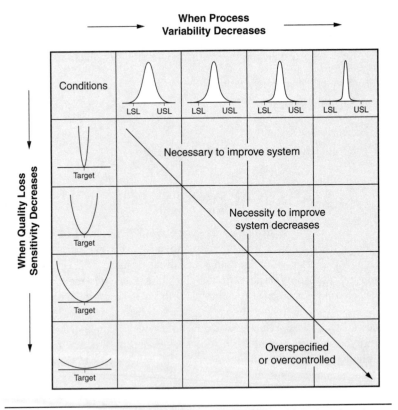

Figure 8.1   The relationship between process variability and the loss function.

Loss function is a degraded performance or operation outside the design specification limits. Loss function is usually the antifunction or the "no function" type of failure mode. Another way of looking at it is the loss that an organization is incurring as the quality drifts away from the target of the specific product or service. Notice that the loss happens in either direction of the target.

For the aerospace industry, the manual may also be very helpful in the sense that it provides the reader with some basic and fundamental concepts about variation, control charts, and capability. For more information see Stamatis (2003a), AIAG (1995).

MEASUREMENT SYSTEMS ANALYSIS

The purpose of the *measurement systems analysis* (MSA) manual is to present guidelines for selecting procedures to assess the quality of a measurement system, primarily for the industrial automotive world. To ensure that the benefit derived from using measurement data is great enough to warrant the cost of obtaining it, attention must be focused not on the quality of the data, but rather on the total measurement system.

Because of this unique focus, this manual is not intended to be a compendium of analyses for all measurement systems. Rather, its primary focus is measurement systems where the readings can be repeated on each part. It is this focus that makes the MSA a manual that all managers and anyone using or reading results of measurement equipment should be using as much as possible. Important characteristics of MSA are:

- Discrimination of the measurement: Is it adequate?

- Stability over time: Is the measurement statistically stable?

- Consistent over range and control: Are properties consistent and acceptable over the expected range and control?

- Bias and linearity.

- Gage repeatability and reproducibility (GR&R) for both variable and attribute data.

Worst-Case Total Uncertainty Formulas

Due to the significance that measurement presents in the quest for quality, we provide a simple approach to determining uncertainty. The following formulas can determine a worst-case total uncertainty on a typical two-gage block method. These formulas are conservative and should only serve as a guide in establishing worst-case scenarios and should not replace individual GR&R testing.

Estimating total uncertainty. The formula for datum uncertainty is:

$$U_d = (U_m^2 + (2\mu \text{ in})^2)^{1/2}$$

where, U_d = datum uncertainty (μ in) and

U_m = uncertainty of master gage block used to set datum (μ in)

where: 2μ in is from instrument uncertainty (2μ in + $0.5L\mu$ in) where L = 0.

Scale Factor Uncertainty. The formula is:

$$U_s = (U_{m1}^2 + U_{m2}^2 + 8\mu \text{ in})^{1/2}/(L_2 - L_1) + 2\mu \text{ in/in/}°F \times dT$$

where, U_s = scale factor uncertainty (μ in/in)

U_{m1} = uncertainty of block 1 (μ in)

U_{m2} = uncertainty of block 2 (μ in)

L_1 = length of master block 1 (in)

L_2 = length of master block 2 (in)

2μ in/in/$°F$ = machine uncertainty as a function of temperature normalized
　　to per inch basis.

dT = room temperature variation during test

where 8 is the sum squared value of two instrument uncertainties with
　　L set to 0.

Total Uncertainty. The formula is:

$$U = U_d + U_s [L - L_d]$$

U = total measurement uncertainty

U_d = datum uncertainty (min)

U_s = scale-factor uncertainty (μ in/in)

L = length of part being measured (in)

L_d = datum point (in)

　　A helpful hint to lessen the total uncertainty is to perform a two-point mastering with the same probes being used in the measurement. For example, when measuring ring gages, perform a two-point master with two master internal diameters and forgo the datum uncertainty. The same holds true when using flat probes (anvils) or any other type of probes. Also, when measuring gages using the bidirectional probes (OD), there is no need to set a datum because the first point acts as the datum.

Measurements Outside Two Masters. If it is necessary to measure outside the two master points, the following formula resultant can be added to the calculated total measuring uncertainty:

$$U_0 = ((U_{m1} + U_{m2}) \times D)/(P_2 - P_1)$$

where,

U_0 = added uncertainty outside the master points (μ in)
D = distance of measurement from nearest calibration point (in)
P_1 = first master point (in)
P_2 = second master point (in)
U_{m1} = uncertainty of first master (μ in)
U_{m2} = uncertainty of second master (μ in)

Measuring k-Sigma Capability for Attributes

Yet another issue of MSA is the concern about capability. Certainly in any SPC program the C_p, P_{pk}, C_{pk}, and so on are taught and rightfully so. They present a measurement in relation to the specifications and the location of the distribution. On the other hand, in the Six Sigma methodology this capability is presented with the sigma metric.

To expedite the process when working with variable data, use of a k-sigma metric provides a way to measure process capability that is linked to a fraction nonconforming as well as a process capability index. According to statistician Luko (2002), the concept of using such a metric is adaptable to situations involving perhaps the two most common types of attribute or count data.

Luko illustrates an example involving attribute data where nonconformities are being counted and any unit inspected may contain a number of nonconformities. In the application described, there are two nonconformities (y) among 5000 units. Here Luko makes use of the Poisson probability distribution to develop the k-sigma metric for the application. The equation for this distribution provides the probability of observing y nonconformities in the inspection unit when the average number of occurrences within units of the same size is λ.

$$F(y) = (e^{-\lambda}\lambda^{\wedge}y)/y! \text{ where y equals 0, 1, 2, 3, and so on.}$$

The goal is to have a 50 percent confidence point estimate for the mean number of nonconformities per unit. When r equals 2 in such a case, he reports lots of the size in this application will have λ of 2.674 nonconformities with 50 percent confidence or 0.000535 (2.674/5000) nonconformities per unit.

According to Luko, the strategy for this and the other type of attribute is to then develop one of the alternate process metrics, such as P_{pk}, and then calculate k-sigma. In this case, he first calculates the probability that a unit will have zero nonconformities for a single-sided P_{pk} lot equivalent. Here, $P(0) = e^{-0.000535}$ or 0.999465. This is the probability of containing no non-conformities, which Luko then translates to the fraction nonconforming in the lot of approximately $p = 1 - 0.999465$ or 0.000535 (not uncommon when p is small and the number of units large).

He then calculates the one-sided P_{pk} equivalent as

$$P_{pk} = Inv(1 - p)/3 = 1.09$$

and the two-sided case as

$$P_{pk} = Inv(1 - p/2)/3 = 1.154.$$

Since the k-sigma metric allows process drift to either side of the center of tolerance of up to 1.5 (sigma), the equation for the metric is

$$K = 3Ppk + 1.5$$

By determining the k-sigma metric for both one- and two-sided cases, a manufacturer can then classify this process as operating between 4.77 and 4.96 sigma.

According to Luko, a similar strategy can be used to find the k-sigma metric for another common type of attribute data where each unit produced either has or doesn't have the defined attribute. In this go/no-go type of application, the binomial distribution is used instead of the Poisson distribution.

FAILURE MODE AND EFFECTS ANALYSIS

The purpose of the failure mode and effects analysis (FMEA) is to identify up front the known and potential failures and take the appropriate action to remove them from the design and/or the process. The earlier the FMEA is done, the better it is. After all, up-front time spent in doing a comprehensive FMEA well, when product/process changes can be most easily and inexpensively implemented, will alleviate late-change crises. An FMEA can reduce or eliminate the chance of implementing a corrective change that could create an even larger concern. Properly applied, it is an interactive process that is never ending. An FMEA is a team activity and a living document.

The need for using the FMEA as a disciplined technique to identify and help eliminate potential concern is as important as ever. However, an additional need is the fact that every company in today's world is looking for ways to continually improve its products and/or services. As such, the FMEA can be used as a formal documentation of continual improvement, since it identifies and proposes corrective actions to specific problems. One of the most important factors for the successful implementation of an FMEA program is timeliness. It is meant to be a *before-the-event* action, not an *after-the-fact* exercise. It is, after all, a prevention methodology, rather than an appraisal one.

Although responsibility for the *preparation* of the FMEA must, of necessity, be assigned to an individual, FMEA input and preparation must be a team effort. A team of knowledgeable individuals should be assembled, for example, engineers with experience, manufacturers, assemblers, and quality and reliability personnel. The use of the FMEA is called out in the APQP and must be done for every production part process. Preparation instructions for an FMEA are in two distinct sections (design and process.) However, having both sections in the same manual facilitates the comparison of techniques used to develop the different types of FMEAs as a means to more clearly demonstrate their proper application and interrelation.

A *design potential FMEA* is an analytical technique used primarily by a design responsible engineer/team as a means to assure that, to the extent possible, potential failure modes and their associated causes/mechanisms have been considered and addressed.

A *process potential FMEA,* on the other hand, is an analytical technique used by a manufacturing responsible engineer/team as a means to assure that, to the extent possible, potential failure modes and their associated causes/mechanisms have been considered and addressed.

The key components of all FMEAs are:

- Header information: provides general information.

- Potential function: provides the task in question.

- Potential causes of failure: provide the root cause(s) of the task. A root cause in the FMEA is defined as an actionable cause.

- Current controls: provide the mechanism(s) that exist *right now* to *detect* and *catch* the failure before the customer does.

- Occurrence (O): provides the frequency of the failure.

- Severity (S): provides the seriousness of the failure.

- Detection (D): provides the level of difficulty of detecting a failure before it reaches the customer.

- Risk priority number (RPN): provides the priority of the failure based on the product of $O \times S \times D$.

- Recommended action(s): provides alternative solutions to eliminate the identified failure.

- Responsibility: assigns responsibility to an individual.

- Action taken: documents corrective action.

In addition to the two predominant FMEAs just discussed, system, machinery, attribute, safety, service, environmental, and other FMEAs exist. All of them have the same intent, however, the focus of prevention is based on their own specific purposes. For more information on FMEAs see Stamatis (2003) and AIAG (2001).

APQP AND CONTROL PLAN

The advanced product quality and control plan manual provides general guidelines for preparing plans and checklists for ensuring that advanced product quality planning is actually carried out by the supplier. It does not give specific instructions on how to arrive at each APQP or control plan entry, a task best left to each component review team. However, a typical approach to an APQP process is shown in Figure 8.2.

The supplier's first step in product quality planning is to assign responsibility to a cross-functional team. Effective product quality planning requires the involvement of more than just the quality department. The initial team should include representatives from engineering, manufacturing, material control, purchasing quality, sales, field service, subcontractors, and customers, as appropriate.

The guidelines given in this manual are intended to cover all situations normally occurring in the early planning, design phase, or process analysis. Each phase output is designed to be the input of the next phase with management support being included at each output level. It was felt that repeating the management support was important to encourage supplier management to be involved with the process through all phases. The initiation of the APQP elements according to each of the five phases is further explained in CD-ROM appendix II.

Dynamic Control Plan

The dynamic control plan (DCP) is a methodology to ensure that the customer expectations in the form of product design requirements are understood, deployed, and controlled in the manufacturing and assembly process.

The dynamic control plan describes the actions required at each phase of the process to assure that all parts produced will be uniform and conform

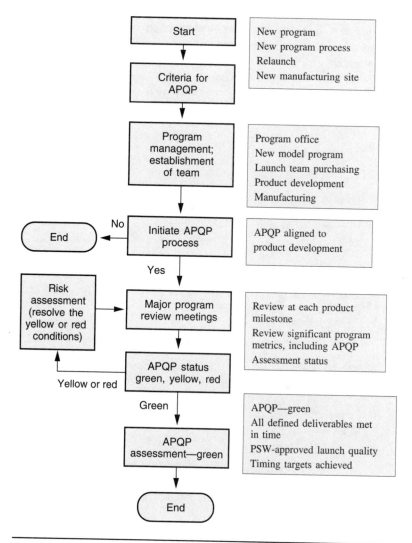

Figure 8.2   A typical approach to an APQP process.

to the customer's satisfaction. The dynamic control plan is a *living document,* which means that it is subject to revision. It is through each department's DCP team participating in DCP meetings that these revisions are discussed and agreed upon.

The difference between a traditional control plan and the DCP is that a traditional control plan identifies only the concerns for controlling parts and processes. In essence, a control plan describes the actions that are required at each phase of the process in a manner that assures that all process outputs will be in a state of control. On the other hand, the DCP is a more detailed control plan offering reaction plan(s) for particular deviations of a process, and it is usually combined with an FMEA. (Both control plans should be driven by the FMEA.)

Key characteristics of the APQP are:

- Milestone schedule dates

- Tracking of critical and significant characteristics

- Status of characteristics

Key characteristics of the control plan are:

- Process description

- Identification of devices, jigs, tools

- Process parameter, product characteristics

- Classification of process steps

- Monitoring methods

- Analysis method

- Reaction when out of control

For more information on APQP and control plans, see Stamatis (1998) and AIAG (2000).

PRODUCTION PART APPROVAL PROCESS

The purpose of the production part approval process (PPAP) is to determine if all customer engineering design record and specification requirements are properly understood by the supplier and that the process has the potential to produce product meeting these requirements during an actual production run at the quoted production rate.

The PPAP should be used by suppliers in the submission of production parts for approval to DaimlerChrysler, Ford, or General Motors and is required for each part prior to the first quality shipment. The supplier shall retain a complete record of findings and the master sample(s) for each submission, including SPC results and, when applicable, appearance approval.

It is imperative that during the production trial run, the capability is established and controlled. It is this capability that is reported during the part submission warrant (PSW) and is the guarantee that the supplier provides to the customer for ongoing performance. While this procedure is intended to cover all situations in normally occurring processes, it must be understood that questions and concerns may be raised during a PPAP. When this happens, they must be directed to the customer for his or her approval. This approval *must* be in writing.

To develop a complete PPAP, the record should show conformance to all test specifications and all other customer requirements. Appropriate signatures and dates are mandatory. The flow and specific requirements of a typical PPAP are explained in CD-ROM appendix I. Key components of PPAP are:

- Sample parts according to the control plan
- Test results
- Change notices following document control procedures
- Process flow information
- Control plans
- GR&R results
- Capability results

For more information on PPAP see AIAG (2000).

REFERENCES

DaimlerChrysler Corporation, Ford Motor Company, and General Motors Corporation. 1995. *Statistical Process Control*. Southfield, MI: Automotive Industry Action Group.

———. 1998. *Quality System Requirements: QS-9000,* 3rd ed. Southfield, MI: Automotive Industry Action Group.

———. 2000. *Advanced Product Quality Planning and Control Plan*. Southfield, MI: Automotive Industry Action Group.

———. 2000. *Production Part Approval Process*. 3rd ed. Southfield, MI: Automotive Industry Action Group.

———. 2001. *Failure Mode and Effects Analysis*, 3rd ed. Southfield, MI: Automotive Industry Action Group.

———. 2002. *Measurement System Analysis*. 3rd ed. Southfield, MI: Automotive Industry Action Group.

International Automotive Task Force. 2002. *ISO/TS 16049:2000*, 2nd ed, AIAG ed. Southfield, MI: International Automotive Task Force.

———. 2002. *IATF Guidance to ISO/TS 16049:2000*, AIAG ed. Southfield, MI: International Automotive Task Force.

———. 2002. *Quality System Assessment Checklist: Checklist to ISO/TS 16049*, 2nd ed., AIAG ed. Southfield, MI: International Automotive Task Force.

Luko, S. 2002. *Metrics and Conversions for Process Quality.* Paper 2002-01-1372. Warrendale, PA: SAE.

Stamatis, D. H. 1998. *Advanced Product Quality Planning.* New York: Quality Resources.

———. 2003. *Failure Mode and Effect Analysis: FMEA from Theory to Execution,* 2nd ed. Milwaukee, WI: ASQ Quality Press.

———. 2003a. *Six Sigma and Beyond: Statistical Process Control.* Boca Raton, FL: St. Lucie Press.

9
Auditing

uditing is a process of evaluating a system to make sure that certain parameters (usually some criteria or standards) have been met.
To do this evaluation, however, one must identify the system and
its requirements. The process for defining this system and finding out
where the needs are for meeting the requirements is called a *needs analysis*
or *assessment* (NA). As a general rule, an NA is conducted much earlier
than the formal audit as its main function is to determine the "gaps" in the
system. Because of its importance in the quality system documentation
process, let us review the topic.

NEEDS ANALYSIS

Imagine you are a doctor. A patient arrives at your office complaining of a
pain somewhere. The patient knows exactly what it will take to "cure" the
pain—a pill, a shot, perhaps surgery—and he tells you. Now you must
decide what to do next. Do you follow his diagnosis and develop the designated "cure?" Do you tell him he's wrong about the hurt and only someone sufficiently qualified and skilled (that is, you) can make such a
diagnosis and prescription? Or do you assure him you'll help with the pain,
then perform your own diagnosis, prescribe the fitting treatment, and, as
appropriate, implement it?

Sound familiar? There are striking parallels between the analytical
processes doctors follow and those you and I follow. Whether we call

ourselves consultants, trainers, instructional designers, organizational efficiency experts, or performance technologists, we are in the business of
eliminating the human performance problem "pain" or lessening it as much
as possible for an organization.

Over the years we have seen many attempts to quantify the process;
however, as of yet, there is no such a thing as "one approach covers all."
What we have been able to accomplish over the years is to define a methodology and a system approach to diagnose the "pain" in any organization.
The more we understand the process, the more successful the implementation efforts on whatever we are trying to establish.

This diagnostic process is called a needs analysis or need assessment.
For our purposes, here, I will identify some of the main ingredients that any
needs analysis should have and provide at least three basic models for
implementation. (I may add that all three models are user-friendly and are
workable. I have personally used them in a variety of applications with
great success.)

An NA is an important ingredient of the larger context of system
planning for it defines terms such as "input," "product," "output," and
"outcome." If this was the only benefit one received from an NA, it still
would be worth the effort. However, a complete NA relates these terms
to two themes for any organization: management commitment and
action plan.

In any needs analysis the implication of the "need" must be that the
organization is about to undergo some kind of change. As such, the needs
analysis must be explicitly tied to the organization's goals. It must also be
introduced in a top-down fashion, if positive results are expected. Overall,
a needs analysis will attempt to solve the organization's performance problems, describe a set of performance-influencing variables, and strive to
identify the "gap" between the present condition and some future condition.

To be effective, however, appropriate support by management must be
given and appropriate time for evaluating the results must be allocated.
When that is done, then the analyst will be able to identify the performance
problem, verify its importance, identify its root cause(s), and select the
appropriate solution(s) for recommended implementation.

To understand the NA concept one must understand the different kinds
of NAs. They are shown in Table 9.1.

So, how does one do a needs assessment? Obviously, you have to focus
on the "gap." A "gap" is the difference between the existing and a future
state of affairs. In terms of quality, the "gap" is defined as the difference
between the existing state and the state that is called for by the quality system (quality manual, procedures, instructions, and so on). Once the gap has

Table 9.1 Different types of NA.

Type	Function	Characteristics	Assumption Base
1	Identify problem based on need	External utility plus partnership-based perceived needs referent for survival and contribution. Single emphasis upon "need" as an outcome gap.	Almost anything may be changed and questioned; there are no "sacred cows"; even laws can be added, deleted, modified; organizations may be challenged, disassembled, rebuilt, or even eliminated.
2	Determine solution requirements and identify solutions alternatives	Partnership-based analysis of output gaps of the system; analysis of process and product gaps within the system	Work is to be conducted within a context, usually organizational, and for the most part, the rules, policies, goals, and objectives of the organization, as they now exist, are the ground rules for planned change.
3	Select solution strategies from among alternatives	Ranking of solution by partners. Cost efficiency models, cost effectiveness models, and so on. Emphasis on processes and inputs.	The existing organizational goals and objectives are useful and appropriate and the change is to find the most efficient and effective manner to meet the objectives. The purpose is to develop products using effective and efficient processes and inputs.
4	Implement	Determination of gaps in prespecified performances. Management objectives, scheduling, cycle time, and so on.	It is known what is to be done and how to do it; the important function here is to successfully administer the jobs to be done and manage the resources to help accomplish the overall organizational mission and identified products.
5	Determine performance effectiveness	Determine discrepancies between results and objectives for the end of term/ project or program for a proper decision. Gaps in outputs and outcomes evaluated.	The jobs have been done; this function is to determine the gaps between the goals and objectives and the accomplishments.

continued

continued

Type	Function	Characteristics	Assumption Base
6	Revise as required	En route evaluation of both processes and progress toward outcomes, with possible changes of inputs, processes, products, and/or outputs.	While the jobs are getting done, or after we have finished any segment of one or more jobs, discrepancies between our goals and objectives are determined and corrective action is instituted, or a decision not to change is accepted and implemented.

been identified, then an action plan is in order. A generic gap analysis based on Kaufman (1979) is the following:

What Is	What Should Be
Suppliers	
Your organization	
Customers	

Once these major categories are identified then the rating should follow. A typical abbreviated structure for a rating scale is the following:

Goal	Current Performance	Probable Increase in Utility	Average Rated Importance	Priority Value and/ or Ranking
1				
2				
etc.				

As to the specific questions one may ask, the following may serve as the starting point:

- What is the extent of the gap between the facts (what is) and the values (what ought to be)?

- How accurate (consistent with facts and values) is the analysis of this concern?

- What degree of effectiveness (employee or company benefit) for dollars spent is likely if this need is satisfied?

- To what extent would satisfying this need help satisfy other needs on the list?

- In comparison to the other needs of the organization, what is the degree of criticality of this need?

- Considering time, cost, and other constraints, how feasible is satisfaction of this need?

As for the specific techniques, tools, and purposes, the following are typical:

Techniques	Tools	Purposes
Current data analysis Task analysis Gap analysis Subject-matter analysis	Interviews Observations Group discussions Surveys Statistical techniques	*Optimals*—performance (P) or knowledge (K) *Actuals*—current P or K *Feelings*—of employees and general culture of organization *Causes*—from many different points of view *Solutions*—from many alternatives and different points of view

A different perspective is given by Harless (1970), who focuses on the high-level strategy of front-end analysis (FEA). The focus is on what major questions need be asked and answered so that one can identify problem(s), causes(s), and solution(s). However, he does not describe how the necessary information should be gathered, other than in general terms (for example, behavioral observation, review of records). In fairness, however, he does provide an approach to streamline the process. For example, during the problem identification phase, he suggests:

- Identify deficiencies at the task level.

- Identify what the deficient performers must do, rather than what they "need to know."

- Refine the customer's problem to statement(s) of performance deficiency plus organizational impact.

- Value the problem (that is, assign a cost to it).

- Use the customer's statement of evidence for when the problem will no longer exist as criteria for evaluating the solution.

In like fashion, when one identifies causes(s), he offers these guidelines:

- Performance is influenced by three domains of variables: skill/knowledge, the environment, and motivation/incentives.

- Examine all three domains for contributing causes to poor performance.

- Once you've generated hypothesized causes, test only those for which you can gather evidence.

- Identify all causes which are really effects linked to prior root causes.

For the final phase, identify solution(s). Harless points out that you should look to these rules of thumb:

- Develop solutions that treat the root cause(s).

- Given general solution goals, select and prioritize specific solution(s).

- If you can't eliminate the root cause, minimize its effects.

- If a skills/knowledge deficiency is part of the cause, determine the mix of job aids, job aids plus instruction, or instruction that will meet the need.

Finally, Harless provides step-by-step procedures for what questions to ask at each point along the way and suggestions to help you decide what's next. You have a strategy for how to move from the initial customer problem statement to the final set of recommendations offered to management for their decision.

Zemke and Kramlinger (1982), on the other hand, provide very specific tactics. Zemke's contribution with his *figuring things out* (FTO) model, has focused on the tactics of information gathering, the investigative techniques one can choose from to solve human performance problems. The model purposely is not limited to conducting an FEA. The methods he proposes can also help the trainer write job descriptions, set training and performance standards, construct competency models, perform task analyses, and so on.

Zemke's approach is through an algorithm that describes 15 procedures for gathering data. They are grouped into three categories: observational techniques, discussion tactics, and instrumental methods. Time and motion studies, task listings, and frequency counts are examples of the first category of observational techniques. Conducting focus groups and doing face-to-face or telephone interviews constitute discussion tactics. Critical incident reports, surveys, and questionnaires are all instrumental methods.

The FTO model offers an algorithm and decision tables that make it easier for anyone to choose among tactics for a desired result. For example, depending on whether the task or information in question is observable, you can find one (or more) tactics that vary in how costly and time-consuming they are to perform. Or you can find out what tactic(s) to employ if employee buy-in is an important concern.

Perhaps one of the most important aspects of any NA is the management presentation. After all, if your presentation of the results is poorly positioned and lacks persuasive power, nothing will change in your organization.

Also, in conjunction with the management presentation and the evaluation of the results, one may bear in mind that a critical factor in the perpetuation of the newly implemented program is the "confirmation" run, based on some kind of "data driven" results. Of course, the data must be generated from a formal evaluation.

A well-designed evaluation phase provides critical information on whether a chosen intervention was a success and to what degree. The evaluation data can assist in isolating problem areas and in developing strategies to improve desired results. The data can also be used to justify similar future programs. There are many reasons for conducting an evaluation, but do the evaluation systems we're using tell us what we need to know?

There are four steps of evaluation. Each step adds a degree of sophistication to the evaluation process.

Step I: Reaction

This step of evaluation is the most commonly used; it is also known as the "popularity contest," or "smiles test." Reaction is the measure of employee or learner, instructor, or observer opinion. Data are gathered using surveys, interviews, and questionnaires.

Step II: Learning

The learning step of evaluation is the measure of knowledge and skill acquisition. Data are gathered from pretests/posttests, simulations or role plays, and task certification exercises.

Step III: Performance

The performance step is the measure of the application of skill/knowledge on the job rather than in the classroom. Data can be gathered by observing on-the-job performance and recording it on checklists or data sheets; auditing printed or computer-generated material; and by obtaining reports from individuals or groups.

Step IV: Organizational Impact

The impact step of evaluation is the measure of the bottom line. It answers the question, "Is the program actually accomplishing what we want?" When the goal of a program is determined, usually the organization is trying to produce an impact on some aspect of the business. If there is a reason for implementing a program, then the program's impact on the organization should be measured. The impact (or bottom line) is not always money. It could be customer satisfaction, number of repeat customers, number of items with quality problems, and so on. Data are gathered using whatever method will provide the necessary information, including questionnaires, interviews, audits, and observations.

The higher the step of evaluation, the more valuable the information. The most commonly used steps are I and II. Step IV is the most critical, most important, most time consuming, yet least used, even though it provides the organization with the most information in relationship to effectiveness. From an NA perspective, step IV is the most crucial because it confirms or negates the action(s) taken.

Several ingredients are needed to set up a good evaluation system:

- Knowledge of evaluation processes.

- Time, money, people, and other resources to design and run the evaluation system.

- A desire to know the results of the program. It is surprising how often managers undertake a performance improvement program but do not care about, or are not held responsible for, the results.

Too many performance improvement programs go without a sophisticated evaluation phase (using steps I through IV); most often the reason is lack of resources (time, money, and people) to set up and maintain the evaluation system. All four levels of evaluation are important and provide good information. However, if an organization cares about the results of its program, the necessary resources should be allocated up front and a step IV evaluation should become a required step in the design process.

Conclusion

In this short overview we have tried to present a cursory discussion about needs assessment. Our focus has been "purpose-based assessment" and as such, we have focused on the approaches used by Kaufman, Harless, and Zemke. We also have tried to incorporate some of Rossett's (1987) concepts, especially those relating to the stages of assessment.

We believe that the issue of assessment is a very important one, since we must find out where we are before we move on to new horizons. A proper NA not only will facilitate the benchmarking of your status quo, but it will also help you in creating an action plan to succumb your shortcomings in an efficient and economical way. This will be accentuated if the NA is followed by the appropriate evaluation as well as a formal audit.

AUDITING

The ISO 8402 defines an audit as "a systematic and independent examination to determine whether quality activities and related results comply with planned arrangements and whether these arrangements are implemented effectively and are suitable to achieve objectives" (ANSI/ISO/ASQC A8402-1994). ISO 9000:2000 defines it a: "systematic, independent, and documented process for obtaining audit evidence and evaluating it objectively to determine the extent to which audit criteria are fulfilled." Thus, an audit is a human evaluation process to determine the degree of adherence to prescribed norms and results in a judgment. The norms, of course, are always predefined in terms of criteria, standards, or both.

To avoid confusion and misunderstandings, it must be understood from the beginning of the audit that the norms are defined by the management of the organization and the auditor has nothing to do with evaluating the suitability of such norms. However, it is the responsibility of the auditor to evaluate the compliance of the organization to those norms. For this reason the audit is usually performed as a pass/fail evaluation rather than a point-system evaluation.

As defined then, an audit is an information gathering activity with the purpose of identifying noncompliances in the system, so that improvement, corrective action, or both may be evaluated and implemented. It should be understood by all auditors and lead auditors that in a given audit there is neither a preestablished number of noncompliances nor a fair ratio of major and minor noncompliances. This is true for the first audit, as well as for subsequent audits. Furthermore, audits are not public hangings.

Quality audits are neither inspection tools nor verification tools for actual acceptance or rejection of the product or service. The orientation of the quality audit is fact finding; its focus is the evaluation of the system or process. The focus of an audit is always prevention and planning, as opposed to inspections where the focus is appraising product quality after the fact.

Quality audits may be internal or external and take one of three forms:

1. *First-party audit.* This audit is conducted by an organization on itself and may be done on the entire organization or part of the organization. It is usually called an internal audit.

2. *Second-party audit.* This audit is conducted by an organization on its supplier and may be done on the entire supplier or part of it. It is called an external audit.

3. *Third-party audit.* This audit is conducted by an independent organization (the third party) on a customer, organization, or supplier. It can be conducted at the request of a customer or on the initiative of a supplier or the organization to gain certification. It is always an external audit.

As already mentioned a quality audit is a systematic and independent investigation to determine whether quality activities, objective evidence, and related results comply with the documented quality system. As a consequence, when we audit something, we audit systems, not people! To do this, we must depend on "objective evidence," which includes: qualitative or quantitative information, records, or statements of fact pertaining to the quality of an item or service that can be verified. Another way of saying it is that objective evidence is the proof presented to auditors for verification. If it is not documented, it is not objective evidence. (It is very important here to recognize that *documented* may mean several things including direct observation, interview finding, item on a record, collaboration of multiple sources, and so on.)

In the course of the audit, an auditor may find an "observation," which is a matter with which an auditor is concerned but which cannot be clearly stated as a nonconformance. It is an identified opportunity for improving the quality system. In other words, the auditor may suspect something; however, there is no proof for the suspicion. An observation is only within the internal auditor's domain. Compliance to an observation is optional, but may prevent a future corrective-action request (CAR), especially from an external auditor.

In the life of the auditor and in any audit it is only a matter of time before the word "nonconformance" is mentioned. ISO 9000:2000 defines it as the nonfulfillment of specified requirements, such as missing a requirement stated using the word "shall." When the requirements of the standard are not met by the system, it is a nonconformance to the standard. The nonconformance may be either major or minor, depending on its severity, and can be found in the quality manual, procedures, instructions, and/or records.

Specifically, a minor nonconformance is a failure of some part of the quality system or a single observed lapse in following one requirement of the system. In either case, the nonconformance is not likely to result in the failure of the quality system or materially reduce its effectiveness.

On the other hand, a major nonconformance indicates the absence of an element or the total breakdown of a system in meeting a standard requirement. A number of minor nonconformances can collectively constitute a major nonconformance. A major nonconformance could result in the shipment of nonconforming product.

Another term that is used in an audit is "recommendation," which is a statement made by the auditor that provides direction to the auditee regarding an activity that may benefit their quality system. A recommendation is only within the internal auditor's domain. However, as with an observation, compliance with a recommendation is optional, but may prevent a future CAR for a nonconformance, or improve the effectiveness of the process. The reader must be cognizant that the terms "observation" and "recommendation" are used only by the internal auditors and never in association with the QS-9000 registration scheme.

Auditing Planning Tools

The audit team uses at least the following tools for an effective audit.

- *Schedule and scope.* To notify auditees who will be audited and to set boundaries of what will be covered.

- *Matrix.* To show which elements of the standard are applicable to each department.

- *Audit checklist and activity sheet.* Used by the audit team to plan each audit. It indicates what to look for relative to each clause when auditing. Appendix IV provides the reader with some typical auditing expectations for ISO 9001:2000 on a per-element basis.

- *Roles and responsibilities.* Review of the management structure and organizational chart to find the responsibility of quality management.

- *Actual work in progress in each department.* Observe actual operations for verification of the quality system.

- *Previous audits documentation.* Review previous audits to see whether corrective action has taken place, management has been informed, and whether prevention and implementation of the "new" changes have taken place.

- *Organizational documentation.* Review all relevant documentation before the actual audit.

The audit team uses these tools to create an audit plan, which all team members agree to follow. The audit plan should specify what activities will be audited, when, where, and by whom. It should also give auditors some direction on where to focus attention. Each auditor on the team must follow the plan, with assistance as needed from the lead auditor.

The Process of Auditing

All audits are processes. Therefore, to conduct an audit, one must follow a process. A typical process for conducting the audit is a four-step approach.

The Opening Meeting

To break the ice, confirm people, times, and places involved in the audit; identify gaps in roles and responsibilities; ensure that the department manager understands the audit process and his or her responsibilities.

Attendees: Audit team and any interested auditee representatives, managers, or designees from each department.

Timing: At the start of each audit.

Agenda:

- Introductions

- Audit objective

- Audit scope and theme

- Audit process

- Confirm details about audit format and schedule

- Confirm auditee availability

- Questions and answers (*only* process-related)

- Confirm dates, times, and locations of debrief meeting(s) and close out meeting

The opening meeting is chaired by the lead auditor and the following records should be saved: sign-in sheet and opening meeting agenda.

The Audit

This is the physical visit where the auditor actually performs the verification of the quality system based on the standard and the documentation of the organization. To have an effective audit, some of the critical factors that the auditor must possess and demonstrate are:

- Professional conduct

- Recognize importance of introductions

- Focus on key issues

- Use effective questioning skills

- Listen actively

- Use silence effectively

- Gain cooperation

- Be persistent and decisive

- Coordinate information with other auditors

- Be alert

- Keep emotions in check

- Examine records

- Verify that system is operating

- Know when enough is enough

Setting the Stage

The auditor must:

- Introduce himself or herself and make time to establish trust and minimize fear

- Ask a general question of personal interest to the auditee to help put them at ease

- Inform each auditee that you will be taking notes, which will be made available to the auditees

- Present himself or herself as an ally who, like the auditee, wants things to get better

- Explain who he or she is, why he or she is here, and the types of things he or she will be looking at

Selecting a Sample

- Select a random sample from the evidence

- Auditor to select sample, not auditee

Debrief Meeting

To inform the department and its managers of the audit status.

Attendees: Department managers or designers and other interested people from the audited department

Timing: Daily

Agenda:

- Thank-yous

- Introductions of new people

  - Department personnel

  - Audit team

- Positive observations/recommendations

- Presentation of CARs

- Presentation of negative observations and recommendations

- Sign and copy CAR

- Department closeout responsibilities

At the end of the meeting make sure:

1. You give a signed copy of CARs and observations/ recommendations to the department managers.

2. Hand all CARs and observations/recommendations to the audit team leader.

3. Remember that departments have a right to question CARs and observations/recommendations. If this happens, handle it amicably. Keep referring back to the objective evidence.

4. If departments refuse to sign CARs, you will have to escalate the matter. In any case, a nonsignature CAR is not a major problem, because it is still part of the report and will remain as such. Even though a CAR may not be signed by a manager, there is a potential problem if that issue is not resolved before an external auditor finds it.

Audit Summary Report

To let the organization know the status of the internal audit and identify areas of concern and trends. Depending on the size of the audit, this summary report may be written as part of the debriefing or as part of the next step, which is the closing meeting.

Contents:

- Departments or activities that were audited
- Audit team members' names and audited department name and number
- Audit duration, dates, scope, objective, and so on
- Summary of the nonconformances, observations, and recommendations that were found
- Attach supporting information to the audit report as applicable

Closeout Meeting

To identify status of quality system, positive observations, recommendations, areas of concern, and trends. To provide a summary of all findings.

Attendees: Audit team, management representative from the audited department or their designees, executive management or their designees.

Timing: End of audit.

Agenda:

- Thank-yous
- Introductions
  - Managers
  - Audit team
- Audit objective
- Audit scope
- Audit summary (start with positive observations first)
- Define CAR response time
- Audit report issue date
- Dates and departments for next audit phase
- Questions and answers (*only* as they relate to the results)

In the closing meeting the lead auditor is in charge. He or she is the one who reviews the agenda with attendees before starting the meeting. He or she is also responsible for the sign-in sheet and handout copies of the agenda. At the end of the meeting, remember to save the following quality records from the meeting: sign-in sheet and closeout meeting agenda.

REFERENCES

Harless, J. H. 1970. *An Ounce of Analysis (Is Worth a Pound of Objectives)*. Falls Church, VA: Harless Educational Technologists, Inc.

Kaufman, R., and F. English. 1979. *Needs Assessment*. Englewood Cliffs, NJ: Educational Technology Publications.

Rossett, A. 1987. *Training Needs Assessment*. Englewood Cliffs, NJ: Educational Technology Publications.

Zemke, R., and T. Kramlinger. 1982. *Figuring Things Out: A Trainer's Guide to Needs and Task Analysis*. Reading, MA: Addison-Wesley Publishing Company.

SELECTED BIBLIOGRAPHY

Chase, W. G., and H. A. Simon. 1973. "The Mind's Eye in Chess." In W. G. Chase, ed. *Visual Information Processing*. New York: Academic Press.

Chi, M. T. H., R. Glaser, and M. Farr, eds. 1988. *The Nature of Expertise*. Hillsdale, NJ: Erlbaum.

Chi, M. T. Fl., R. Glaser, and E. Rees. 1982. "Expertise in Problem Solving." In R. J. Sternberg, ed., *Advances in the Psychology of Human Intelligence*. Hillsdale, NJ: Erlbaum.

Das, J. P., J. A. Naglieri, and J. R. Kirby. 1994. *Assessment of Cognitive Processes*. Needham Heights, MA: Allyn & Bacon.

Ericsson, A., ed. 1996. *The Road to Excellence*. Mahwah, NJ: Erlbaum.

Ericsson, K. A., and N. Charness. 1994. "Expert Performance: Its Structure and Acquisition." *American Psychologist* 49: 725–747.

Ericsson, K. A., R. T. Krampe, and C. Romer Tesch. 1993. "The Role of Deliberate Practice In the Acquisition of Expert Performance." *Psychological Review* 100: 363–406.

Feuerstein, R. 1979. *The Learning Potential Assessment Device*. Baltimore: University Park Press.

Feuerstein, R. 1980. *Instrumental Enrichment: An Intervention Program for Cognitive Modifiability*. Baltimore: University Park Press.

Kilpatrick, D. 1959. "Techniques for Evaluating Training Programs." *Journal of the American Society of Training Directors* (November/December/January).

McClelland, D. C. 1985. *Human Motivation*. New York: Scott Foresman.

Naglieri, J. A., and J. P. Das. 1997. *Cognitive Assessment System*. Chicago: Riverside Publishing Company.

Nickerson, R. S. 1986. *Reflections on Reasoning*. Hillsdale, NJ: Erlbaum.

Parsowith, B. S. 1995. *Fundamentals of Quality Auditing*. Milwaukee: ASQC Quality Press.

Russell, J. P., ed. 2000. *The Quality Audit Handbook*, 2nd ed. Milwaukee: ASQ Quality Press.

Stamatis, D. H. 1996. *Documenting and Auditing for ISO 9000 and QS-9000*. Chicago: Irwin Professionals.

10

Process-Oriented Audit (Assessment)

TYPES OF AUDITS

For quality purposes, there are two basic kinds of audits. They are:

1. *Conformance audits.* They compare the requirements to what is audited. In other words, they compare something to a standard.

2. *Process audits.* They look at the actual activities within a process and determine the effectiveness of those activities. Process audits examine the actual process and then look at the requirements that are associated with the activities. Because of the actual process being investigated it is important to consider and take into account the following:

   - Process audits have a higher level of difficulty

   - Process audits require more interpersonal skills

   - Process audits require more preparation

   - Process audits focus on continual change

The cornerstone of ISO 9000, ISO/TS 16949, and AS9100 is the process model. In its simplest form the process model may be shown as in Figure 10.1.

Therefore, the *process audit* is the focal point for the organization in the sense that it has the opportunity to be an excellent reconnaissance methodology to identify potential as well as real problems. The process

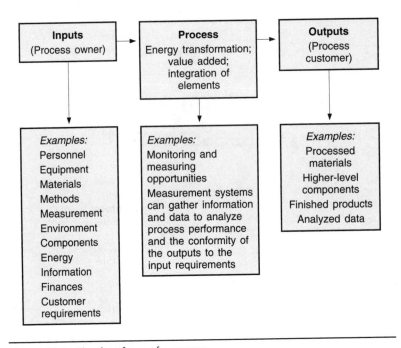

Figure 10.1 Simplest form of a process.

audit is management's tool/methodology for continual improvement. It always focuses on effectiveness regardless of the area or management level. For example: One may want to evaluate effective design, prevention orientation, linkage to customers, suppliers and partners, the focus on value creation for all key stakeholders, operational performance, cycle time, evaluation on continual improvement, organizational learning, and so on. All of these and many others may be helped by *process auditing*.

A typical model for conducting a process audit is shown in Figure 10.2, which follows the PDC(S)A model.

The PDC(S)A model is designed for continual improvement of any management system. This cycle is critical to understanding the new standard and its requirements. The basic concepts of the PDC(S)A cycle are straightforward:

- *Plan.* This is a critical stage and ISO 9001:2000 has planning requirements and suggestions in nearly every clause. But the basic concept is simple—formulate a plan to fulfill your quality policy and the objectives of the system.

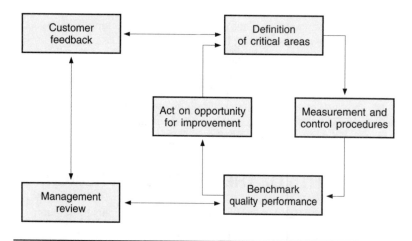

Figure 10.2   A typical process audit following the PDC(S)A model.

- *Do.* This is a fairly simple concept as well. It means implement the processes you've laid out in your plan.

- *Check.* This means monitor and measure what you're doing so that you have data with which to evaluate and improve the processes and overall system.

- *Act.* After you have data, you must do something with it to improve, and, of course, plan for the improvement (which begins the cycle again). The "act" usually stems from management reviews, internal audits, customer audits, data gathering, or even third-party assessments.

Internal quality audits are required by ISO 9001:2000, TS 19649, AS9100, and ISO 14001 (not discussed here) standards, to ensure the quality system is performing as planned. *All* activities must train internal auditors to make sure that they are capable of identifying deficiencies in the system. It is through internal audits that organizations can make sure that they run effectively and profitably.

Specifically, process audits are holistic approaches to evaluating: 1) customer requirements and satisfaction, and 2) organizational profitability. Therefore, the scope of the process audit is on effectiveness and streamlining, or removing nonvalue activities through proper identification.

Process audits are not surprise visits. Each activity to be audited will receive written notification of the time and scope of the internal audit.

Internal audit frequency depends on the activity being audited, that is, some need to be more frequently than others.

At the conclusion of the internal audit, a CAR may be issued and presented to management. Management is responsible for following up on the effectiveness of the corrective action.

Finally, *all* process audits depend on independent auditors to carry out the activity(ies) being audited. In other words: auditors from Paint can audit Body but not their own area.

BENEFITS OF THE PROCESS APPROACH

- Holistic approach (provide value-added from inputs to outputs).

- Broadens the outlook of the auditors.

- Helps the organization understand the role of the process in achieving certain business results.

- Pushes lessons learned back to the previous process.

- Enables the organization to stay focused on what is important.

- Employees become more involved and are willing to share for the common good of the organization.

- Keeps processes streamlined.

- Keeps focus on organizational goals for achieving customer satisfaction and profitability.

- The organization can solve problems faster with a mature information database.

GENERAL COMMENTS ABOUT PROCESS AUDIT

The transition from element-based auditing (ISO 9000:1994) to process-based auditing (ISO 9001:2000) is mandatory, and it is imperative that the organization's personnel as well as the auditors know that they are successful in process auditing when they can conduct a process audit focused on performance improvement and evaluate audit results for effectiveness. The performance metrics, more often than not, are already established at the corporate level. Typical metrics are associated with safety, quality, delivery, cost, manufacturing, and environment. Of course, these metrics are translated at the plant floor levels as required.

By far the most important objectives of all process audits are based on two principles. They are:

1. To evaluate a process for effectiveness from a holistic approach.

2. To show the linkages of the process to inputs, outputs, and interfaces.

Given these two core objectives, one of the most troubling items with the new standards is the notion of what the auditors will look for. The answer, of course, is very easy, if we think of the purpose of the audit. That is, we must look for effectiveness. Consequently, we look for:

- Effectiveness of the process through evaluating at least the following:

  - Interfaces of process

  - The inputs and outputs of the process

  - The appropriateness of the metric

- Problem areas such as:

  - Untagged scrap

  - Tagged scrap not segregated from good parts

  - Unidentified parts and materials

  - Materials, supplies, and parts in unauthorized areas

  - Damaged shipping containers

  - Parts out of normal production process flow

  - Poor housekeeping

  - Work and inspection instructions

  - Adherence to standards, procedures, and instructions

  - Conditions of tools and equipment

  - Use of processed parts, tools, and parts

  - Unidentified gages

  - Calibration procedures and records

- Training issues, records, and certifications, if applicable
- Preventive maintenance
- Inspection and test records
- Surveillance records
- Correction and prevention of customer complaints
- Obsolete documents

NINE STEPS IN PREPARING FOR THE PROCESS AUDIT

The Boy and Girl Scouts are both known for the motto: "Be prepared." To be successful in auditing we must be prepared. That means:

1. Know the organization's quality policy and be familiar with both quality and environmental (optional) procedures and instructions.

2. Know your metrics.

3. Know your job and where your work instructions are located (if you do operate under a "road map" make sure you are able to navigate through it—especially if the road map is computerized).

4. Know your tools and gages, and their calibration requirements.

5. Do not ask or create unauthorized documents (procedures, instructions, visual aids, and so on).

6. Do not use unauthorized tools and gauges—all must have traceability to a standard and must be identified appropriately.

7. Understand what to do if you cannot complete your job.

8. Understand what to do with nonconforming materials.

9. Answer all questions that come your way—be factual and brief.

The idea of a successful audit is predicated on planning. The nine items identified will help in that effort. In real terms these may be interpreted as specific tasks that the audit team under the leadership of the lead auditor is responsible for generating. Some of the tasks should be to:

- Gather and review the necessary documentation, checklists, and/or information.

- Develop your audit strategy.

  – Order of interviews or process evaluations

- Follow a natural flow.

- Use information from one interview/process to lead into the next interview/process.

- Select your audit object/target sample.

- Customize your audit checklist. This is perhaps one of the most important tasks in planning the audit. Items that should be considered as the input for generating a thorough checklist include the following:

  – Ask for an overview of the process.

  – How are processes measured?

  – What is the purpose of the process?

  – How are the metrics in the process used to evaluate process performance?

  – How are process interrelationships identified, managed, resolved, and improved?

  – How is the process controlled?

  – Are controls effective?

  – What procedures relate to the activities that you are evaluating?

FOUNDATIONS OF AUDITING

To appreciate the process audit we must realize that a process is a continuum made up of inputs, the process, and the outputs (see Figure 10.1). A process is something that:

- Transforms inputs into outputs

- Transforms energy

- Creates or adds value

- Integrates elements to achieve a certain objective

It is imperative to understand that even though we showed the process as a holistic entity and linear, that doesn't mean that it is the case in the real world. Many times we have to adjust the process with specific requirements such as:

- Specifications
- Customer requirements
- Corporate requirements
- Process requirements
- Legislative/regulatory requirements
- Process goals and objectives

And/or controls, such as:

- Control plans
- Operational controls
- Procedures
- Work instructions
- SPC

The intent of the specific requirements and the controls is that we in the end produce effective and efficient products and we can focus on the "improvement efforts" as defined by the organization.

Inputs are the items that make the process go. They are the signals, the beginning, the starting point of everything. They also can be the:

- Customer needs
- Product requirements inputs
- Good parts
- Trained operators
- Defined methods
- Capable equipment
- Defined customer needs

Outputs are the results of the process. They are the answer to the question of "What should we deliver?" The assumptions of the outputs are based on:

- Good product

- On-time delivery

- Satisfied customers

- Records

- Process and product data

- Environmental impact

Therefore, the outputs may be in a variety of forms such as:

1. Products that meet customer expectations

2. Equipment/installations (with what?):

   - Gaging

   - Assembly fixtures

   - Test stands

3. Training, knowledge, skills (with whom?):

   - Engineers

   - Operators

   - Inspectors

4. Performance indicators (how many?):

   - ppm defects

   - Throughput

   - Returned goods

5. Instructions, procedures, methods (how to?):

   - Control plans/inspection plans

   - Standard work instructions (SWIs)/instructions

   - Test methods

THE PROCESS AUDIT
METHODOLOGY

We already have said that the focus is on effectiveness of the system. Therefore, by the end of the questions you should be very comfortable addressing opportunities for improvement that can be identified, tracked, verified, and validated. Key questions are:

- Are all the process inputs in place?

- Are the process requirements specified?

- Is the process controlled to the extent necessary?

- Do the outputs meet process, product, customer, and interested party requirements?

- Is the process effective (measurements, criteria, condition)?

Typical questions that may be asked for identifying customer expectations and linking them with business objectives are:

- Can the processes perform to expectations?

- Are the customer's expectations understood?

- Are there linkages between business and process objectives?

- Are the organization's scorecard measures being met?

Typical questions that may be asked in identifying customer-related processes and process measurables are:

- Are they cascaded?

- Are they linked at different levels and to customer requirements?

- How are the measurables identified, defined, analyzed, responded to, and communicated?

Here we must recognize that all organizations' scorecards—linking measurements—are derived from:

- Zone (cell) measures

- Process/departmental measures

- Plant measures

- Customer impact

Above all, auditors should also verify that the system is getting expected results. For example, if metrics are available, focus on:

- Production

- Maintenance

- Environmental

- Safety

- QMS measurables

On the other hand, if there are no metrics:

- State the purpose of the element or process in simple terms

- State how you would know if the element or process was *not* accomplishing its purpose. The audit process is not effective if it is not finding the systemic weaknesses in the QMS.

- Develop a strategy and/or describe the indicators you will use to evaluate if the process/activity is accomplishing its purpose.

- In essence, where there are no metrics, we evaluate the results of our internal audits against the audit results of our customers.

So, the question then becomes: How can an auditor be effective in auditing? We suggest that the components of an effective audit program lie with understanding and utilizing, at least at a minimum level, the following:

- Process map

- Conduct the audit in the actual *environment* of the process

- Debrief final reports

- Final report

- Verification of closing of findings

While these are very important, they need to be supported by appropriate and applicable questions. Typical questions for a successful audit are:

- Are all the process inputs in place?

- Are the process requirements specified?

- Is the process controlled to the extent necessary?

- Do the outputs meet process, product, customer, and interested party requirements?

- Is the process effective (measurements, criteria, condition)?

- Can opportunities for improvement be identified, tracked, verified, and validated?

Key parameters, to ensure the success of an audit program:

- Must be tied to organization's metrics—scorecard/plant boards
- Indicate number of improvements realized

MECHANICS OF PROCESS AUDIT

In any methodology, including an audit, there is a series of activities that have to be performed. These activities are team-oriented and facilitate the task of auditing. Specifically, they are:

1. *How to plan the process audit.* All audits should begin with some level of planning. Planning in this case refers to asking the right questions. Typical questions are:

- Do all processes need to be assessed in a location?
    - Not every manufacturing *operation* has to be assessed in the location, but the sample has to be representative of the number and type.
        - A process may need to be audited on a regular basis if it continues to have major issues.
        - The processes should be selected on the basis of status and importance.

2. *Defining the scope of the audit.* All audits should have boundaries. Therefore, before one begins the audit everyone should be familiar with the scope of what is expected from the audit. Key considerations are:

- Natural process flow
    - How interdependent are the activities?
    - Natural work unit/process.
- Well-defined boundary points
    - Quality planning/design to production
    - Forming/bending/machining to assembly
    - Assembly to final testing
    - Final testing to packaging/storage/delivery
- Process metrics

- Known problem areas
  - Previous audit reports
  - Audit database
  - Problem reports/issues
  - Organizational metrics and/or indicators not being met
  - Process owner
  - Other performance measures
- Time available
- Delivery
  - List some of the items relating to delivery that could affect the process.
- Process availability

3. *Process inputs considerations.* Once the scope has been defined then the audit team should focus on the inputs. Typical issues and concerns that should be investigated are:

- Process information
  - Operator instructions
  - Control plans
  - Drawings, sketches, bill of materials
  - Environmental aspects
    - List some of the items relating to environmental aspects and related controls that you would evaluate during a process audit.
- People
  - Process operators
  - Inspectors
  - Engineering and support personnel
    - List some of the items relating to personnel that you would evaluate during a process audit.
  - Process information
    - List some of the items relating to process information that you would evaluate during a process audit.

- Tooling and equipment

  - List some of the items relating to tooling and equipment that you would evaluate during a process audit.

4. *Conducting the audit.* After the preparations are complete, the audit team, under the direction of the lead auditor, will conduct the audit. The actual audit is a four-part process. The first part is the opening meeting. It is followed by the actual physical audit, then the debriefing, and the closing meeting. Every audit must have an opening meeting.

The purpose of the opening meeting is to:

- Break the ice.

- Confirm people, times, and places involved in the audit.

- Identify gaps in roles and responsibilities

- Ensure that the department manager understands the audit process and his or her responsibilities.

The agenda of the opening meeting is to:

- Introduce the attendees (audit team and any interested auditee representatives; managers or designees from each department).

- Review the audit objective.

- Review the scope, schedule, and theme of the audit.

- Review the audit process. Q and A is offered by the lead auditor, but only in reference to the process. That is: questions are allowed only as they relate to "how" the audit is going to be conducted.

The actual audit is performed based on a predetermined structure (the checklist) that follows these steps:

- Based on the understanding of the business objectives, the audit will proceed to identify and evaluate the effectiveness of the QMS.

- The focus is based on priority of processes after examining the process map of the specific processes.

- Proper identification has to be made for inputs and outputs for each process examined.

- Characterization of appropriate and applicable metrics has to be identified and followed through the audit.

- Investigate the relevance of the performance and metrics of the process investigated against the business objectives.

- Investigate the process controls and all other pertinent information that documents and/or ensure that the process is stable, in control, and capable.

- Investigate process performance to identify opportunities for improvement.

Obviously the audit is conducted to find good, marginal, and bad issues, concerns, and problems. Therefore, all findings must be documented by appropriate and applicable:

- Description of the nonconformity

- Reference to the requirement that is being violated

- Effectiveness of the process

- Impact on the process

- Background information

At the end of the audit a debriefing meeting is held between auditors and area management. (This may vary from audit to audit, depending on the length of the audit and whether it is a departmental audit or an organizational audit). In any case, the debriefing meeting is to communicate:

- The level of involvement of senior management

- The type of key measures selected

- Effectiveness of the review process

- The use of quantifying tools

- Effectiveness of problem-solving activity

- The effectiveness of the deployment methods

- The documentation system

- Demonstrated overall business improvement

The intent of this communication is to let the area or process owner be aware of possible issues with this particular process. It is also the intent of this communication to give the opportunity to the process owner to fix any questionable items before the close of the audit.

Another function of the debriefing meeting is to allow the auditors to come together and discuss the findings as well as to arrive at a consensus about specific nonconformances. This step is quite important because it is the basis of the corrective action report that is issued at the end of the audit.

Furthermore, depending on the length and type of audit, a summary report may be initiated at the debriefing meeting to be presented during the closing meeting. Typical contents of the summary report are:

- Departments and activities that were audited

- Audit team members' names and audited department name and number

- Audit duration, dates, scope, objective, and so on

- Summary of observations, nonconformances, and recommendations that were found

- Supporting documentation for the findings

The last step in the audit is the closing meeting, which is a mandatory step for all audits (every audit must have a closing meeting at the end of the audit). Its purpose is to identify status of QMS, positive, observations, recommendations, areas of concern, and trends, and to provide a summary of all findings. Q and A is appropriate during the closing meeting as long as the questions deal with the results of the audit and not the process.

A typical closing meeting agenda will have the following content:

- Thank yous

- Introductions (managers and audit team)

- Audit objective

- Audit scope

- Audit summary of findings

  - Specific positives

  - Nonconformities

  - Areas of concern

  - Improvement opportunities

- Ensure auditee understanding of findings

- Define CAR response time

- Provide clarification as to what will happen next

- Emphasize that the audit is only a sample

- Process for responding to findings

- Timing of actions
- Q and A

RELATIONSHIP OF PROCESS AUDIT AND PDC(S)A

Plan

Establish the audit program (objectives):

- Resources
- Responsibilities
- Procedures
- Criteria
- Frequency

Do

Implement the audit program (schedule audits):

- Evaluate competence of auditors.
- Establish program to certify internal auditors.
- Select auditors.
- Direct audit activities.
- Maintain records.

Check

Monitor audit program (monitor and review activities):

- Evaluate types of CARs written
- Identify needs for corrective action
- Take action by:
  - Identifying opportunities for improvement
  - Tracking acceptance and implementation for opportunities for improvement

Act

Improve the audit program (reaction plans):

- Corrective action

- Performance evaluation

- Results

CHECKLISTS

As mentioned earlier, one of the most fundamental issues in any auditing practice is to recognize that preparation is not only a *must* requirement, but it is such an essential process that it has to be started far ahead of time and be specifically related to the process at hand. One of the most basic tools used in auditing is the checklist. As important as the checklist is, the person who is using it must recognize that it is a guideline and not a document that has to be followed regardless of the situation. It provides the auditor with a sequence of questions that may help the process evaluation; however, depending on the responses of the auditee, the checklist may even prove to be of somewhat limited value.

Nevertheless, the checklist is important and for this book we are trying to make it generic enough so everyone can benefit from it. Obviously it is not an exhaustive document, but rather it focuses on the mental process that one has to follow to create and develop a checklist.

Specifically, we have tried to develop two paths in the generation of the checklist. The first is a very generic approach for a process auditor to pursue an audit with management. The second is more specific, oriented to operational levels. The first is included here. The second is found in the CD-ROM appendixes V and VI.

In both cases, we want to assure the reader that these checklists are *only* guidelines and they can be drastically changed, modified, or even ignored. Feel free to add or delete items that you think are important or not important to the process.

Checklist for Management Orientation

Note: Issues that concern management are holistic in nature and, therefore, the focus of the checklist should be to generate information to prove the value creation of the process. In other words, the questions asked should examine the organization's key product, service, and business processes, with the aim of creating value for their customers and other key stakeholders, and improving their marketplace and operational performance.

To do that, the auditor has to ask questions that will identify their key value creation processes and their requirements. Process auditing for management and executives calls for information on the management and improvement of key value creation processes. The information required includes a description of the key processes, their specific requirements, and how performance relative to these requirements is determined and maintained. Increasingly, these requirements might include the need for agility—speed and flexibility—to adapt to change. Therefore, management should be asked:

- How these processes are designed, implemented, and performed to meet all their requirements and how they incorporate input from customers, suppliers, and partners, as appropriate

- How they address key factors in design effectiveness, including cycle time, productivity, and cost control

- How their processes create value for all key stakeholders and how they contribute to business profitability and success

- To identify their key performance measures for the control and improvement of their value creation processes, including how in-process measures and customer and supplier feedback are used

- How they minimize costs associated with inspections, tests, and audits through the use of prevention-based processes

- How they improve their value creation processes to achieve better performance and to keep them current with their changing business needs and directions

- How improvements are shared to achieve organizational learning

In addition to their own process(es), management should be asked about their support processes, that is, their input processes that do contribute to value generating and aim to improve the overall operational performance. The support processes are those that support daily operations and product and service delivery but are not usually designed in detail with the products and services. The support process requirements usually do not depend significantly on product and service characteristics. Support process design requirements usually depend significantly on the internal requirements, and they must be coordinated and integrated to ensure efficient, effective linkage and performance. Support processes might include finance and accounting, facilities management, purchasing, engineering, human resources, and other inputs or even administrative services. Therefore, management should be asked:

- To identify their key support processes and their design requirements.

- How their organization's key support processes are designed to meet all their requirements and how they incorporate input from customers, suppliers, and partners, as appropriate.

- How day-to-day operation of their key support processes ensures meeting the key requirements, including how in-process measures and customer and supplier feedback are used.

- How they minimize costs associated with inspections, tests, and audits through the use of prevention-based processes.

- How they improve their key support processes to achieve better performance and to keep them current with their changing business needs and directions.

- How improvements are shared to achieve organizational learning.

Foundation of the Creation of the Checklist

To be effective in any audit, especially in a process audit, as an auditor you must be familiar with your organization, its culture, its system of operation, and certainly the standards/procedures/instructions that you will be auditing against.

Your organizational profile is critically important because it:

- Is the most appropriate starting point for self-assessment and for writing an application of a nonconformance

- Helps you identify potential gaps in key information and focus on key performance requirements and business *results*

- Helps the auditor to understand the organization and what is considered important

Understand Your Organization (Facility)

Can you describe your facility's business environment and your key relationships with customers, suppliers, and others?

Depending on the response, you should include:

1. What are your organization's (department's) main products and services? What are the delivery mechanisms used to provide your products and services to your customers?

2. What is your organizational culture? What are your stated purpose, vision, mission, and values? How do you use them in your process (job)? How do they affect the result?

3. What is your employee profile? What are their educational levels? What are your organization's workforce and job diversity, organized bargaining units, use of contract employees, and special health and safety requirements?

4. What are your major technologies, equipment, and facilities? How do you make sure they are appropriate, applicable, and up to date?

5. What is the regulatory environment under which your organization operates? What are the applicable occupational health and safety regulations; accreditation, certification, or registration requirements; and environmental, financial, and product regulations?

6. What is your organizational structure and governance system? What are the reporting relationships among your employees and management, and your parent organization, as appropriate?

7. What are your key customer groups and market segments, as appropriate? What are their key requirements and expectations for your products and services? What are the differences in these requirements and expectations among customer groups and market segments?

8. What role do suppliers and distributors play in your value creation processes? What are your most important types of suppliers and distributors? What are your most important supply chain requirements?

9. What are your key supplier and customer partnering relationships and communication mechanisms, as appropriate?

Organizational Challenges

Describe your organization's competitive environment, your key strategic challenges, and your system for performance improvement.

Depending on the response, you should include:

1. What is your competitive position? What is your relative size and growth in your industry or markets served? What are the numbers and types of competitors for your organization?

2. What are the principal factors that determine your success relative to your competitors? What are any key changes taking place that affect your competitive situation? What are your key available sources of comparative and competitive data from within your industry? What are your key available sources of comparative data for analogous processes outside your industry? What limitations, if any, are there in your ability to obtain these data?

3. What are your key business, operational, and human resource strategic challenges?

4. What is the overall approach you use to maintain an organizational focus on *performance* improvement and to guide systematic evaluation and improvement of key processes?

5. What is your overall approach to organizational learning and sharing your business objectives?

Organizational Leadership (Management)

Describe how management guides your organization. Describe your organization's governance system and how senior leaders review organizational performance.

Depending on the response, you should include:

1. How does management set and deploy organizational values, short- and longer-term directions, and performance expectations? How does management include a focus on creating and balancing value for customers and other stakeholders in their performance expectations? How does management communicate organizational values, directions, and expectations through your leadership system, to all employees, and to key suppliers and partners? How does management ensure two-way communication on these topics?

2. How does management create an environment for empowerment, innovation, and organizational agility? How do they create an environment for organizational and employee learning? How do they create an environment that fosters and requires legal and ethical behavior?

3. How does your organization address the following key factors in your governance system?

   • Management accountability for the organization's actions

- Fiscal accountability

- Independence in internal and external audits

- Protection of stockholder and stakeholder interests, as appropriate

4. How does management review organizational performance and capabilities? How do they use these reviews to assess organizational success, competitive performance, and progress relative to short- and long-term goals? How do they use these reviews to assess your organizational ability to address changing organizational needs?

5. What are the key performance measures regularly reviewed by your management leaders? What are your key recent performance review findings? How do they compare to past performances?

6. How does management translate organizational performance review findings into priorities for continual and breakthrough improvement of key business results and into opportunities for innovation? How are these priorities and opportunities deployed throughout your organization? When appropriate, how are they deployed to your suppliers and partners to ensure organizational alignment?

7. How do you evaluate the performance of your management, including the chief executive? How do you evaluate the performance of members of the board of directors, as appropriate? How does management use organizational performance review findings to improve both their own leadership effectiveness and that of your facility and leadership system, as appropriate?

Social Responsibility

Describe how your organization addresses its responsibilities to the public, ensures ethical behavior, and practices good citizenship.

Depending on the response, you should include:

1. How do you address the impacts on society of your products, services, and operations? What are your *key* compliance processes, measures, and goals for achieving and surpassing regulatory and legal requirements, as appropriate? What are your key processes, measures, and goals for addressing risks associated with your products, services, and operations?

2. How do you anticipate public concerns with current and future products, services, and operations? How do you prepare for these concerns in a proactive manner?

3. How do you ensure ethical behavior in all stakeholder transactions and interactions? What are your key process and measures or indicators for monitoring ethical behavior throughout your organization, with key partners, and in your governance structure?

4. How does your organization actively support and strengthen your key communities? How do you identify key communities and determine areas of emphasis for organizational involvement and support? What are your key communities? How do your management and your employees contribute to improving these communities?

Strategic Planning

Describe how your organization establishes its strategic objectives, including how it enhances its competitive position, overall performance, and future success.

Depending on the response, you should include:

1. What is your overall strategic planning process? What are the key steps? Who are the key participants? What are your short- and long-term planning time horizons? How are these time horizons set? How does your strategic planning process address these time horizons?

2. How do you ensure that strategic planning addresses the key factors listed here? How do you collect and analyze relevant data and information to address these factors as they relate to your strategic planning?

   • Customer and market needs?

   • Competitive environment?

   • Technological and other innovations?

   • Strengths and weaknesses?

   • Changes—of any kind?

   • Factors unique to your organization?

3. What are your key strategic objectives and your timetable for accomplishing them? How did you arrive at them? What are your most important goals for these strategic objectives?

4. How do your strategic objectives address the challenges identified in response to your organizational challenges and in your organizational profile? How do you ensure that your strategic objectives balance short- and long-term challenges and opportunities? How do you ensure that your strategic objectives balance the needs of all key stakeholders?

Strategy Deployment

Describe how your organization converts its strategic objectives into action plans. Summarize your organization's action plans and related *key* performance measures or indicators. Can you project your organization's future performance on these key performance measures or indicators?

Depending on the response, you should include:

1. How do you develop and deploy action plans to achieve your key strategic objectives? How do you allocate resources to ensure accomplishment of your action plans? How do you ensure that the key changes resulting from action plans can be sustained?

2. What are your key short- and long-term action plans? How were they developed? Are they related to the metrics? What are the key changes, if any, in your products and services, your customers and markets and how you will operate?

3. What are your key human resources plans that derive from your short- and long-term strategic objectives and action plans?

4. What are your key performance measures or indicators for tracking progress on your action plans? How do you ensure that your overall action plan measurement system reinforces organizational alignment? How do you ensure that the measurement system covers all key deployment areas and stakeholders?

5. For the key performance measures and indicators identified, what are your performance projections for both short- and long-term planning time? Are they doable? Is there documentation for such projection? How do your projections compare with actuals and competitor's performance? How do your projections compare to benchmarks and past performance?

Customer and Market Knowledge

Describe how your organization determines requirements, expectations, and preferences of customers and markets to ensure the continuing relevance of your products and services and to develop new opportunities.
Depending on the response, you should include:

1. How do you determine or target customer groups and market segments? How do you include customers of competitors and other potential customers and markets in this determination?

2. How do you listen and learn to determine key customer requirements and expectations (including product and service features) and their relative importance to customers' purchasing decisions?

3. How do determination methods vary for different customers or customer groups? How do you use relevant information from current and former customers, including marketing and sales information, customer loyalty and retention data, win/loss analysis, and complaints? How do you use this information for the purposes of product and service planning, marketing, process improvements, and other business development?

4. How do you keep your listening and learning methods current with business needs and directions?

Customer Relationships and Satisfaction

Describe how your organization builds relationships to acquire, satisfy, and retain customers; to increase customer loyalty; and to develop new opportunities. Describe also how your organization determines customer satisfaction.
Depending on the response, you should include:

1. How do you build relationships to acquire customers, to meet and exceed their expectations, to increase loyalty and repeat business, and to gain positive referrals?

2. What are your key access mechanisms for customers to seek information, conduct business, and make complaints? How do you determine key customer requirements for each mode of customer access? How do you assure that these requirements are deployed to all people and processes involved in the customer response chain?

3. What is your complaint management process? Is it effective? Is there appropriate documentation? How are complaints generated? How are they analyzed? Are they aggregated into a learning database for "things learned?" Is there a history of complaint resolution?

4. How do you keep your approaches to building relationships and providing customer access current with business needs and directions?

5. How do you determine customer satisfaction/dissatisfaction? How do these determination methods differ among customer groups? How do you ensure that your measurements capture actionable information for use in exceeding your customer's expectations, securing their future business, and gaining positive referrals? How do you use customer satisfaction and dissatisfaction information for improvement?

6. How do you follow up with customers on products, services, and transaction quality to receive prompt and actionable feedback?

7. How do you obtain and use information on your customer's satisfaction relative to customers' satisfaction with your competitors and/or industry benchmarks?

8. How do you keep your approaches to determining satisfaction current with business needs and directions?

Measurement, Analysis, and Knowledge Management

Describe how your organization measures, analyzes, aligns, and improves its performance data and information at all levels and in all parts of your organization.

Depending on the response, you should include:

1. How do you select, collect, align, and integrate data and information for tracking daily operations and for tracking overall organizational performance? How do you use these data and information to support decision making and innovation?

2. How do you select and ensure the effective use of *key* comparative data and information to support operational and strategic decision making and innovation?

3. How do you keep your performance measurement system current with business needs and directions? How do you ensure that your performance measurement system is sensitive to rapid or unexpected organizational or external changes?

4. What analyses do you perform to support your management's organizational performance review? What analyses do you perform to support the organization's strategic planning?

5. How do you communicate the results to the appropriate operations to enable effective support for their decision making?

Information and Knowledge Management

Describe how your organization ensures the quality and availability of needed data and information for employees, suppliers and partners, and customers. Describe how your organization builds and manages its knowledge base.

Depending on the response, you should include:

1. How do you make needed data and information available? How do you make them accessible to the personnel that needs them (employees, customers, suppliers)?

2. How do you ensure that hardware and software are reliable, secure, and user-friendly?

3. How do you keep your data and information mechanisms, including software and hardware systems, current with business needs and directions?

4. How do you manage organizational knowledge for: a) collection and transfer of knowledge, b) transfer of relevant knowledge, and c) identification and sharing of best practices)?

5. How do you ensure the following properties of your data and information: a) integrity, b) timeliness, c) reliability, d) security, e) accuracy, and f) confidentiality?

Human Resource—Work Systems

Describe how your organization's work and jobs enable employees and the organization to achieve high performance. Describe how compensation, career progression, and related workforce practices enable employees and the organization to achieve high performance.

Depending on the response, you should include:

1. How do you organize and manage work and jobs to promote cooperation, initiative, empowerment, innovation, and your organizational culture? How do you organize and manage work and jobs to achieve the agility to keep current with business needs?

2. How do your work systems capitalize on the diverse ideas, culture, and thinking of your employees?

3. How do you achieve effective communication and skill sharing across work units, jobs, and locations?

4. How does your employee performance management system, including feedback to employees, support high-performance work? How does your employee performance management system support a customer and business focus? How do your recognition and related reward and incentive practices reinforce high-performance work and a customer and business focus?

5. How do you identify characteristics and skills needed by current and potential employees?

6. How do you accomplish effective succession planning for management and nonmanagement positions? How do you manage effective career progression for all employees? What is your policy and practice for recruiting, hiring, and retaining employees?

Human Resource—Employee Learning and Motivation

Describe how your organization's employee education, training, and career development support the achievement of your overall objectives and contribute to high performance. Describe how your organization's education, training, and career development build employee knowledge, skills, and capabilities.

Depending on the response, you should include:

1. How do employee education and training contribute to the achievement of your action plans? Does the training address the organizational needs? Does it relate to performance measurables, improvement, and technological change(s)? Are your short- and long-term training objectives balanced to reflect the business strategy?

2. Does the training reflect the organizational needs for diversity, ethical business practices, and management development?

3. How do you seek and use input from employees and their supervisors? How is corporate knowledge built into the training?

4. How do you reinforce the use of new knowledge and skills on the job?

5. How do you evaluate the effectiveness of education and training, taking into account individual and organizational performance?

6. How do you motivate employees to develop and utilize their full potential?

Human Resource—Employee Well-Being and Satisfaction

Describe how your organization maintains a work environment and an employee support climate that contribute to the well-being, satisfaction, and motivation of all employees.

Depending on the response, you should include:

1. How do you improve workplace health, safety, security, and ergonomics? How do employees take part in improving them? What are your performance measures or targets for each of these key workplace factors? What are the significant differences in workplace factors and performance measures or targets if different employee groups and work units have different work environments?

2. How do you ensure workplace preparedness for emergencies or disasters? How do you seek to ensure business continuity for the benefit of your employees and customers?

3. How do you determine the key factors that affect employee well-being, satisfaction, and motivation? Are these key factors representative of the diverse workforce?

4. What formal and informal assessment methods and measures do you use to determine employee well-being, satisfaction, and motivation? Are safety, productivity, employee retention, absenteeism, and grievances used as additional indicators to assess and improve employee well-being, satisfaction, and motivation? If so, how?

Process Management—Value Creation

Describe how your organization identifies and manages its key processes for creating customer value and achieving business success and growth. Depending on the response, you should include:

1. How does your organization determine its key value creation processes? What are your organization's key product, service, and business processes for creating or adding value? How do these processes create value for the organization, your customers, and your other key stakeholders? How do they contribute to profitability and business success?

2. How do you determine key value creation process requirements, incorporating input from customers, suppliers, and partners, if appropriate? What are the *key* requirements for these processes?

3. How do you design these processes to meet all the key requirements? How do you incorporate new technology and organizational knowledge into the design of these processes? How do you incorporate cycle time, productivity, cost control, overall equipment effectiveness (OEE), and other efficiency and effectiveness factors into the design of these processes? How do you implement these processes to ensure they meet design requirements?

4. What are your key performance measures or indicators used for the control and improvement of your value-creation process? How are the key process requirements being monitored on a daily basis? Are the results of the monitoring used to manage these processes? Is there documentation for past performance or historical tracking? How are customer and supplier input used to manage the process?

5. How do you minimize overall costs associated with inspections, tests, and process audits?

6. How do you prevent defects and rework, as well as minimize warranty costs?

7. How do you improve your value-creation process to achieve better performance, to reduce variability, to improve products and services, and to keep the process current with business needs and directions? How are the improvements shared with other organizational units or processes?

Process Management—Support Processes

Describe how your organization manages its key processes that support your value-creation processes.

Depending on the response, you should include:

1. How does your organization determine its key support processes? What are your key processes for supporting your value-creation processes?

2. How do you determine key support process requirements, incorporating input from internal and external customers and suppliers? What are the key requirements for these processes?

3. How do you design these processes to meet all the key requirements? How do you incorporate new technology, organizational knowledge, cycle time, productivity, cost control, and other efficiency and effectiveness factors into the design of the process? How do you make sure that they meet requirements?

4. What are your key performance measures or indicators used for the control and improvement of your support process? How are the key support process requirements being monitored on a daily basis? Are the results of the monitoring used to manage these processes? Is there documentation for past performance or historical tracking? How are customer and supplier input used to manage the process?

5. How do you minimize overall costs associated with inspections, tests, and process audits?

6. How do you prevent defects and rework, as well as minimize warranty costs?

7. How do you improve your support process to achieve better performance, to reduce variability, to improve products and services, and to keep the process current with business needs and directions? How are the improvements shared with other organizational units or processes?

Following is a typical checklist for anyone conducting a process audit.

AREA OF QUESTIONS/ INTERACTION/OBSERVATION

Resources—Identify and provide resources (personnel, training, equipment, tools) to support the quality system. Describe how the local management has defined the work. Are process maps (flowcharts, machine flows, and so on) available for this area?

1. Does the process account for the seven types of waste:

   - Product defects

   - Overproduction

   - Inventory

   - Transportation

   - Processing

   - Motion

   - Waiting

2. How effective are:

   - SWIs—Are they all accounted for? Does everybody follow them? Is the SWI correlated with the actual process?

   - Five S's (sort, clean, organize, standardize, and improve the standard)—Is total preventive maintenance (TPM) being followed? How is the process reporting each one of the five S's? Are they effective?

   - Is preventive maintenance (PM) conducted as scheduled? Is there a record of such scheduling and repair?

   - Is statistical process control (SPC) conducted in the process? How are the limits figured out? Is the capability appropriate for the parts you are producing? Who is responsible for evaluating the charts? Is SPC an integral part of the decision in the behavior of the process? Is the corrective action appropriate and applicable?

3. Are any of the process steps outsourced? If so, describe how things are controlled. Does it seem that parts/information are flowing smoothly (look at the relationship of input–process–output or the interfaces as well as interactions)? Describe the communication process used by top management in this organization with people working in the area being audited.

4. Are line boards/scoreboards available for this area? Does the scoreboard:

   • Define the purpose

   • Establish/support objectives

   • Plan involvement

   • Evaluate against the six criteria (balanced, owned, actionable, simple, accurate, and predictive)

   • Establish processes to support improvement

   • Plan for maintaining the board. Is the board information correct, timely, and updated? Do the personnel have an understanding of the information posted on the board?

5. What factors are green, yellow, or red? Is the local management addressing any red factors? If so, describe in observations. If red areas are evident, do they suggest any audit trails to follow? Describe them.

6. What is the effectiveness of the requirements, controls, measures, and outputs in your process?

   • *Responsibility and authority.* Define and document responsibility and authority for individuals and departments that manage and verify quality activity. Is all proper paperwork designated for this work area present, used, and understood? Are records being tracked/stored using appropriate statistical analysis methods? Is everything up-to-date?

   • *Performance feedback.* Provide ongoing constructive feedback regarding an employee's activities. How is feedback generated? Are all stakeholders active participants in the feedback process? How effective is the feedback? How do you verify the effectiveness?

- *Manufacturing policy.* Ensuring that the manufacturing policy is defined, documented, and understood. How is the policy affecting your job? What does the policy mean to you? Is it effective?

- *Management review.* Regular management reviews of the management quality system (MQS) to ensure that it is suitable and effective. Is the review with the appropriate owners? Is it effective? Do the process owners have the opportunity to be heard? Are their opinions/suggestions heard?

- *Business plan.* Develop a business plan in support of our business for both short term and long term. How do you know if the plan is effective? How is the plan generated? Is it related to your job? How?

- *Assurance system.* Develop a documented quality system, which is defined in MQS. Is the system appropriate and applicable for the process? Can you demonstrate that the system is working effectively?

- *Use of cross-functional teams.* Defines the requirements for employee involvement through cross-functional teams for continuous improvement and quality planning. Are teams working for improvement of the process? How are the teams formed? Do they have the appropriate training? Are they familiar with at least some basic problem-solving techniques?

- *Training.* Identifies training needs, provides training, and evaluates the effectiveness of training in support of MQS. How are the needs identified? How is training conducted and what are the steps taken to transfer the learning back to the process?

- *Quality planning.* Provides a system to ensure quality from prototype to prelaunch, to production. Is quality planning effective? Can you document its effectiveness?

- *Purchasing.* Controls the quality of purchased product and components, and maintains an approved supplier list. How do you control the purchased product? Is the product appropriately labeled, stored, and transferred? Can you document the effectiveness?

- *Contract review.* Establishes procedures that ensure customer requirements can be met. How do you verify that the requirements are being met?

- *Delivery* (production scheduling, one-piece flow). Provides a system for the delivery of product to meet internal requirements and those of the customer. How do you track the delivery of your products internally? Is the tracking effective?

- *Inventory.* Provides a system for managing inventory. How do you evaluate inventory needs? Are they appropriate? Are they effective?

- *Continuous improvement.* Provides a system to ensure continuous improvement initiatives are identified and implemented in safety, quality, delivery, cost, and morale. How do you document the continual improvement for each of these indicators? Are the criteria for evaluation appropriate? Realistic? Is the improvement real and can it be verified?

- *Corrective and preventive action.* Actions taken to correct problems and prevent future occurrence. How do you verify the corrective and preventive action? Is the corrective and preventive action treating the symptom or the root cause of the problem? Is there evidence to prove the effectiveness of corrective and preventive actions in the long term? Are treated problems recurring?

- *Manufacturing capabilities.* Planning for facilities, equipment, processes, tooling, and mistake-proofing activities. How is mistake-proofing implemented? Is it effective? How are capabilities of the process evaluated? Are they effective? Are the tools capable of performing their task? Are they effective?

- *Analysis and use of company data.* Measurement of internal safety, quality, delivery, cost, and morale or other indicators. How are data gathered? Are the data appropriate and applicable for the specific indicator? How is the analysis performed? Is it appropriate and applicable given the data? How do you evaluate improvement for each of the indicators?

- *Customer satisfaction.* Measurements of customer quality indicators. How do you know what the customer's requirements are? How do you know if the customer's requirements are met? Is there evidence that the requirements are met? How do you verify their effectiveness, accuracy, and integrity?

- *Assurance system assessment.* Perform regular audits and document the results including follow-up of corrective actions on any items found nonconforming with MQS. How are audits scheduled? Do the auditors have appropriate and applicable training? Are the findings of the audits corrected, reviewed, and implemented across the plant? Is there documentation to that effect?

- *Document and data control.* Controls the creation, distribution, revision, and disposal of documents and ensures that documents are readily available to all personnel. How do you know that the record, instruction, or procedure is the most current document? How do you make sure that obsolete documents are not in the work area? How are new items distributed to all parties concerned? Is there documentation to prove that the document and control data are effective?

- *Control of customer-supplied product.* Controls and secures any product or material supplied by a customer. How do you control the control of customer-supplied product? How do you verify that the process of control of customer-supplied product is effective and working?

- *Product identification and traceability.* Where appropriate, product is identified and traceable through the entire process. How do you know that the identification and traceability are correct, appropriate, and effective?

- *Process control.* All production processes are planned and controlled, and standard work instructions are available. Are the SWI's available and current for the process and personnel? How do you make sure that they are current? How effective are they? How do you verify their effectiveness?

- *Inspection and testing.* Maintains appropriate receiving, in-process, and final quality testing and inspection to verify quality. Is incoming SPC utilized for appropriate quality? How do you handle incoming nonconforming quality? Is it effective? Is there documentation to verify the overall incoming quality?

- *Inspection and test status.* Identification is maintained throughout the process, to ensure that all inspection and testing has been performed and documented. How do you verify effectiveness for inspection and test status? Is there appropriate documentation to verify the effectiveness?

- *Handling, storage, packaging, and preservation.* Defines procedures for handling and storing materials to maintain quality. How do you make sure that the handling, storage, packaging, and preservation is being performed according to the requirements? Are they effective? Is there documentation to verify the effectiveness?

- *Control of quality records.* Establishes a system of storing and retrieving key MQS records to provide evidence. Are the controls effective for the process? How do you verify their effectiveness?

- *PPAP (sign-off).* The process of approving production parts through all phases of design and manufacture. Are the steps verified for the final approval? How do you make sure that all changes have the appropriate documentation? What happens when the documentation does not match with the particular product? Who is responsible for the final sign-off but is not on the active list of the appropriate personnel?

- *Design control.* Requires careful control of design activities through the use of cross-functional team design reviews and approval procedures. Are there any design failure mode and effects analyses (DFMEAs)? How are they completed? Is there a relationship between the DFMEA, process failure mode and effects analysis (PFMEA), and control plan? Who is the team that completes the PFMEA? How is the PFMEA reviewed?

- *Control of nonconforming product.* Defective or suspect material or product is tagged or marked then segregated to prevent unintended use or installation. How is the nonconforming product controlled? Is it effective?

- *Statistical techniques.* Defines the use of SPC.

- *Preventive maintenance.* Identifies key process equipment, develops preventive maintenance procedures, schedules and performs maintenance activities. Who is responsible for SPC? Are the control charts updated regularly? Who defined the frequency of the review? Is the frequency of the sample appropriate? Is SPC part of the decision making in reference to the behavior of the process?

- *Control of inspection, measuring, and test equipment.* Assures that all inspection equipment meets required accuracy and is calibrated regularly. How is calibration defined? What are the intervals? Are the intervals appropriate? Is there traceability? Is GR&R performed? Are the tests and equipment appropriate for the tests? Is there documentation for their effectiveness?

- *Employee safety.* Develop a system to provide a safe and healthy work environment for your employees. How do you document the safety program for effectiveness? Are the personnel aware of the policies as they relate to safety programs? Is there documentation that verifies safety improvement?

- *Environmental.* Maintain and document planned environmental activities that will ensure compliance with all environmental standards. How does the environmental policy affect your job? Is there documentation that verifies environmental improvement? How do you contribute to environmental issues and to their solution?

TYPICAL CORRECTIVE ACTION REPORT

Corrective action reports (CARs) are the instruments that auditors use for their findings. Two typical examples are shown in Figures 10.3 and 10.4. The information on a typical CAR is basically divided into two categories— of course, there are many variations of these. The categories are as follows.

Requester Information

- *Subject (15 words or less).* Note: Briefly describe the content of the CAR. Example subject: *"The current procedure for defective product labeling is not followed."*

- *Description of issue or opportunity for improvement.* Note: This item must be based on careful and investigative evaluation of the process. Outline the issue/opportunity in descriptive terms. Provide enough detail to aid the assignee in problem solving. Example description: *"Defective product has been placed into the good parts bin. Process XYZ's defective product bin is not labeled as noted in procedure ABC123. Moreover, the sorting area is not organized or conducive to meeting intended product sorting standards."*

THISVI Corporation	
Corrective Action Request Completed and Approved	
Date requested: July 10, 2004 Date completed and approved:	CAR control number: xxxa
Requester: C. D. Stamatis Location: manufacturing line	Dept: MQS process audit Phone: xxxxx

This Section to Be Completed by the Requester

Department cited: furnace	Priority code: Short-term due date: Long-term due date:	Escalation path:
Subject (15 words or less): Cost issue—furnace lid replaced less than two weeks before entire furnace replaced.	How issue was discovered/identified: Internal process audit Doc link:	Audit type: internal Associated procedure(s): 05, 16, and 34

Description of issue or opportunity for improvement:
    Lack an integrated PM system (operators, TMS, electricians, and so on) to review the operation of entire machine(s) to ensure effective operations within the department.

Description of findings:
Review of operator "clean and skim" forms showed that several weekly reports were missing (four weeks missing over a three-month period—element issue). While reviewing these reports, furnace #81 had been noted by operators as needing a new furnace door for the last 10 of 12 reporting weeks that were found. This led to a review of other PM items related to furnace #81.

Electricians conducted furnace temperature sweeps twice per shift on more than 100 machines. Reports of each sweep (target temperature, actual temperature, and amp draw) were recorded and copies turned in to the PM office. Only the AM report from first ship was saved in a three-ring binder. The PM manager used that one report to review the operation of the plant at the morning plant operations meeting each day. Other reports were left on a central table and thrown out each day. No graphical analysis studies were being done.

The plant total maintenance system (TMS) was reviewed for furnace #81–related items. Six items had been recorded during a three-month period. Four of the references indicated that new lids had been installed on the furnace.

PM reports were conducted on machine #81 every three months. During these checks, it was found that the furnace was *not* reviewed as part of the formal PM system.

The information found between the four reports had no correlation to each other. The operator on the line indicated that a new furnace had finally been installed about two weeks prior, but no information could be found as to when the new furnace was actually installed at machine #81.

The plant had installed a new lid (manufactured internally at a high cost—no information on how much) just days before the new furnace was installed (thus another new lid with the rebuilt furnace).

Related element or process (optional):
Source of the requirement and related documents (optional):
Non–system 9000 related documents (optional):
Requester's short-term recommendation (optional): Use electrical data in a run chart at each machine to help determine overall performance of the furnace. PM and repairs should be based on data analysis of the machine and recorded into TMS. Initial study of one machine may need to be made to determine the optimum sample time for operators and electricians.

Routing Information	
Assigned to: Department: Copy to:	Phone: Location:

This Section May Be Completed by the Assignee

Reassignment/Delegation:	
Assigned to: Department: Copy to:	Phone: Location:

Figure 10.3 Example of a typical CAR.

THISVI Corporation	
Corrective Action Request Completed and Approved	
Date requested: August 16, 2004 Date completed and approved:	CAR control number: xxxb
Requester: S. D. Stamatis Location:	Dept: MQS auditor Phone: xxxxx

This Section to Be Completed by the Requester

Department cited: line department	Priority code: Short-term due date: Long-term due date:	Escalation path:
Subject (15 words or less): Identification of critical/ essential/support (C/E/S) equipment contributes to more effective PM.	How issue was discovered/identified: Internal process audit Doc link:	Audit type: internal Associated procedure(s): 05, 17, 18, 24, and 34

Description of issue or opportunity for improvement:
  The XYZ line experiences frequent problems with delivery (downtime) and quality and is not meeting its goals. Only one piece of equipment (a pump) is classified as C/E/S. The evaluation used in ZI #MTWI0303 is not effective in identifying C/E/S equipment. These forms for XYZ were last reviewed in April 2002.

Description of findings:
  ZI 69344: 5.4 The equipment should be reevaluated if significant changes to the throughputs of the line: equipment changes, cycle time, or redundant equipment are added. PLSP 0312 defines critical (key) equipment as: equipment required to maintain the process capability requirement of the control plan, equipment required to support compliance to environmental requirements, or the bottleneck equipment that effects product delivery.

Related element or process (optional):
Source of the requirement and related documents (optional):
Non–system 9000 related documents (optional):
Requester's short-term recommendation (optional): Review all forms annually and expand the scope of the design process to include the effectiveness of equipment to be used.

Routing Information	
Assigned to: Department: Copy to:	Phone: Location:

This Section May Be Completed by the Assignee

Reassignment/Delegation:	
Assigned to: Department: Copy to:	Phone: Location:

Figure 10.4   A second CAR example.

Assignee Information

- *Short-term or interim action taken.* (Attachments optional.) Note: Indicate the actions taken to address the concern temporarily. These steps are intended to provide improved output but are not intended to be permanent corrective actions.

- *Short-term or interim action effective date.* Note: What date was the interim action deemed effective?

- *Root-cause analysis.* Note: Utilizing the five why technique, provides likely root-cause identification. Each "why" question level provides a deeper investigative analysis of the problem.

  1. Why?

  2. Why?

  3. Why?

  4. Why?

  5. Why?

- *Alternative root-cause analysis (if not five why).* (Attachments optional.) Note: If the five why technique was not used, provide the root-cause analysis comments justifying the proposed root-cause conclusion. A common and excellent analytical tool is the eight discipline (8-D) approach formulated by Ford Motor Company and used throughout the automotive industry. In a summary and modified version the 8-D, as it is commonly referred to, is:

  - *Step 1:* Establish a team.

    ○ Does the leader have the authority to be effective?

    ○ Are the people most knowledgeable about the problem, product, or process on the team?

    ○ Does the team know to whom they will be accountable?

  - *Step 2:* Describe the problem

    ○ Has the problem been defined in measurable terms? Have trends been evaluated?

    ○ Has the team gone beyond "symptoms" to define the specific problem or defect?

- Is there a final, concise problem statement from which to measure results?

- *Step 3:* Interim containment actions—problems and symptoms

  - Has containment been documented, implemented, and verified to be effective?

  - Have relevant process data been collected during containment actions?

  - Have customers (internal and external) confirmed effectiveness of containment?

- *Step 4:* Identify all potential root causes

  - Has a thorough list of several or more potential root causes been documented and numbered?

  - Are potential root causes substantiated by data?

  - Has the team identified why the defect escaped and the problem was not detected?

  - Are all the root causes actionable?

- *Step 5:* Select the real root cause and permanent corrective action

  - Has every root cause listed in step 4 been accepted or rejected based on logic?

  - Has the team's reason for accepting and rejecting been documented and numbered?

  - Has the cause been verified? Can this root cause(s) turn on/turn off 100 percent of the problem?

  - Is there a permanent corrective action identified for every real root cause?

  - Is the "permanent" corrective action really permanent?

- *Step 6:* Implement and validate permanent action

  - Have FMEAs, control plans, work instructions, training, and so on, been updated?

  - Was the removal of containment actions documented?

- ○ Has the team determined that the permanent corrective actions do not cause negative side effects?

- ○ Does subsequent data confirm that the problem has 100 percent disappeared?

- ○ Have the champion and customer concurred that the cause(s) has been eliminated?

- *Step 7:* Institutionalize

  - ○ Has the team identified the management systems that failed?

  - ○ Has the team corrected the management systems that allowed the problem to occur and escape?

  - ○ Was the solution applied to similar processes?

  - ○ Does the organization's FMEA process anticipate and prevent similar problems?

  - ○ Have lessons learned been documented and communicated?

- *Step 8:* Celebrate success!

  - ○ Was the team appropriately recognized after management approval of the completed process?

  - ○ Was the success communicated throughout the organization?

- *Long-term action taken.* Note: Indicate the long-term actions addressing the root cause(s). The long-term actions must connect to the root cause, as well as provide a confident level of predictability and effectiveness. The assignee must verify that the long-term actions include addressing all necessary and related documentation, training, and systemic elements that require change.

- *Evidence of effectiveness (verification).* Note: Indicate the evidence that demonstrates the effectiveness of the long-term action(s). Effectiveness is demonstrated through levels of process control. To be effective, the corrective actions must either prevent or detect (100 percent of the time) the failure's occurrence. Prevention mechanisms are the preferred strategy.

- *Systematic verification (optional—describe similar potential problem areas you verified as preventive actions).* Note: Indicate what other processes can benefit by applying the same long-term actions. The benefit to the plant can be multiplied when incorporating this CAR's specific improvement to other processes as well.

- Were any organizational indicators affected as a result of implementing the short-/long-term solution? Note: The true test of effectiveness is the resulting measurable improvement after implementation. The process's performance should improve notwithstanding other variable impact.

11

Issues and Concerns About Auditing

The latest rush of high-profile accounting scandals is adding fuel to the debate over reporting relationships in the quality auditing field.* No longer satisfied with a simple certification, organizations demand that quality improvements be truly documented and effective.

Internal auditors especially, who until recently have typically slaved away in anonymity, focusing mostly on broad corporate controls and risk management approaches, are also being asked to take on added responsibility. This responsibility translates into independence and reporting *objective evidence* as it is found in the overall quality system. Furthermore, this responsibility means that auditors must report *any* and *all* findings, especially if a corporation is engaging in activities beyond the understanding of the internal audit's purpose and scope. If not, that is a warning sign.

Internal auditors have the responsibility to ensure the integrity of the quality system, while external auditors have the responsibility to certify the quality system based on preset requirements not only from the applicable standards, but also from the quality manual, procedures, and instructions that the organization has defined for itself.

How do auditors do this? In the last 20 years, auditing has come a long way beyond its humble roots. To perform good audits we need better skilled auditors with an understanding of statistics as they apply to sampling.

---

* Some of the material in this chapter has been adopted from: 1) Som, R. K. 1996. *Practical Sampling Techniques,* 2nd ed.: 19-21, 31, 147, and 229; and 2) Willburn, J. 1984. *Practical Statistical Sampling for Auditors:* 55-67. The material is used here with permission from Marcel Dekker, Inc.

As for training of the auditors, there are many providers that do an excellent job in disseminating the appropriate core knowledge of auditing. On the other hand, even the most successful training programs fail to provide adequate statistical training for the auditors. We hope that in this chapter we will address this issue with some of the most basic statistical approaches.

ISSUES/CONCERNS BEFORE THE AUDIT

Before the audit begins, the audit team, under the leadership of the lead auditor, must plan the audit for effectiveness. That means the team must identify and plan for the method and strategy for evaluating the QMS of the organization. The key methodologies to consider for auditing are:

1. Nonstatistical approaches, referred to as judgmental methods

2. Statistical sampling

Both are used today and they both provide important information. Some of the nonstatistical approaches are:

1. *Cross-section testing.* An attempt to get an across-the-board sample that includes items from all parts of the area being tested. It is common under this type of testing to designate a fixed percentage (usually 10 percent) of items to be included in the test. Sometimes a fixed interval is used instead of the percent, that is, every 15th or 20th item. Of course, if the start is random, then this method will fall under the systematic selection of sampling.

2. *Block testing.* Includes all items in a given time period or in a given section of the audit area being tested. For example, the auditor may select one week's or one month's production, invoices, contracts, blueprints, and so on, and examine all items in those blocks.

3. *Purposive testing.* Its purpose is to highlight known or suspected problem areas with the least amount of effort. This type is generally professionally inadequate and does not reflect good audit practice because it usually concentrates on a limited area where prior experience indicated major problems, and implies that the whole system is as bad as the limited area examined.

4. *Convenience testing.* A type of testing where convenience is the prime consideration in selecting items. This type of testing is generally professionally inadequate and does not reflect good audit judgment, because auditors may not realize that missing or inaccessible records may be missing because the auditee does not want them reviewed.

5. *Large dollar testing (or variation of that).* This type of audit emphasizes the materiality of the items selected. In a sense, it is a form of stratified audit.

Statistical sampling, on the other hand, is a procedure that conforms to the theory and principles of probability for the selection and statistical evaluation of results obtained from a portion (sample) of a group of items or records to estimate some characteristics of the entire group, as a basis for some action or decision. When statistical sampling is used, the auditor can calculate the risk associated with the use of sample data in lieu of a complete audit of all the records.

In using statistical sampling, the auditor can select transactions in a more objective manner. However, as many attempts to develop a practical approach to the application of statistical sampling to auditing have shown, we still have not completely satisfied the needs of audit activities. The reason for this dissatisfaction is that the size of the sample, per se, is no indication of its precision. Also, an auditor cannot offset poor auditing or sampling procedures by increasing the sample. (Stratification and the choice of sampling units are more significant. After these are properly handled, then an increase in the sample improves the precision but the point of diminishing returns is reached rapidly.)

The size of the universe is of no practical importance in determining the size of the sample. In fact, the universe size is usually ignored in calculating the sample precision, except when the sample is a significant part of the universe. The sample size for a universe of 10,000 may be about the same as for a universe of 1,000,000 if the number of strata and the degree of variability of the primary variables or characteristics are the same. It is the absolute size of the sample and not its proportion of the universe that determines its precision.

For example, there are no basic distinctions between a national and a local sample. Thus, a statistical sample of an institution (corporate-level organization), city, county, or state requires similar procedures, and probably the same size sample as a national sample. It is therefore more efficient and economical to direct the sampling activities to the highest organizational or geographic level consistent with the audit objectives. Obviously, the results of a nationwide sample (on the corporate level) are not applicable to individual plants (facilities) unless stratified by plants, cities, and states (individual plants) with sufficient sampling for each strata. The same rationale works for a single department rather than the whole plant or vice versa.

The auditor cannot delegate to the statistical sample the responsibility for specifying the kind of information needed, the criteria and methods of eliciting the information, the segregation or stratification of material and sensitive items, nor the rationale of the audit opinion that integrates the sample results with other audit evidence. The statistical sample only provides a range of probability precisions. The auditor must translate these into meaningful audit opinions and decisions.

The precision of the sample results is often thought to include errors of observation or measurement. If the methods of examination, of obtaining information, or of analyzing and appraising findings are not satisfactory, no sample, not even a 100 percent examination, will provide useful audit information. Many auditors who have been exposed to classical statistical methods may remember mathematical formulas or tables for determining sample sizes if the desired precision and confidence level are specified. Such formulas and tables, however, merely shift the problem from specifying sample size to one of specifying the sample precision.

The most critical factors in determining sample size for audit purposes are the value of the information and the availability of evidence from other sources of reliance. The value of information depends on how likely it is to influence a decision. Given auditing's present state of the art, the value of the information is made subjectively by the auditor.

Also, there is a basic difference between classical and nonclassical statistical methods. Nonclassical procedures incorporate prior judgments, other information, and subjective probability into the decision process. For more information as to how we can use judgment in a logical and explicit manner see Kraft (1968) and Tracy (1969ab).

RANDOM SELECTION OF SAMPLES

Statistical sampling is dependent upon the principle of random selection, which eliminates personal bias and subjective considerations. However, audit stratification makes provisions for handling subjective considerations without invalidating the statistical sampling portion of the audit. Before a random sample can be drawn, the sampling frame or listing of sample items must be established. The frame should be an adequate representation of the universe, since the statistical evaluation of the results applies only to items in the frame.

(A frame is a listing of the sampling units, as well as procedures that account for all the sampling units without the effort of actually listing them.)

The random selection of a sample from 50 purchasing contracts or invoices may be accomplished by: 1) recording the identification number of each of the 50 vouchers on a separate slip of paper, 2) placing the folded slips of paper in a container and thoroughly mixing, and 3) withdrawing the required number for the sample, thoroughly mixing after each selection. This procedure may be feasible when the universe is very small, but difficulties are apparent when the universe consists of thousands of items. Random digit tables and computer selection routines provide means to overcome such difficulties. Such devices provide numbers that are thoroughly mixed, that is, randomly arranged. Obviously, considerable time can usually be saved if a computer selection program is used instead of manually selecting from a random digit table; however, it is important that the auditor understand the random selection process.

There are two basic random selection methods: unrestricted or simple random selection, where each item is drawn at random from the sampling frame; and systematic or interval random selection, in which, after a random start, items are selected from uniform intervals. Other statistical sampling procedures involve the use of one or both of these two basic methods, or a modification or a combination of them.

SAMPLE DESIGN

The sample design is the scheme of a sampling process; it covers the procedures for selecting a random sample from a specific frame. Although there are a variety of techniques for selecting a random sample, feasibility and economy are the prime considerations in deciding which scheme to use in a particular situation. For any audit situation, there are usually several possible sampling schemes, all valid, but of varying degrees of difficulty with some more appropriate and others more economical. The strategy is to choose the sampling scheme that will provide the required information with a reasonable assurance at the lowest possible cost and within the least amount of time consistent with resource constraints.

Feasibility refers to procedures that are practical, simple, reasonable, and easy to execute. Simple procedures reduce the risk of making human or nonsampling errors. Thus, simplicity is desirable even if there is some sacrifice in theoretical efficiency, because the reduction in nonsampling errors may provide better overall sampling precision. Each sample design should be considered an adaptation of sampling theory and techniques to the particular audit objectives, modified by the environment and resource limitation. Economy concerns the accomplishment of the audit objectives with minimum effort for a reasonable precision.

In addition to feasibility and economy, the following considerations influence the optimal selection techniques: 1) complexity of the audit objectives, 2) complexity of frames for the most critical characteristics to be tested, 3) desired sampling precision, 4) availability and quality of other evidential material, 5) availability of computer programs to assist in the sample selection and evaluation of results, and 6) time limitations.

The ideal sample design would be feasible, economical, efficient, and effective.

SAMPLING PLAN

The plan defines the sampling frame or listing to be used, the characteristics to be appraised and evaluated, the types of factual determinations to be made about the characteristics, and the criteria and judgments to be exercised. It also indicates the method of randomly selecting the sample, the sampling assurance desired, and the minimum and optimum sample sizes deemed necessary for flexibility of the sampling operation.

A sampling plan is necessary to coordinate the requirements for the various test-checks that may appear in different parts of the audit program, and to assure that no pertinent facts or steps have been omitted in the preliminary planning of the sampling process or in conducting the sampling operation. Failure to adequately plan the entire sampling operation may result in considerable rework and often a complete revision of the sampling procedure after some sample items have been examined.

Another principal value of a sampling plan, aside from its control function, is the support it provides to the audit findings and opinions by revealing the factors and conditions considered in the planning and execution of the sampling operation. This support is important, especially when the audit findings and work papers are subjected to review and critical analysis by auditees and by higher authority (the registrar).

SAMPLING AND NONSAMPLING ERRORS

The three principal sources of error in sampling are: 1) sampling variability, generally referred to as sampling error or precision, which depends on the sample design and, to a much lesser extent, on the sample size; 2) sample selection biases, which reflect how accurately the sample design is carried out; and 3) effects of defective frames, erroneous criteria, and mistakes in collecting, processing, analyzing, and interpreting data that cause differences between what is observed and actual conditions or characteristics. The latter two types of errors are called nonsampling errors and are not covered in the statistical evaluation of the sample results.

One procedure for controlling nonsampling errors is for two or more auditors in widely scattered locations to collaborate. The results obtained by combining efforts are substantially better than the sum of separate audits. Also, experience indicates that tighter control can be maintained over smaller groups of auditors in several locations than over a larger group in one location, although it may require more supervisory effort.

Another method for increasing sample credibility is to compare the current audit results with those of similar prior audits. If the results replicate those of earlier audits, both the prior and current audits gain in credibility, even if the auditing and sampling procedures differ. If, however, the results of a current audit contradict the results of similar earlier audits, the auditor should investigate to determine whether the differences are caused by sample differences, different criteria of observation and measurement, or something else, such as organizational, operational, or system changes. Any of these changes could affect the results.

SUBJECTIVE AUDIT APPRAISAL OF SAMPLE RESULTS

The audit examination and appraisal of a statistically selected sample are the same in all essentials as the examination and appraisal of a sample selected by any other method. The same characteristics and variables are examined; criteria of acceptable and reasonable transactions and operations are the same; and the same level of judgment should be exercised in appraising the findings for audit significance. Also, the methods of analysis and the precautions to avoid incorrect conclusions are the same. However, for statistically selected samples, the auditor has an additional capability of estimating the reliability of his or her factual findings. However, these findings should be in consonance with other evidence. The consideration of all of these interacting factors is called *audit appraisal.* This process involves separately investigating the nature, cause, and audit significance of each individual finding. The auditor should be alert to ascertain whether the findings are systematic or in clusters, or whether they seem to follow no pattern, or are nonrecurring.

Thus, it is essential that all findings, both factual and judgmental, be correctly and adequately recorded. This should be accomplished for any audit, but when the reliability of the results is not involved, as in the case of judgment sampling, there is a tendency to be less disciplined in the recording and analysis of findings.

The checklist provides a simple means of tabulating the audit findings for each characteristic examined in the sample. The checklist, besides the questions to be asked, has a place where observations, findings, recommendations, and other items may be recorded.

STATISTICAL EVALUATION OF SAMPLE RESULTS

The sample result is objectively (mathematically) evaluated by the computation of the standard error for the estimate, which, in turn, may be used to compute the precision associated with any desired probability, or confidence, level.

Briefly, the process involves: 1) computing a point estimate from the sample, 2) computing the estimated standard error for the estimate, and 3) then computing from the standard error the precision for the desired confidence level.

One estimates a total amount by *blowing up* or projecting the sample result to the universe. This single value obtained from this process is called a *point estimate*. Such an estimate may be computed in a number of different ways, which are called estimators or estimation techniques. Examples of estimators are ratios, means, and regression coefficients. For the same estimator, the point estimate is computed in an identical manner for either a judgment sample or a statistical sample. In both cases, if the auditor were using the ratio of audited dollars in a sample to the dollars examined to estimate total audited costs, the computed ratio would be multiplied by the book value to obtain a universe estimate. For example, suppose $9500 were the audited amount in vouchers totaling $10,000. Then the ratio of audited to recorded amounts would be 0.95. If the total book value of vouchers was $500,000, the ratio point estimate of audited costs would be $475,000 (500,000 × 0.95).

The major advantage of statistical sampling over judgment sampling is that the calculated risk associated with the results can be estimated. Statistical sampling evaluation provides an estimated probability associated with the actual universe value being in a range of values (confidence interval) around a point estimate. For example, the statistical evaluation might indicate that there is an 80 percent probability that the universe total is $200,000, plus or minus $15,000, or between $185,000 and $215,000. In other words, if repeated samples of the same size were selected from the universe, using the same care and procedures, the computed probability intervals of about 80 out of 100 of the samples would be expected to include the actual universe value of interest.

AUDIT STRATIFICATION

It is perhaps one of the most common approaches to auditing. The process of separating audit areas into different segments for separate and varying degrees of examination is known as stratification. The aim is to isolate the major problem items for separate handling, thereby reducing the risk of missing significant undocumented transactions. In addition, by separating selected items from the universe, the auditor decreases the variability among the items to be sampled, thereby reducing the required amount of testing and increasing the precision of the subsequent sampling results.

SAMPLE SIZE CONSIDERATIONS

The determination of an adequate audit sample is more sophisticated and less straightforward than auditors have been led to believe. So, let us examine the issue in more detail.

The number of sampling units into which the universe is divided is called the universe size. The number of sampling units selected is called the sample size. One cannot determine sample size merely by looking at a listing of data. Before sample size can be determined, an auditor must decide how the universe is divided for sampling purposes, that is, what constitutes the sampling unit. For instance, in testing accounts receivable the universe may be divided so that a sampling unit consists of: 1) a single amount such as a debit, credit, or balance, 2) the amounts on a single line of a ledger, 3) the amounts for one account, 4) the amounts for a particular customer, 5) the amounts on one of several ledgers, 6) the amounts in some group of columns on a page of a computer listing, 7) the amounts on a single page or card, 8) the amounts on cards or other records in a single file cabinet drawer. (We can also use the same rationale for engineering blueprints or purchasing contracts, and so on.) Additionally, there may be *empty* sampling units corresponding to pages or lines containing no relevant audit data.

The division of a universe into sampling units is dictated primarily by feasibility and convenience. In order to easily identify the sampling units, the division is made so that different units are associated with different individuals or items such as accounts, pages, cards, or lines.

The size of a sample is no criterion of its reliability. Hence, an auditor cannot offset poor testing procedures by selecting a larger sample. Stratification and the choice of sampling units are more important. After these are properly handled, then an increase in the sample improves the reliability, but the point of diminishing returns is reached rapidly.

Also, the auditor cannot delegate to the sample the responsibility for specifying: 1) the kind of information needed, 2) the criteria and methods of eliciting the information, 3) the segregation of material and sensitive items, nor 4) the rationale of the audit opinion, which integrates the sample results with other audit evidence. A statistical sample only provides a range of probable tolerances. The auditor must translate these into meaningful audit opinions or actions.

After the auditor has delimited the original universe to exclude material, sensitive, nonrecurring, and any other items or groups of items he or she feels warrant special or detailed treatment, he or she is then confronted with determining sample size. There is no single way to approach the problem of sample size, which is difficult to determine precisely. There is a tendency to use sample sizes that have been used by other auditors under similar circumstances.

The idea that a precisely predetermined sample size is always possible is probably the most widespread misconception about statistical sampling methods among quality auditors.

NEED FOR A MINIMUM SAMPLE

The use of samples to estimate characteristics of universes from which they are drawn is based on the premise that some sample items will overestimate the actual universe value and other sample items will underestimate the value. But when these values are combined into an overall sample the tendency is to approximate the value of the universe characteristics. For this tendency to operate effectively, the sample size must be sufficiently large. Fortunately, through audit stratification of material, extreme, nonrecurring, and sensitive items, the minimum for the remaining sample items is often smaller than in other disciplines, because items in the delimited universe are much more similar than those of the original universe. Also, there are other possible sources of audit evidence to support the decision. Nevertheless, the minimum sample must be large enough to allow any undesirable condition to manifest itself.

A sample is too small if its results are not precise enough to contribute to an audit opinion or decision. Conversely, a sample is too large if its results are more precise than is warranted by its intended use or if nonsampling errors caused by human mistakes overwhelm the sampling precision. This suggests some trade-off between the cost of designing and executing the sample and the value of the results in the formulation of an audit opinion, especially in light of additional information from other sources of evidence and audit experience.

SAMPLING COST VERSUS PRECISION

Too often in audit situations, both the cost of sampling in terms of resources and sample tolerance or precision are specified in advance. Since these are competing factors, usually one or both will have to be modified during the course of the audit. Also, predetermined sample tolerance for a specified confidence level may be vague when the audit has several objectives, with conflicting demands on the allocation of the sample. Furthermore, the overall accuracy is usually less than the computed precision because of the adverse effects of nonsampling (human) errors, about which knowledge is generally inadequate.

When considering the sample size necessary to achieve a specified precision or tolerance, the auditor desires to have a satisfactory degree of certainty that the sample point estimate does not differ from the value being estimated in the universe by more than a specified amount or a specified proportion, which may be considered the permissible tolerance. It is difficult to fix the sample size and the sampling rate, or fraction, if the critical factors of unit variance and unit cost of collecting data are subject to considerable uncertainties. Even when a predetermined sample size is specified, the sampling rate, or fraction, cannot be specified if the size of the universe is unknown.

If an arbitrary sampling rate, or fraction, is used, the selection process should not be terminated when the desired sample size is reached. This is especially true with systematic sampling procedures, where the items are selected at, or are within, uniform intervals after random starts. Such truncations would preclude the selection of some sample items.

MINIMUM AUDIT SAMPLES

Any arbitrary sampling rate, or fraction, should be a sensible minimum based on a reasonable expectation of unit variance. Experience reveals that the absolute minimum audit sample for attributes is 50 when controls and conditions are deemed to be excellent, and at least 100 when estimating dollar amounts. If errors are found, these minimums are generally insufficient to provide a reasonable precision for the confidence levels desired by most auditors. Obviously, in situations where the sample data are the sole basis for an opinion, the auditor would want more precision and less risk, thereby requiring a larger minimum sample. However, effective stratification is usually more efficient than merely drawing a larger sample.

REPLICATED SAMPLING

In replicated sampling, the total sample n is selected in k independent samples of equal size so that each of the k samples is a separate sample covering the entire universe or sampling frame. Usually the use of replication does not change the sample size; however, when used in conjunction with flexible sampling, which is described briefly in the next section, the overall sample size may be reduced.

Replication provides a simple and direct way of calculating point estimates and their standard errors (precisions). Replication can also be used to avoid the complexities associated with multistage sampling. For example, one replicated sample may be applied to the total universe, while another replicate is applied to an area or stratum of special interest. Additionally, one or more replicates may be used for detection or as a probe. This is the basic procedure of flexible sampling, where the size of each replicate constitutes a minimum sample, assuming no finding.

Although the number of independent subsamples may range from two to 20, most often there are two, four, five, or 10. It is possible to replicate any sample design merely by dividing the sample size in half and repeating the same sampling procedure twice to make two replications. For more on this see Deming (1960).

FLEXIBLE SAMPLING

In considering sample size it would seem that the auditor is more concerned with the minimum sample, since he or she has many other sources of information and evidence. His or her primary use of sampling is to reduce the risk associated with undetected adverse conditions and material amounts of undocumented costs. Thus, if the sample reveals a single undesirable condition that he or she was not aware of, his or her audit strategy should change. The auditor should immediately become concerned with the nature, source, and potential impact of the finding. The minimum sample feature of flexible sampling is consistent with this concept, and also it prevents the wasting of resources through oversampling. Briefly, under flexible sampling, a minimum sample provides a specified probability, such as 95 percent, that the occurrence rate in the unaudited records will not exceed a specified percentage, such as three percent, provided no error is detected in this minimum sample. For example, if 100 transactions are selected by simple random sampling and no error is found, the auditor has a 95 percent assurance that the error rate in the remaining transactions is less than three percent. If, however, there are findings, the concept of a minimum sample no longer applies. At this point, the auditor has a number of options, among which are sample replication, or terminating sampling and resorting to other acceptable audit techniques. Probably the most appealing aspect of flexible sampling compared with classical approaches is that it is not necessary to estimate or postulate any expected universe characteristics.

Supplemental sampling should be planned in advance; otherwise, the risks associated with the sample results may be greater than calculated (see next section). Often a large initial sample can be selected, then separated into subsamples to be used as supplements after an initial subsample is examined. Replicated sampling, because of its ease of application and estimation of standard errors, may be a better procedure. The overall large sample should represent a reasonable maximum, assuming the highest estimate of unit variance. The size of the initial replicate may correspond to a minimum sample, assuming there are no findings. The replicates, after the first two, could be held in reserve to be used if necessary.

Experience indicates that for most audit activities, a sample three or four times the size of the minimum sample, assuming no errors are found, may be considered a maximum. In other words, if an audit decision has not been reached by that time, it is usually best to cease sampling and resort to other acceptable audit techniques. However, if the frame is highly skewed with a low error rate that exhibits a high monetary tainting, a larger sample may be necessary to adequately support an audit opinion.

SAMPLE ENLARGEMENT INCREASES RISK

If an auditor concludes that more verification is required and he or she enlarges a preliminary sample, the sampling risk from the enlarged sample is greater than if the larger sample were selected in the first place. Since there is a tendency among auditors to expand preliminary samples that are too small for the intended purpose, it is significant to understand that this problem can be avoided by using replication.

CLASSICAL DETERMINATION OF SAMPLE SIZE

Mathematical Formulas

Classical sampling theory provides formulas for computing sample sizes for various sample designs. To use these formulas, however, information is required that may not be known. For example, precision for the estimate must be specified. This procedure merely shifts the problem from one of specifying sample size to specifying precision and assurance. However, neither the size nor the precision of a sample can be determined accurately until after the sample data have been examined, analyzed, and evaluated.

Predetermined Sample Sizes and Uncertainty

There are mathematical formulas that relate sample sizes to the permissible tolerance and assurance of a particular sampling scheme. However, the computed sample sizes may not be precisely accurate, since the necessary parameters in the formulas are subject to uncertainty. Thus, any predetermined sample size reflects the uncertainties of the particular parameters used in the computation. Nevertheless, one advantage of statistical sampling is that the underlying theory enables the construction of these formulas.

On the other hand, it is somewhat paradoxical that the mathematical formulas used to determine sample sizes generally are the same formulas originally derived to compute the precision of the results after the samples have been examined. Hence, as has been mentioned, the formulas require the estimation or postulation of some information that the samples are intended to provide. Thus, exact predetermined sample sizes are not needed as the formulas may lead one to believe that precision exists where, in fact, it may not. If the estimations or postulations are not sustained by the sample results, the predetermined sample size is said to reflect poor planning. Obviously, undersampling can be handled, but oversampling has already wasted critical resources. One way to avoid oversampling is to use a flexible sampling plan with equal replications, where each replicate constitutes a minimum sample if there were no audit findings. If there are any findings, the prescribed minimum sample would be insufficient. Thus, the sampling scheme should provide for at least two, and preferably four, replicates of the same or approximately the same size.

SAMPLE PRECISION

The precision of a sample estimate is measured and gauged by the standard error of the estimate, which is computed by mathematical formulas derived from sampling theory. The smaller the standard error, the greater the mathematical precision of the results. The standard error is associated with the 68 percent probability or confidence level. Other confidence levels are merely multiples of the standard error. The standard error varies from zero if the sample consists of the entire universe to that associated with a sample of two, which is the minimum size for computing variability.

If simple random sampling is used and the sample size is less than five percent of the universe, the standard error is computed by dividing the universe standard deviation (which is the square root of the universe variance) by the square root of the sample size. As a verbal equation, this may be stated as follows:

$$\text{sample size} = \frac{\text{universe standard deviation}}{\text{square root of sample size}}$$

The importance of this equation is that the standard error does not decrease in proportion to the increased sample size. That is, doubling the sample size does not reduce the standard error by one-half. This is because the denominator in the formula is the square root of the sample size. Actually, there is a rapidly diminishing return in improved precision for increased sample size. It should be remembered that the single value (point) estimate with which the tolerance or precision (standard error) is associated is expected to remain somewhat stable for increased sample sizes. Thus, the value of the standard error is relative to the value of the point estimate and to the significance of tighter tolerance in support of the audit opinion.

COMPONENTS OF A SAMPLE SIZE EQUATION

If the aforementioned verbal equation for computing the standard error for simple random sampling is solved for sample size, the following equation results:

$$\text{sample size} = \frac{\text{universe standard deviation squared}}{\text{standard error squared}}$$

In practice, this equation is further modified to provide for confidence levels different from the 68 percent level of the standard error, and a permissible tolerance is substituted for the standard error, resulting in the following:

$$\text{sample size} = \frac{\text{estimate of universe standard deviation}^2 \times \text{confidence coefficient}^2}{\text{permissible tolerance}^2}$$

ESTIMATING UNIVERSE VARIANCE

The formula requires an estimate of the universe variance to compute sample size. Unfortunately, in practice, the universe variance is generally not known, and hence, must be postulated or estimated from experience or from a preliminary sample. Obviously, the computed sample size will be affected by the postulation or estimation of the universe variance, which is one of the most significant factors in determining sample size. In other words, the formula for computing sample size depends on some characteristic of the universe that is to be estimated through sampling.

Despite these uncertainties, some ways of estimating the universe variance are by: 1) using information from an audit survey, 2) using results from previous audits in the same or similar areas, 3) taking a preliminary sample and using its variance as an estimate of the universe variance, and 4) using audit experience and judgment.

TOLERABLE ERROR AND ALLOWANCE FOR SAMPLING RISK

After an estimate of the universe variance (or standard deviation) has been made, the next consideration is the amount of error tolerance for some specified confidence level. Auditors often specify a higher level of confidence than that associated with the standard error (68 percent confidence level), thereby disregarding other relevant audit evidence in many situations. Also, allowable tolerance or precision may be expressed either as an interval or as an upper or lower limit. It may be expressed in terms of a percentage or proportion, such as an occurrence rate, or it may be in terms of an amount, such as dollars.

If the auditor is sampling to estimate a percentage or a rate, he or she may specify a range of allowable percentage tolerance for the estimate of the actual occurrence rate at a given confidence (probability) level, say 90 percent. In other words, if repeated samples of the same size were taken from the universe, using the same audit and sampling procedures and care, the computed confidence (probability) intervals of about 90 out of 100 of the samples would be expected to include the actual occurrence percentage. If the audit objective can be achieved with a one-sided confidence interval, such as a maximum occurrence rate, a smaller sample will result.

CONFIDENCE LEVEL OR DEGREE OF ASSURANCE

The confidence level indicates the degree of assurance (probability) that the results of a sample are reasonable estimates of specific universe characteristics. Whenever one takes a sample, he or she is taking a risk that the sample results may not be reasonable. By specifying the confidence level, the auditor has a means of measuring this risk, which is the converse of the confidence level.

The selection of a confidence level depends upon how much risk one is willing to take of having the universe value lie outside the computed tolerance range or confidence interval. When one speaks of a 90 percent assurance, it is expected that if repeated samples were selected, the actual value would fall within the confidence intervals of about 90 out of 100.

Confidence levels are usually expressed in percentages such as 68 percent, 80 percent, 90 percent, or 95 percent, or in proportions, 0.68, 0.80, 0.90, or 0.95. However, in the formulas for computing sample size, equivalent Z factors are used.

ILLUSTRATION OF SAMPLE SIZE COMPUTATION

If the maximum allowable tolerance, the desired confidence level, and an estimate of the universe standard deviation are specified, an estimate of sample size for simple random sampling can be computed by applying the aforementioned sample size formula. To illustrate the computation of sample size, suppose the universe standard deviation is estimated to be 10 units, the maximum allowable error is prescribed to be two units, and a 95 percent confidence is desired. The Z confidence factor for 95 percent is 1.96. Substituting these values in the sample size formula, the results are:

$$\text{sample size} = \frac{10^2(1.96)^2}{2^2}$$

$$= \frac{100 \times 3.8416}{4}$$

$$= 96 \text{ or approximately 100 random samples}$$

BAYESIAN APPROACH TO SAMPLE SIZE

Bayesian methods take their name from Thomas Bayes, an 18th century English cleric, who derived a formula for dealing with prior probabilities. Bayesian statistical methods, which are controversial among statisticians, incorporate prior information from experience and subjective probability (Kyburg and Smokler 1964) that reflects judgment into the decision-making process. These methods are based on the notion that the theory of probability does not replace audit judgment and experience.

Thus, in the Bayesian decision approach, judgment and experience are permitted in assigning probabilities when dealing with uncertainties. This approach appeals to auditors because their decisions regarding uncertainties are not based merely on sample data, but on other sources of evidence, experience, and judgment. In other words, Bayesian methods enable the auditor to use his or her judgment in a logical manner.

The Bayesian approach to sample size determination emphasizes the relative value of new sample information in the light of evidence already available from other reliable sources. The value of new information is regarded as the most significant and critical element in determining the sample size. Also, the value of the new information depends on how likely it is to influence an action or an opinion. Obviously, the value of any information is personal and depends on the knowledge, maturity, and beliefs of the individual auditor.

In many audit situations, it may be difficult to justify a sample that is not expected to reflect a financial impact or to aid in sustaining a significant decision. The use of a sample to estimate an overall error rate that merely reinforces information already gained from an audit survey or other evidence may not be justified, especially if there is little or no financial impact. In other words, the cost of conducting an audit sample must be weighed against the value of the elicited information in influencing an audit opinion or decision.

If an auditor has concluded from an audit survey that an operation is grossly unacceptable, then there is little value in additional information from a sample. On the other hand, if he or she is not sure about an opinion or a decision, the additional information could be useful, such as assisting in stratification. Usually examples of poor internal control can best be located judgmentally during an audit survey. Also, if the cost of sampling exceeds the value of the reduction in uncertainty about a decision, an auditor should seriously consider the use of other audit techniques. Thus, if an auditor has a strong opinion about an activity or an account, the relative decrease in uncertainty due to additional sampling may be small, and therefore, may not be justified.

Inasmuch as Bayesian statistics are controversial, it is useful to summarize the pros and cons of the method.

- Bayesian inference is the optimal statistical method if there is adequate known prior information. Compared with classical methods, the Bayesian approach often yields more credible point estimates and smaller confidence intervals.

- Bayesian methods are particularly useful in applications where sample sizes are small.

- The major criticism of Bayesian methods is that they are highly subjective. Often there is inadequate prior relevant information, and assumptions are necessary. However, classical methods also involve assumptions that are often implicit in the techniques.

SAMPLING RISK

Sampling risk relates to the probability that the sampling procedures for both compliance and substantive testing might produce different results if the same procedures were applied in a similar manner to all transactions. Therefore, the sampling risk can be objectively computed and controlled when statistical sampling is used. In fact, the special feature of statistical sampling is that it permits the use of the theory of probability for the computation, from the sample data, of the margin of sampling error (precision) with the associated risk that has been introduced by using a sample in lieu of a complete review.

The other aspect of overall audit risk is associated with the possibility that the auditing procedures, even if applied to a complete review, might fail to detect material errors or fail to reveal compliance deviations that would influence the auditor's decision. This aspect of audit risk is referred to as the nonsampling risk, and it is attributable to the nature of the auditing procedures, the timing of the application of the procedures, the system or operation being reviewed, and the maturity, skill, and thoroughness of the auditor.

In summary, there are three principal sources of risk in audit sampling applications: 1) sampling variability, generally called sampling error or precision, which depends on the design and, to a lesser extent, on the sample size; 2) sample selection biases that reflect how accurately the design is executed; and 3) the effects of erroneous criteria, assumptions, and observations, which cause differences between observed and actual characteristics or variables. The latter two sources are usually called nonsampling risks and are not covered by the statistical evaluation aspect of the sample results.

When the auditor uses statistical sampling to estimate a universe characteristic, the Central Limit Theorem provides a basis for calculating the impreciseness of the estimate for a specified sampling risk. Two interrelated concepts are used for this purpose. One is the precision, which estimates the probable proximity of the estimate from the sample to the corresponding unknown universe characteristic or value. The other is the reliability (confidence, assurance), which measures the frequency with which the difference between the sample estimate and the actual universe characteristic or value does not exceed the estimated precision, if repeated samples of the same size are taken.

Replication provides an intuitive way of minimizing the acceptance of higher sampling risks through comparison of the results of individual replicates. Any significant differences noted among the replicates should be analyzed for cause. If there seems to be a systematic pattern, the auditor might subjectively examine additional items that fit the pattern, and thus augment the sample results with judgmental testing in support of an audit opinion. In auditing, one often proceeds from an effect (finding) to the cause. In doing this, there is an assumption that the occurrences of a characteristic in a sample will follow a pattern similar to the universe, provided the sample is large enough.

In statistical sampling, a reliability statement consists of two parts: a) a confidence or precision interval, and b) a confidence or reliability (or assurance) level. The terms confidence interval and confidence level are used in the consideration of the following, based on information obtained from the sample:

- The probability alpha (α) (or confidence level 100 α percent) that the unknown universe characteristic or value will lie within specified limits (or confidence intervals)

- The confidence interval within which the unknown universe characteristic or value may be expected to lie with a specified confidence level of 100 α percent

For most purposes, the auditor desires to know how likely the universe estimate derived from the sample deviates from the actual universe characteristic or value. Knowledge from the Central Limit Theorem that the sampling distribution of means approaches the normal distribution as the sample size increases, and that the mean of the sampling distribution is equal to the mean of the universe, together with properties of the normal distribution, enables the auditor to make statistical evaluation or reliability statements. The concept of the normal distribution is significant in stating the reliability of sample estimates of universe means and aggregates. The sample means of distributions of any shape tend to form normal distributions as the sample sizes increase. This tendency is more rapid for those universes that are only moderately skewed. Sample size, however, is not the sole determinant of the reliability of the results. Smaller samples from carefully designed and executed samplings provide more useful information than loosely improvised larger samples.

If the sample is effectively stratified and large enough, the underlying sampling distribution is approximately normal, and therefore the chances are 68 out of 100 (68 percent assurance) that the universe estimate derived from the sample does not deviate from the actual universe characteristic or value by more than one standard error (the standard deviation of the sampling distribution), and the chances are 95 out of 100 that the deviation will not exceed two standard errors.

Often the interval is assumed to be such that equal areas are excluded from each tail, resulting in what is referred to as a two-sided confidence interval. In the case of a 95 percent confidence level, this would mean the exclusion of 2.5 percent of the area from each tail of the distribution. On the other hand, a one-sided confidence interval excludes only 2.5 percent of the area from one tail, depending upon whether an upper precision limit or a lower precision limit is of interest. Thus, the confidence level is increased to 97.5 percent. The conversions from two-sided to one-sided probabilities, and vice-versa, may be accomplished by applying the following relationships:

$$C = 2C_1 - 1, \text{ for conversion to two-sided}$$

$$C_1 = \frac{1}{2} + \frac{C}{1}, \text{ for conversion to one-sided}$$

where

   C = probability for two-sided interval corresponding to a specified value
   C_1 = probability that either the mean is greater than the lower limit or that
      it is less than the upper limit

   After the sample has been selected, examined, and analyzed, the results
are used to estimate universe characteristics or values. The statistical procedures for deriving universe estimates from sample data are referred to as
estimators. For example, the sample mean is a random variable because it
varies from sample to sample, and thus has a sampling distribution. The
sample mean is also an estimator because it can be used to estimate the universe mean. Statistically, the best estimator is unbiased, consistent, efficient, and sufficient. The bias of an estimator is not the same as a selection
bias, since an absence of selection bias does not guarantee the avoidance of
procedural or estimation bias.

   Any selection, observation, measurement, recording, or estimation
procedure that systematically distorts an estimate from the actual universe
value is considered biased. Although there may be distortions in individual
samples, they average out to zero in the long run if the method is unbiased.
This is one of the reasons replication is so significant in audit sampling.

ESTIMATION AND EVALUATION

Although it is seldom used with audit sampling, the mean-per-unit estimator may be used in projecting (estimating) a universe characteristic or value
from a sample. The mean estimation of the total audited amount Y is computed from the following relationship:

$$Y = N\bar{y}$$

[mean estimation of total audited amount] = [number of audit units in uni-
verse] × [mean of sample audited amount]

   With an estimate of the standard deviation, one can compute an estimate
of the standard error of the estimated audited total using the following:

$$\hat{\sigma}_{\bar{y}} = \frac{S_y}{\sqrt{n}} N \sqrt{\frac{N-n}{N-1}}$$

[estimated standard error of audited total] = [product of estimated standard
deviation of audited amounts, and universe size, and finite universe correction factor] × [square root of sample size]

The reader should notice that the expression

$$\left[\frac{N-n}{N-1}\right]^{\frac{1}{2}}$$

is the factor that adjusts for sampling without replacement.

The estimated total difference D between the audited amounts and the recorded amounts is computed from the following:

$$D = N(\bar{y} - \bar{x})$$

[estimated total difference] = [number of audit units in universe] × [mean of sample audited amounts − mean of sample recorded amounts]

Ratio analysis is yet another way to estimate. Even though the ratio estimate and its standard error are slightly biased, they are consistent and they are very helpful to auditing. Deming (1960) describes how the detection and correction of an estimation bias can be accomplished through replication. Sometimes, as Quenouille (1956) has suggested, we may be interested in calculating the equivalent to an extrapolation of the ratio regression line through zero. For example, suppose, r denotes the ratio derived from the two replicates combined, and r_1 and r_2 denote the ratios derived from the two replicates individually, then the

$$\text{extrapolated ratio} = 2r - \frac{1}{2}(r_1 + r_2)$$

In the use of ratio estimation, the auditor uses two sample values (audited amount and the corresponding recorded amount) and one known universe value (total recorded amount) to compute an estimated universe value (total audited amount). The ratio estimate of the universe audited amount Y_r is computed as follows:

$$Y_r = rX$$

[ratio estimate of total audited amount] = [ratio of sample audited amount to recorded amounts] × [universe recorded amount]

When the correlation between the audited amount and the recorded amount is not zero, the regression estimate is more efficient than the mean-per-unit estimate. To be sure, the linear regression is similar to the difference estimator, except the adjustment is multiplied by b, where b is the regression in the simple regression equation. The linear regression estimate of the total audited amount Y_g is computed from the following equation:

$$Y_g = N\bar{y} + b(X - N\bar{x})$$

[regression estimate of total audited amount] = [product of universe size and mean of sample audited amounts] + [estimated regression coefficient] × [(universe recorded amount) − (product of universe size and mean of sample recorded amounts)]

ATTRIBUTE SAMPLING EVALUATION

As we already have seen, using the flexible sampling strategy, the auditor desires to estimate the universe occurrence rate. He or she also wishes to state at a specified confidence level that the universe occurrence rate does not exceed his or her maximum tolerable occurrence rate. Thus, as we have implied, flexible sampling is concerned with a one-sided confidence level.

Attribute sampling involves the estimation of an overall occurrence (error) rate and a related confidence interval. That is, attribute sampling is concerned with a two-sided confidence level, such as five percent plus or minus two percent, corresponding to an interval from three percent to seven percent at a specified confidence level. In other words, it is the qualitative counterpart of sampling for variables or dollars. Except for the sampling units and the formulas for the computation of the standard error, all other aspects are the same.

Unfortunately, the attribute sampling strategy requires the auditor to specify an expected occurrence rate in order to determine the sample size. If the auditor overestimates this rate, he or she will oversample. By contrast, the flexible sampling strategy prevents oversampling by using minimum sample sizes. Thus, no prior estimate of the universe occurrence rate is necessary in flexible sampling. To determine the minimum sample under flexible sampling, the auditor only needs to specify his or her maximum tolerable occurrence rate, his or her desired confidence level, and a very rough estimate of the universe size. [Note: For those readers who desire to pursue the attribute sampling strategy, the following discussion is provided; however, a flexible sample may be converted into an attribute sample whenever desirable. Thus, to conserve audit resources, the flexible sampling strategy is suggested as the initial approach even when attribute sampling is an objective. Usually sampling for attributes is considered prior to discussions of sampling for variables, since the concepts and the computations are easier. On the other hand, the theory of sampling for attributes may be considered a special case of the general sampling theory for variables, where the variable can assume only two values: zero or unity. Thus, the universe may be represented by the symbols "0" (to mean "does not possess the characteristic") and "1" (to mean "does possess the characteristic"). If the universe proportion of the occurrence of a characteristic is P, then the proportion of the absence of the characteristic is 1 − P. Then P is the universe rate of occurrence and the universe variance is P (1 − P).]

To calculate the standard error, we follow the equation

$$\text{standard error of proportion} = \left[\frac{\text{proportion} \times (1 - \text{proportion})}{\text{sample size} - 1} \right]^{\frac{1}{2}}$$

In sampling attributes, the hypergeometric distribution is used without replacement and the binomial distribution is used with replacement. On the other hand, when the occurrence is small (less than 5 percent) and the sample size is large, the Poisson distribution becomes a good approximation of the bimodal. Sometimes the normal distribution is used as an approximation to the hypergeometric, binomial, and Poisson distributions for reliability statements when the sample size is not too small and the occurrence rate is not too rare.

To avoid oversampling when using attribute sampling, it is suggested that a preliminary sample, at least the size of a minimum sample, be selected as in flexible sampling, and then be evaluated using the following formula:

$$\text{total sample} = \left[\frac{\text{achieved precision}}{\text{desired precision}} \right]^2 \times \text{initial sample size}$$

For example: An initial sample of 100 is selected and the error rate is five percent with an achieved precision of ± four percent when ± two percent is desired at the same confidence level. Using the aforementioned relationship, one gets:

Total sample = $(4/2)^2 \times 100 = 400$. Since 100 items have already been examined, the additional sample would be 300. If the supplementary sampling is large, replication should be considered with a cumulative evaluation after each replication to avoid oversampling.

To calculate the standard error S_p of a proportion we use

$$S_p = \sqrt{\frac{N - n}{N(n - 1)} p(1 - p)}$$

Estimated standard error = [(universe size − sample size) (sample error rate) (1 − sample error rate) / (universe size) (sample size − 1)]$^{\frac{1}{2}}$

After the standard error is obtained, the computation of confidence limits is easy and straightforward, as follows:

Confidence limits =
(sample error rate) ± (confidence factor) × (standard error)

Replicated sampling is the procedure of selecting from the entire universe two or more independent random samples of the same or about the same size. Replication provides an easy way to estimate and evaluate both variables and attributes, such as means, aggregates, ratios, frequencies, proportions, and so on. Replicates provide a simple and direct method of calculating standard errors of any kind of estimate. It can also be used to identify any localized abnormal errors where an unusual frequency or value occurs in a replicate and to adjust for bias in ratio estimations.

To calculate the standard error for proportion (attribute) estimate we follow:

$$P_\alpha = \frac{\text{activity } A \text{ minutes for area } k \text{ employees}}{\text{number of replicates}} \times \frac{\text{number of employees}}{\text{in activity}}$$

To estimate the standard error we use:

$$\text{Estimated standard error } P_\alpha = \frac{P_{max} - P_{min}}{m}$$

That is, estimated standard error = [largest estimate from a replicate – smallest estimate from a replicate]/number of replicates.

To calculate the standard error for dollar (variable) estimate we follow:

$$Y_\alpha = \frac{\text{minutes per work day}}{\text{number of replicas}} \times \frac{\text{sum of products cents per minute and}}{\text{the number of employee minutes}}$$

$$\text{estimated error } Y_\alpha = \frac{y_{max} - y_{min}}{m}$$

If we want to use the method of sums of squares the estimates are:

1. For proportion (attribute):

$$P_\alpha = \frac{\text{number of sample occurrences for activity } A}{\text{total number of sample occurrences}}$$

$$s^2 = \frac{1}{m(m-1)} \sum \left(p_j - p \right)^2$$

= [1/[(number of replicates × number of replicates minus one)] × [sum of squares of the difference between individual replicate proportions and overall sample proportion]

   2. For a dollar aggregate estimate:

$$s^2 = \frac{1}{m(m-1)} \sum \left(y_j - \bar{y}\right)^2$$

= [1/[(number of replicates × number of replicates minus one)] × [sum of squares of the difference between individual replicate estimates and the mean estimate for the sample]

ISSUES/CONCERNS DURING AUDIT

Just like in the planning stage of the audit, during the audit there are issues and concerns of which the auditor should be aware. For starters, it is important that the auditor establish a rapport with the auditee and make him or her feel comfortable before the actual audit begins. The opening moments are crucial, for they set the tone of the entire audit. They may make the difference between a successful and not so successful audit. Therefore:

- Learn how to use the: who, what, where, when, how, and why

- Learn and practice a questioning strategy that should start with broad, open-ended questions to obtain maximum information; then, use closed-ended and clarifying questions to "funnel" down to the missing information and to fill in the gaps

   Here we must remind the reader that there are basically four question types in any audit: 1) open-ended questions, 2) closed-ended questions, 3) clarifying questions, and 4) leading questions. Use open-ended questions to get as much information as possible; closed-ended questions to research or to pinpoint specific points; clarifying questions to make sure that the item under discussion is clear to both you as an auditor and the auditee; and leading questions to lead the auditee toward a specific answer. Try not to use the latter. It may introduce a "bias" into the answer. Typical questions are:

- Are you aware of our quality policy and can you relate it to your job?

- What kind of training is required for this activity?

- Do you have any questions?

- Is there anything we overlooked?
- Where is . . . , How do you . . . , Why do you . . . , Are the operating criteria defined?
  - Where are the procedures located?
  - Are the records maintained?
- When would it be:
  - Appropriate?
  - Applicable?
  - Necessary?
  - Desirable?

COMMUNICATION AND AUDITING

The thrust of any audit activity is communication. That is, it is the communication process that will reveal nonconformities, explain the process, negotiate the CARs, interact with owners of the process, and so on. Therefore, in order for the auditor to be effective, he or she must make sure that:

- The message is understood. The communication pathways (verbal and body language) are in synch. When the words, tone, pace, inflection, and nonverbal communication elements do not agree, dig deeper.
- Active listening is practiced. The auditee and the process are the focus.
- Attention must be given to the words that are used:
  - Listen and consider the tone, the pace, and the inflection (how the words are used)
  - Watch the nonverbal communications
  - Eyes
  - Facial expression
  - Body posture
  - Hand
  - Words

VERIFICATION

Auditing is an activity that verifies the effectiveness of the QMS. It does that by objective evidence. Therefore, all auditors must be very careful how the objective evidence is defined, collected, and reported. It is imperative that auditors should always look for ways to provide positive feedback to the auditee. Internal auditors should typically share their findings with the auditee—not only at the debriefing meeting but also as the audit is in progress. Give them an opportunity to either fix the problem or to start the improvement process. Objective evidence may include:

- Metrics
  - Records
  - Lists
  - Meeting minutes
  - Personnel observation
- Activity being performed (observations)
- Interview results of individuals who have ownership of the process
- Collaboration of multiple sources
- Condition of area or item
- Confirmation by other individuals involved in the activity

DO'S AND DON'TS DURING INTERVIEWS

Especially during interviews, the auditor must be very sensitive about his or her behavior. Here are some guidelines:

- Do:
  - Ask one question at a time.
  - Conclude one topic before going to the next.
  - Make the auditee feel like he or she is a member of the team.
  - Stay within the scope of the audit.
  - Be a good listener.

- Don't:

  - Use emotional words or opinions.

  - Ask unsafe questions (questions that may provoke the auditee in a negative way).

  - Argue.

  - Offer opinions.

  - Use the "I" word.

    ○ Use "I think . . . "

    ○ Use "I feel . . . "

    ○ Use "I've seen."

  - Feel confined to asking only questions on your checklist.

It is also possible that as an auditor you may come across an individual who is uncooperative. That means as an auditor you must be ready, willing, and prepared to deal with individuals who are:

- Excessively nervous

- Time wasters (too much detail)

- "Disturbed" for some reason either related to the audit or even something totally unrelated

- Talkative escorts (or supervisor)

REFERENCES

Deming, W. E. 1960. *Sample Design in Business Research*. New York: John Wiley and Sons.

Kraft, W. 1968. "Statistical Sampling for Auditors: A New Look." *Journal of Accountancy* (August): 63–69.

Kyburg, H., and H. Smokler, ed. 1964. *Studies in Subjective Probability*. New York: John Wiley and Sons.

Quenouille, M. 1956. "Notes on Bias Estimation." *Biometrica* 43: 356–66.

Tracy, J. 1969. "Bayesian Statistical Methods in Auditing." *Accounting Review* (January): 45–48.

———. 1969. "Bayesian Statistical Review in Accounting." *Accounting Review* (January): 56–64.

12

Implementing ISO 9001, AS9100, and TS 16949

As in any quality system, to excel it must have excellent foundations. For ISO 9001 and its specific derivatives (TS 16949, AS9100) the foundation is shown in Table 12.1. The table identifies the council, which is made up of top management, as the key and pivotal point in the entire organization and its specific overall requirements for success.

The key issue of Table 12.1 is that it focuses on performance standards and their application. And that, of course, is the intent of the ISO 9001:2000 standard, that is, effectiveness and improvement.

The performance that Table 12.1 implies embodies the following steps:

1. *Take a system view.* Look at and evaluate your objectives from a systemic perspective. That is, business view, organizing system view, performer view, and management view. The intent here is to understand the need to eliminate suboptimization of the organization by understanding the context of your implementation project within the overall system.

2. *Focus on outcomes.* Tie performance improvement initiatives to critical business issues. Demonstrate the effectiveness of what you are about to implement.

3. *Add value.* Link the implementation strategy with the expected results to specific critical business issues.

Table 12.1 Overview of the foundation for a quality system.

	Select Functional Group (Quality Council)		
General Goals of Management	**Production Goals and Production Support**	**Training Goals**	**General Goals for the Workforce**
	The Organization:		
• Human resources • Accounting and finance • Research and development • Marketing • Engineering • Manufacturing • Quality assurance • Service • Etc.			
Goals for Management:	**Goals for Production and Support:**	**Training Goals:**	**Current Goals for the Workforce:**
• Provide realistic goals • Empower employees • Focus and preach the concepts of consistency, stability, and continual improvement • Eliminate fear as part of the decision-making process • Encourage teamwork • Remove *all* barriers to pride of workmanship	• Do not depend on mass inspection • Buy on statistical evidence (be a data-driven organization) • Do not allow accepted levels of defects (aim for excellence)	• Train in statistical tools and methods • Train supervisors to ménage • Train and educate all appropriate employees in methods, materials, and technology, as applicable	• Search for better ways • Use statistical methods
Business objectives for each function	Business objectives for each function	Business objectives for each function	Business objectives for each function
Implement yearly (this means: plan; execute; measure progress; control and review). The information gained in this step should be fed into the organization (specific areas) for appropriate action.			

4. *Apply systemic needs analysis.* Learn to analyze gaps in your system and then design appropriate action. This will require working in teams.

5. *Systemic cause analysis.* Systematically learn to analyze results and evaluate based on the criteria set. The analysis strategy here is of paramount interest. This means: finding results improvement opportunities; establishing the results chain (cascading the results through the system) from individual performance to organizational results; and evaluating alternative "points of entry" into a client organization.

6. *Systemic design.* Follow an established design or a new one based on the specific needs and expectations of the organization.

7. *Systemic development.* Follow an established developmental design or a new one based on the specific needs and expectations of the organization. Make sure that the proposed development is appropriate and applicable to what your organization needs.

8. *Systemic implementation.* Follow an established implementation design or a new one based on the specific needs and expectations of the organization. Make sure that the implementation strategy is doable within the constraints of your system.

9. *Systemic evaluation.* Evaluate by assessing the impact of the implementation project on the critical business issue and results gap. Fundamental to this evaluation are: determining performance improvement project feasibility within stated and expected constraints; planning and executing the strategy; capturing and assessing interview data in a formal record; linking the data, observations, and results of interviews to a rigor analysis and final recommendations; organizing recommendations for organizational change and eliminating the gaps.

One can see that an organization gradually may bring internal processes and systems under control only by consolidating its management and resources. It has become clear that management by objectives (MBO) or its derivative methodologies alone do not address the needs of the new competitive environment (for more on this see Crow 2002). Most organizations need corporate cultural changes that focus on the premise that through quality awareness, substantial improvements in business efficiency would be obtained. This is where ISO comes in.

Certainly, an easy beginning may be an adaptation of Deming's 14 points and setting specific, timely, measurable objectives against each point. However, in conjunction with the ISO standards, organizations have been making substantial progress by:

- Creating a corporate creed that focuses on establishing consistency and continuity.

- Creating and implementing an employee suggestion program to help eliminate fear and encourage communication. Suggestions can save more than $250,000 per company per year (see pp. 11–13).

- Developing a corrective-action process for continual improvement that encourages teamwork and increases efficiency.

- Creating and implementing an employee recognition program to help remove the barriers to pride of workmanship.

- Investing in people and training to help educate and train supervisors, particularly in improving methods and productivity.

- Developing and beginning to implement a quality awareness program that defines management's commitment to quality and productivity. It is imperative to note here that when an organization begins the road to improvement with any kind of quality philosophy, including standards such as ISO, substantial opportunities exist, particularly in setting realistic R&D schedules, implementing SPC into the manufacturing process, implementing employee training programs in the tools of quality, and helping supervisors do a better job. As with any program that defines objectives, quality objectives that are not totally achieved must be reset and aggressively addressed by all available resources on a continuing basis.

It is not unusual that in a brief period of time an organization may experience success, and opportunities for improvement may become highly visible when the management by quality objectives (MBQO) process has been applied. Timely quality objectives must be created around each of Deming's 14 points and progress measured periodically. If the process is implemented continuously, the organization should expect a complete cultural metamorphosis, in which quality objectives become the business strategy and continuous quality improvement becomes a way of life.

However, for any implementation or methodology, or even a culture change, speed of implementation and user-friendliness are the top priorities. As a consequence, management must be committed, and must set criteria and milestones for achieving and evaluating the journey of the implementation. A typical and very detailed approach is discussed in Stamatis (1995) and (1999). The core approach to the implementation journey is shown in Table 12.2.

Table 12.2 The core approach to the implementation journey.

Standard (Core Requirement)	Management Commitment	Quality Plan	Inspection of Incoming Material	Measurement of In-Process Work	Traceability	Training	Continual Improvement
Purpose	Confirm top management is committed.	Plan and document the implementation of the quality system.	Ensure all materials used in production meet the set standards.	Ensure all work is performed according to standards to reduce variation.	Ensure material is traceable from incoming material to shipped product.	Ensure all employees are fully trained and capable to perform their duties.	Ensure problems and opportunities for improvement are continuously addressed and resolved.
Who is responsible	Senior management.	Quality manager (QM).	Purchasing and QM.	Production manager and QM.	Production manager and QM.	Senior management, HR, supervisors, and QM.	Senior management, QM, and supervisors.
Elements of success	1.1 Appoint responsible individual in senior management.	2.1 Create a quality manual and determine structure for handbook and critical work procedures.	3.1 Create procedures and standards for acceptance testing of critical supplies.	4.1 Create a general process flowchart and a facility layout.	5.1 Implement an identification system for machines and equipment.	6.1 Establish policies for employee career development and training.	7.1 Establish quality teams and determine how they function.
	1.2 Define a budget for the WoodMark Quality System (WQS).	2.2 Create templates of data collection sheets, quality charts, and related information.	3.2 Establish contracts with performance criteria for critical supplies.	4.2 Create process flowcharts for critical processes.	5.2 Implement an identification system for tracking orders through the plant.	6.2 Determine specific training requirements for the WQS and critical processes.	7.2 Use brainstorming to determine critical areas of problems and opportunities for improvement.

continued

continued

Standard (Core Requirement)	Management Commitment	Quality Plan	Inspection of Incoming Material	Measurement of In-Process Work	Traceability	Training	Continual Improvement
Elements of success	1.3 Appoint QM.	2.3 Create a system for dissemination of information.	3.3 Implement performance checklists and procedures for selecting suppliers.	4.3 Create work procedures for critical processes.	5.3 Implement a tracking system for parts flowing through critical areas.	6.3 Establish training records and maintain training documents.	7.3 Determine customer satisfaction.
	1.4 Develop quality policies and broad quality goals.	2.4 Create a system for storing and maintaining quality documents.		4.4 Apply statistical process control tools for critical processes.			7.4 Act on the opportunities for improvement.
	1.5 Create organizational flowchart and table of responsibilities.			4.5 Control nonconforming products.			7.5 Develop goals and benchmarks for in-process improvement.
	1.6 Conduct annual internal review of the WQS.			4.6 Test and control measuring tools.			

The table identifies seven core requirements as the foundation of the implementation journey. They are:

1. *Management commitment.* Individual elements require a representative of senior management to be responsible for the quality system, a quality manager to be appointed, and a budget to be set aside for the program. Senior management is responsible for setting an organization's quality policies and goals, and the quality manager is responsible for overseeing a system that responds to those priorities.

An organizational chart pertaining to the quality system should include a table of responsibilities so each person knows what aspects of quality he or she is responsible for. Management must conduct an annual internal review of the quality system and make any necessary improvements in policies and responsibilities.

2. *Quality plan.* This relates to documentation, information sharing, and record keeping. An organization must create a manual explaining the quality system. The manual should contain detailed information on how data are collected, analyzed, and used in the quality system. The manual should consist of two parts: a detailed quality manual for use by employees and auditors and a quality handbook that can be distributed to customers.

The manual is very useful for employee training and annual employee reviews. To be actively involved, all employees must have access to the information used in the quality system. The auditors must ensure that employees understand the information provided with respect to the quality system.

3. *Inspection of incoming material.* This core requirement assures and/or implements a system for acceptance testing of critical supplies purchased by the organization. The acceptance testing procedures must be tied to formal criteria used on purchase orders and contracts. A supplier rating system based on past performance is then used to rate suppliers. While acceptance testing procedures are usually standard business practices in most sectors, they were purposely added here to emphasize the need for such standard business practices.

4. *Measurement and control of in-process work.* This is a main focus of any system, especially if incoming raw material is of a heterogeneous nature. In such cases, many problems that are part of the product, such as moisture, are not visible to the human eye. Another reason for the dominance of measurement and control procedures is the amount of scrap and rework typically found in a plant because of machining problems that could have been detected in-process rather than at the end of the production line. In addition, this requirement covers work procedures for critical processes. It is not necessary to have written work procedures for all

processes in a plant, but they are required for processes the organization deems to be critically important to success. SPC tools must be applied to these critical processes. The choice of tools is up to the organization. Proper training (see item 6) and outside assistance are key to the successful application of these tools.

Finally, this requirement requires implementation of a system to properly label and isolate nonconforming products found in the inspection process. Additionally, you must label and regularly calibrate and test the sensitive measuring tools often used for quality control work. You also must keep good records on the status of these tools.

5. *Traceability.* Product traceability is becoming an important issue in any industry for several reasons. First, due to international environmental standards, it is becoming increasingly important to produce products from raw materials that originate from sustainably managed sources. Environmental certification provides this assurance, and many systems are currently in place. Second, poor raw material quality or problems in an earlier process frequently cause scrap and rework. To successfully identify the root cause of the problem, it is often necessary to trace the product back to an earlier process. This item ensures that a process is in place to track orders and parts through the plant. You should design this tracking system so any parts flowing through critical processes can be traced back to their origin. To aid in tracking, you must create an identification system for all machines and equipment in the plant. The tracking system will both reduce quality costs and make problem solving easier.

6. *Training.* No quality system can function without proper training. This item ensures that training is structured, continuous, and part of the career path development of employees. Training is designed to familiarize all employees with the quality system of the organization, so they can participate in continuous improvement activities.

7. *Continual improvement.* In ISO 9000:2000, "continual improvement" is defined as: "Recurring activity to increase the ability to fulfill requirements." It is a continual process using audit findings and audit conclusions, analysis of data, management reviews, or other means, and generally leads to corrective or preventive action.

Making the decision to become registered to ISO 9001:2000 is often a very simple one, as the benefits are well documented (some of them discussed in the introduction and chapter 1). A more difficult task is putting together and successfully completing an implementation plan that balances the requirements of the standard, your deadline to become registered, and the normal pressures of your business.

There is no single blueprint for implementing ISO 9001:2000 that will work for every company; however, there are some common steps that will allow you to balance the often conflicting requirements and prepare you for a successful registration assessment.

Stamatis (1995; 1999) has developed a very detailed implementation strategy based on a project management approach. Rather than repeating the process all over again, we will examine and address some practical considerations and key phases in the implementation process and suggest some "best practices" from start to finish for each, and we will try to direct you to some further resources as you embark on your ISO 9001:2000 journey.

THINK OF IMPLEMENTATION AS A PROJECT

The way to treat the implementation process is as a project, which means appointing a project team with a project manager, preparing a project plan, and evaluating and monitoring progress according to the plan. This demands certain prerequisites, including top management commitment, good communication at all levels, and ownership of the quality system by all. If ISO 9001:2000 management systems is a completely new subject area for your organization, or you lack time, expertise, or objectivity, you may want to consider the use of a quality management system consultant to assist with implementation.

An experienced consultant can be a very beneficial part of your project team, particularly if you have an implementation deadline, as they can undertake the project manager role. However, a consultant should not write your quality system for you, as ownership of processes and procedures is important for a successful management system.

UNDERSTAND THE PROCESS APPROACH

ISO 9001:2000 promotes a process approach to QMSs. Successful management system implementation depends on understanding the process approach in addition to the standard's requirements. Begin your understanding by ordering the ISO 9000:2000, ISO 9001:2000, and ISO 9004:2000 family of standards. Copies can be purchased through a variety of sources including ASQ, any registrar, and the ISO organization. It is of paramount importance that before opening the ISO 9001:2000 requirements standard, review the quality concepts described in the *ISO 9000:2000 Fundamentals and vocabulary* standard.

When you examine ISO 9001:2000, pay particular attention to the process approach described in its introduction. A "process" is a system of activities that uses resources to transform inputs into outputs. The "process approach" promoted by ISO 9001:2000 requires that you systematically identify and manage these processes and their interaction within a QMS. An advantage of the process approach is the ongoing control it provides over the linkage between individual processes within a system of processes, as well as their combination and interaction. According to clause 4.2.2 in ISO 9001:2000, the quality manual must describe the interaction of the processes within the QMS. ISO 9004:2000 provides guidance on performance improvements beyond the basic requirements of ISO 9001:2000. More current information may be obtained from the ISO Web site www.iso.ch. Pay attention to the section on "Key Concepts of ISO 9001:2000," as it covers the major principles of the standard.

ASSEMBLE AN IMPLEMENTATION TEAM

Choosing the right team to implement your ISO 9001:2000–based QMS is key to any successful quality program, but it's not easy. There is no right or wrong way to choose a team because organizations vary in size, scope, and complexity. It is optimal to have people with different skill sets on the team, from cross-functional parts of the business to provide valuable input to the implementation process. This allows business synergies and communication to occur across the business.

Team members for implementation and assessments should be identified early in the process, but make sure you have people who represent all relevant departments. It is vital that senior management is represented on the team, as overall responsibility for the QMS lies with them, but it is equally important that staff from all levels form part of the team, as everyone can provide a valuable insight. It is key to have team members who understand how the interdepartmental interfaces function and processes link so that a process-based management system can be effectively implemented.

Additionally, it is a good idea to consider the personality traits of the members of the team. For example, because there will likely be a lot of meetings in the beginning for implementation planning, setting objectives, and the quality policy, you should consider personnel who work well together in groups. Group decisions can generate a lot of creative feedback, which is often critical in providing more employee ownership and buy-in to the project. Other personality traits you should consider include:

- *Action-oriented.* The team needs to be ready to act and implement change.

- *Experienced.* It is a good idea to have team members who know the business of the organization. People who have been around a while and know how things operate can be invaluable to your team.

- *Detail-driven.* Documentation and implementation means dotting the "i" and crossing the "t", and deadlines are often absolute.

- *Holistic thinkers.* When implementing ISO 9001:2000 for an organization, team members must be able to see the "big picture."

- *Good communicators.* Once the system begins, awareness and understanding is crucial. This is where a strong team becomes essential, because spreading the word about quality is important. Also, ensure that the information that is communicated is consistent and relevant.

GET MANAGEMENT SYSTEM TRAINING

Many of your implementation team members will require ISO 9001:2000 management system training to aid understanding of the requirements, and to plan and develop your management system. It is important to get training early in the implementation project as it will bring significant time and money savings to your organization in the long term if staff members are correctly trained.

IMPLEMENTING THE SYSTEM

Now you are appropriately prepared with an understanding of the fundamentals, and have a project plan and a trained team assembled. Next is the hard part, the actual implementation. Here we will present the three core elements of implementation.

Gap Analysis

A gap analysis is a process an organization goes through to determine the difference between what the process or QMS is like now and what it should be when it conforms to the requirements of ISO 9001:2000 (or any management system standard). At the early implementation phase, a gap analysis should focus on:

- Whether procedures have been established when necessary and/or required

- Compliance to established procedures and processes

- Proper resource allocation

- Effective communication of objectives and responsibilities

- Competency of personnel and training programs

- The organization's ability to make changes when necessary

Once you have a full understanding of these issues, you may realize that you are a long way on the road to ISO 9001:2000 already. You can then evaluate the best way to formalize what you have and make strategic decisions on how best to fill those gaps that were discovered so that established requirements can be met and customer satisfaction enhanced. Later in the implementation process a gap analysis may include the following areas:

- The organization's quality culture

- Knowledge of the QMS and ISO 9001:2000

- Awareness of the quality policy and quality objectives

- The suitability and effectiveness of the quality system

Write and Develop Documentation

Everyone on the team must have a clear understanding of what documentation needs to be created and this includes identifying the needs and expectations of your customers, as they form the basis for many of your processes and procedures. All of the ISO 9001:2000 documentation requirements are laid out clearly in clause 4.2. The following list details these and splits the required documents into a simple four-level hierarchy.

1. Quality manual

2. Procedures

3. Instructions

4. Records, forms

The reader will notice that "documents" means the total written system of your quality system and not an individual document. For purposes of ISO, there is one quality manual, six procedures, and as required instructions and records/forms.

The six documented procedures shown in Figure 12.1 are the minimum needed for your management system, and it may be necessary to retain or write other procedures to ensure effective operation of the QMS. For example, you may wish to look at design, control of monitoring and measurement devices, and other areas, depending on the organization. Other processes may or may not be documented, depending on whether the organization needs the documents for effective planning, operation, and control of its QMS. There are other issues that you should consider during the documentation phase as well. ISO 9004:2000 suggests that you should satisfy the "contractual, statutory, and regulatory requirements, and the needs and

---

1. Documented statements of a quality policy (5.3) and quality objectives (5.4.1)

2. A quality manual (4.2.2)

3. Documented procedures that are required by ISO 9001:2000. These are:

   a. 4.2.3—Control of documents

   b. 4.2.4—Control of records

   c. 8.2.2—Internal audit

   d. 8.3—Control of nonconforming product

   e. 8.5.2—Corrective action

   f. 8.5.3—Preventive action

4. Documents needed by the organization to ensure the effective planning, operation, and control of its processes

5. Records required by ISO 9001:2000 (see 4.2.4)

Figure 12.1 Required ISO 9001:2000 documented procedures (clause 4.2.1).

expectations of customers and other interested parties" concerning the nature and extent of the documentation. This means that items such as contracts, standards used by the organization, applicable regulations, and other information regarding the needs of your stakeholders should be considered.

Communicate Implementation

As you write your documentation, you should also simultaneously begin the process of implementing your QMS. The key to implementation is *communication and training*. During the implementation phase, everyone must operate to the procedures and collect records that demonstrate that the organization is doing what it says it's doing. Consequently, if personnel are to implement the system correctly, they need to be aware of what they're supposed to do. If staff have been involved in writing the documentation, implementation and compliance with the procedures should be easier. All staff members should be briefed accordingly about the procedures, although because the procedures should essentially be what they currently do, only changes need to be highlighted. Training can then be entered in the training records as evidence that proper instruction has been provided.

Once the training process has been completed and staff are implementing the procedures, periodically walk around the business, informally asking if the procedures are working or being implemented.

These activities cannot be done in series, but must be done at the same time and often done multiple times.

IMPLEMENTATION TIME SCALE

The time scale to implement a QMS that conforms to the requirements of ISO 9001:2000 depends on a number of factors such as resources, a sound plan, commitment from top management and personnel, and the complexity of the system. It is very important that you consider all of these issues during the planning phase. You also need to take into account time constraints if you are implementing ISO 9001:2000 due to a contractual requirement.

Ideally, the implementation phase should last about six months to allow sufficient time to collect enough records to verify that the system is working, but you should be getting data back for analysis within two to three months. Some good examples of records are purchase orders, sales records, contracts, internal audits, meeting minutes, test data, and anywhere ISO 9001:2000 requires a record to be maintained. Records must be legible and retrievable in a reasonable time frame. (You decide what is reasonable to your organization.)

Also, registrars usually want to see at least three months of system operation before conducting a third-party audit. This operating period should also include an entire internal audit cycle and a management review. You will need to collect records as evidence your system is complying with planned arrangements, meeting requirements, and effectively achieving the planned results.

REVIEW MANAGEMENT SYSTEM EFFECTIVENESS

One of the final stages of implementation and also a continual improvement process is to check that your system is working effectively and conforming to the requirements of ISO 9001:2000. This is the check and act part of the PDC(S)A cycle and involves monitoring your system by recording and interpreting data and conducting internal audits. ISO 9001:2000 requires that data generated as a result of monitoring and measurement should be analyzed as a means of determining where continual improvement can occur. Specific areas where data should be collected are customer satisfaction, product conformity, processes and products trends, including opportunities for preventive action, and suppliers.

CHOOSE A REGISTRAR

Registration to ISO 9001 takes place when an accredited third party visits an organization, assesses the management system, and issues a certificate to show that the organization meets the requirements of ISO 9001:2000. A number of factors should be considered when choosing a registrar, including industry experience, geographic locations, price, and service level offered.

THE REGISTRAR CONDUCTS THE AUDIT

The last step in the implementation process is the audit by the third-party registrar. Providing that your organization has done a good job of documenting and following the ISO system of quality, the registrar will issue the certificate of registration. At that point, recertification will occur as per the guidelines of the registrar and the ISO requirement.

REFERENCES

Crow, R. 2002. "A Prescription for Disaster." *Human Element: A Publication of the American Society for Quality* (Winter): 12–14.

Stamatis, D. H. 1995. *Understanding ISO 9000 and Implementing the Basics to Quality.* New York: Marcel Dekker.

———. 1999. *Integrating QS-9000 with Your Automotive Quality System,* 3rd ed. Milwaukee: ASQ Quality Press.

Appendix A
Readability Index

READABILITY

With all written documents, the intent is to communicate. Therefore, it behooves the individuals who will create any level of document to make sure that the reader will comprehend the content and the message. In this section of the appendix we provide two common methods of identifying the readability of a document.

The Fog Index

Robert Gunning (1968) developed a way to measure how hard something is to read. His Fog Index in *The Technique of Clear Writing* is considered the most reliable formula for testing your writing. It is not an index of how *good* your writing is but of how *easy* it is *to understand.* Good writing is another subject. But all writing must be clear before it can be good. Here is the Fog Index formula:

1. Take a sample of your writing. Count the words in several complete sentences until you have about 100 words. Divide the number of words by the number of sentences to get the average sentence length.

2. Count the words with three or more syllables. Don't count those that are capitalized or combinations of short, easy words (like bookkeeper or garbageman), or that are made three syllables by adding –ed or –es (like expanded or confesses).

This gives you the percentage of "hard" words if your sample is about 100 words.

3. Add the average sentence length and the percentage of hard words (like 15.25 percent, not .1525). Multiply by .4.

4. Make number whole (round it off)—without the decimal.

Example: Apply the Fog Index to the three items of the previous paragraphs, without the samples in parentheses. Figures like 100 count as we read them—one hundred (two words). Likewise, we read ".4" as point four or four tenths (two words either way). The three previous paragraphs have 98 words and eight sentences—an average of 12.25 words per sentence. The "hard" words total 10—slightly more than 10 percent. Adding average sentence length (12.25) and percentage of hard words (10.20) gives you 22.45. Multiply that by .4 and you have 8.98. Round this to the closest number. In this case: 9. See what this means below.

It should be noted that the ideal reading level for most, if not all, quality documentation should be 7 or 8. If you have a Fog Index of more than 12, you run a serious risk of not being understood—or even read. This chart is not a measure of intelligence level, or of subject-matter level, but only of reading level. (ISO 9001:2000 is written on a 17th grade level. AS9100 is written on an 18th grade level. ISO/TS 16949 is written on a 17th grade level). To give you an idea what the numbers represent, here is a list of indices, grades, and popular magazines.

Fog Index	Reading Level by Grade	Magazines at This Level
17	College graduate	No popular magazines at these levels
16	College senior	
15	College junior	
14	College sophomore	
13	College freshman	
12	High school senior	*Atlantic Monthly*
11	High school junior	*Time, Harper's*
10	High school sophomore	*Newsweek*
9	High school freshman	*Reader's Digest*
8	Eighth grade	*Ladies' Home Journal* and typical newspapers
7	Seventh grade	*True Confessions*
6	Sixth grade	Comic books

The following is an example of a policy statement that would be difficult for most people to read. The Fog Index (calculated below) is 13.2.

This policy addresses access to and data residing in computerized administrative systems (hereafter referred to as the systems and the data) supported by Administrative Information Services (AIS). This includes but is not limited to financial and student systems. It does not include institutional reporting databases [that is, fast reactor database (FRDB), research reactor database (RRDB), staff demographics reporting database (SDRDB), and so on], departmental systems, hard-copy files, or systems or databases maintained by any unit other than AIS. It does not supersede applicable statutes that guarantee either the protection or accessibility of data.

The intent of this policy is to: a) maximize the strategic value of the systems and the data by promoting its effective use in management decisions, daily operations, and analyses being conducted by faculty, staff, and students; b) provide clear assignment of responsibility for protection against unauthorized use; and c) promote security measures for the purpose of maintaining the integrity of the systems and the data.

Figuring the grade:

1. Count the *number of words* in the sample 148

2. Count the *number of sentences* 13

3. Count the *number of big words* (three or
   more syllables) 33

4. Divide the number of sentences into the
   number of words . . . . $148/13 = 11$

5. Divide the number of words into the number
   of big words . . . . $33/148 = 22\%$

6. Add the *result of step 4* to the *result
   of step 5* . . . . $11 + 22 = 33$

7. Multiply by .4 . . . . $33 \times .4 = 13.2$

The Flesch Method

Microsoft Word. Under the Tools menu, Microsoft Word contains a word counter, grammar checker, and thesaurus you can use to help simplify your writing style. The grammar checker doesn't use the Fog Index. It uses three Flesch (1974) tools to analyze style:

1. Flesch Reading Ease (100 = easiest, 70–80 = average)

Typical Reading Ease Score	Difficulty	Flesch Grade Level
0–29	Very difficult	Post graduate
30–49	Difficult	College
50–59	Fairly difficult	High school
60–69	Standard	8th to 9th grade
70–79	Fairly easy	7th grade
80–89	Easy	5th to 6th grade
90–100	Very easy	4th to 5th grade

2. Flesch Grade Level (assigns a grade level reader must have to understand your writing, 6 = average)

3. Flesch Kincaid (Another formula for determining reader grade level)

The grammar checker will also report the percentage of sentences written in the passive voice. (Acceptable percentages for sentences with passive voice are *zero!*) The grammar checker will also find typos that spell checkers miss, like transpositions, capitalization errors, and double words.

You can use the thesaurus to find simpler words or when you find yourself using the same words over and over. The grammar checker reported the following for the previous policy sample:

- Percent passive—14 percent
- Flesch Reading Ease—26.8
- Flesch Grade Level—17
- Flesch Kincaid—14.9

WordPerfect. WordPerfect has its own readability calculator. Word generates readability statistics using several different methods including Flesch Reading Ease and Flesch Kincaid. To determine readability of any document, first, use the grammar tool to check grammar. After the grammar check is completed, the document's readability statistics will be displayed.

In WordPerfect select Grammatik from the Tools menu. Select the Options button and then analysis and readability. WordPerfect generates statistics on the Flesch Kincaid, passive voice, sentence complexity, and vocabulary complexity. It also compares the scores of the document you are analyzing with another document.

In all cases when analyzing text you will get better results by analyzing longer passages or taking three 100-word passages from different sections of a book.

REFERENCES

Flesch, R. 1974. *The Art of Readable Writing.* New York: Harper & Row. (Original work published 1949.)

Gunning, R. 1968. *The Technique of Clear Writing.* New York: McGraw-Hill.

Appendix B
Training

The following training programs are generally associated with ISO and its derivative standards. Here we provide the scope and objectives of the training, rather than the actual outlines of the specific programs.

Quality Systems Documentation (two days). Teaches the skills required to write documents that meet the requirements of the standard. The documents are: quality manual, procedures, work instructions, forms, guidelines, and other specific items such as logs and check sheets. Furthermore, the training provides the knowledge base for the auditor as to the rationale and specifications of the actual documentation. As the auditors gain understanding about the documentation process, it helps them in their auditing so that they are not causing interruptions in the work flow of businesses and employees.

Implementing ISO 9001:2000 (two days). Introduces the concepts needed to understand and create a QMS. It is ideal for anybody involved in planning or implementing a QMS to be compliant with ISO 9001:2000. The thrust of this training is based in the explanation of the process that an organization has to follow to be in compliance with the standard.

Understanding ISO 9001:2000 (one day). An interactive, intro-
ductory course that summarizes the requirements of the
ISO 9001:2000 standard. It is ideal for those with little
knowledge of the standard, as well as those starting an
implementation project.

Management Briefing (one day). Provides participants with a
background of management systems, an overview of the
primary requirements of ISO 9001:2000, and an in-depth
interpretation of the requirements in clause 5, Management
responsibility.

Transition to ISO 9000:2000 (one day). Provides participants
with the knowledge and background of the changes from the
1994 to 2000 version. Emphasis is given in the areas of
"process," "customer satisfaction," and "effectiveness."

Understanding ISO/TS 16949 (two days). Introduces the
concepts needed to understand and create a QMS in the
global automotive industry. It is ideal for anybody involved
in planning or implementing a QMS to be compliant with
ISO 9001:2000. The thrust of this training is based in the
explanation of the process that an organization has to follow
to be in compliance with the automotive standard.

Understanding the AS9100 Standard (two days). Introduces the
concepts needed to understand and create a QMS for the
aerospace industry. It is ideal for anybody involved in planning or implementing a QMS to be compliant with ISO
9001:2000. The thrust of this training is based in the explanation of the process that an organization has to follow to
be in compliance with the aerospace standard.

Appendix C
Aids In Helping Formulate an FMEA

The content of this appendix should help the quality professional in creating and/or evaluating an FMEA. We begin by focusing on the thought starters: how and where to start the FMEA, identify appropriate and typical verbs and nouns for applicable "function," and give some typical generic examples of the verb–noun relationship.

BRAINSTORMING THOUGHT STARTERS

Adapt	What else is like this?
	Does the past offer similarities?
	What could we copy?
	What other ideas does this suggest?
Combine	Use a blend, alloy, assortment?
	Can we combine units?
	Combine purposes, functions?
	Combine ideas?
Magnify	What can we add?
	Thicker?
	More frequent?

	Stronger?
	Duplicate?
Minimize	What can we subtract?
	Smaller?
	Lighter?
	Condensed?
	Omit?
	Streamline?
Rearrange	Can we interchange components?
	Different layout?
	Different sequence?
	Change pace?
	Different pattern?
	Different schedule?
Reverse	What's the opposite?
	Can we turn it around, upside down, backward?
	Can we reverse roles?
Modify	Could we change the color, sound, motion, form, shape, meaning, odor?
	What new twist?
Substitute	What can we use instead?
	Who else can?
	Another approach?
	Another material?
	Another ingredient?
What if	You were spending your money?
	Money was no object?
	You combined two functions?
	You were a man from Mars—what questions would you ask about this?

What if	You were eight years old—what questions would you have?
	You knew your managers would buy an idea you came up with—what would it be?
	You were from 1000 years in the future?
	You didn't perform the function at all?
	You had the perfect material—what would you expect?
	You performed the function backward?
	Gravity did not exist—what would you do then?
	You were trying to prevent the function from being performed?
	You had an unlimited amount of time?
	Nothing was sacred?

VERB–NOUN LISTING: PRODUCTS

Verbs		Nouns	
*absorb	generate	access	friction
access	guide	air	heat
actuate	improve	appearance	impact
*allow	increase	bending	light
apply	isolate	circuit	mass
attach	limit	climate	material
attract	maintain	cold	moisture
circulate	pivot	comfort	motion
conduct	position	component	noise
connect	prevent	corrosion	occupant
contain	protect	current	parts
control	*provide	deflection	path
convert	reduce	dirt	performance
create	regulate	drag	pressure
decrease	resist	energy	stability
direct	rotate	entry	surface
enclose	seal	environment	torque
enhance	sense	flow	travel
extend	support	fluid	vibration
*facilitate	transmit	force	weight

*Try to avoid use of these verbs.

VERB–NOUN LISTING: PROCESS

Verbs		Nouns	
*allow	join	alignment	flash
apply	load	assembly	gage
assemble	maintain	burr	gas
assure	make	casting	heat
blend	move	cause	hole
clean	position	cleanliness	inventory
control	prevent	cold	length
convert	protect	component	locator
create	*provide	container	machine
decrease	receive	correction	material
deliver	release	damage	mold
*facilitate	remove	defect	operation
fasten	repair	device	part
fill	rotate	die	priority
finish	seal	dimension	schedule
form	store	dirt	shape
identify	supply	environment	surface
improve	thread	equipment	tool
increase	transport	finish	uniformity
inspect	verify	fixture	waste

*Try to avoid use of these verbs.

FUNCTIONS IDENTIFICATION EXAMPLE FOR A PRODUCT

Team Members: Date:
Project:

Listing of Functions Performed	
Active Verb	**Measurable Noun**
Improve	Appearance
Position	Parts
Enhance	Stability
Prevent	Vibration
Improve	Assembly
Assure	Location
Reduce	Margin variation
Enhance	Cooling
Control	Location
Support	Part
Limit	Deflection
Fasten	Parts

FUNCTIONS IDENTIFICATION EXAMPLE FOR A PROCESS

Team Members: Date:
Project:

Listing of Functions Performed	
Active Verb	**Measurable Noun**
Transfer	Material (parts)
Move	Material
Position	Material (parts)
Apply	Material (sealer)
Actuate	Circuit
Weld	Assembly
Remove	Assembly
Position	Assembly
Store	Assembly
Produce	Assembly
Ship	Assembly
Supply	Material
Repair	Assembly

GENERIC FMEA EVALUATION

Any auditor reviewing an FMEA should at least question and/or look for: a one to one relationship between failure mode and root cause, high severity, high occurrence, high detection, empty columns, criticality, significance, appropriate identification of special characteristics, preparation (must be created by team), connection of FMEA, and control plan and date of revision.

For the convenience of the auditor we provide the generic failures for all products and services. They are: 1) no function, 2) degradation over time, 3) surprise (unintended) failure, 4) intermittent failure, 5) partial failure, and 6) over-function.

Appendix D

Guidelines for Process Selection and Metrics Evaluation

This appendix focuses on "how" to go about selecting the process and the metrics in a given audit for any organization.

PLANT METRICS

- Interview plant personnel to determine what the plant metrics are.
- Inquire and/or determine to what extent they relate to the metrics of the organization.
- Consider if there are any additional metrics being used.

USE OF PLANT METRICS

- Review the scoreboard and identify what exists.
- Evaluate if the metrics are current.
- Determine how the metrics are used. Are they reviewed regularly? Who does the review? To what extent is the information communicated to the workforce?

PROCESSES

- Make a list of some key processes within the facility.

- Identify the measures for each process.

- Determine the extent to which these measures relate to those monitored by the plant.

- Determine how process owners are made aware of process performance.

- Ask questions to determine process performance and major problems experienced with each process.

- Observe whether the metrics for each process are regularly reviewed.

- Determine whether the metrics for the process are visible.

- Identify who has the responsibility to maintain the measures for the process.

- Determine how each measure is defined and documented. This will help assess the reliability of the data.

- Determine how plant personnel respond to performance metrics for the processes. Is structured problem solving being used to respond or react to measures showing an unfavorable trend?

As important as these are, it must be emphasized that not all OEMs require the ISO/TS standard. In fact, the IATF's direction is to provide for the following options:

- *Compliance.* Certification is not required but must conform to the requirements.

- *Optional with upgrade urged.* A partial list of OEMs and their direction toward ISO/TS 16949:

OEM	Direction
BMW	Compliance
DaimlerChrysler	Optional through 7/1/04
Fiat Auto	New certification/renewal
Ford	Optional
GM	Optional
Nissan Motor	Optional/compliance only
Peugeot-Citroën	Optional through 2003
Renault	Optional through 3003
Volkswagen	Optional

- *Phase in.* Start with lead, major commodity supplier organizations, and the rest will follow.

- *Mandate.* Establish a deadline for first-tier suppliers that fall under applicability.

Appendix E

A Cross-Reference between ISO 9001:1994 and ISO 9001:2000 Standards

ISO 9001:1994 AND ISO 9001: 2000

As we already discussed, the structure of the new standard (2000) is quite different than the old one (1994). However, most of the requirements are the same, though they have been rearranged in a different scheme. This appendix compares the two and is based on the ISO 9001:2000 standard.

ISO 9001:1994	ISO 9001:2000
1 Scope	1
2 Normative reference	2
3 Definitions	3
4 Quality system requirements [title only]	
4.1 Management responsibility [title only]	
4.1.1 Quality policy	5.1 + 5.3 + 5.4.1
4.1.2 Organization [title only]	
4.1.2.1 Responsibility and authority	5.5.1
4.1.2.2 Resources	6.1 + 6.2.1
4.1.2.3 Management representative	5.5.2
4.1.3 Management review	5.6.1 + 8.5.1
4.2 Quality system [title only]	
4.2.1 General	4.1 + 4.2.2
4.2.2 Quality system procedures	4.2.1

continued

ISO 9001:1994	ISO 9001:2000
4.2.3 Quality planning	5.4.2 + 7.1
4.3 Contract review [title only]	
4.3.1 General	
4.3.2 Review	5.2 + 7.2.1 + 7.2.2 + 7.2.3
4.3.3 Amendment to a contract	7.2.2
4.3.4 Records	7.2.2
4.4 Design control [title only]	
4.4.1 General	
4.4.2 Design and development planning	7.3.1
4.4.3 Organizational and technical interfaces	7.3.1
4.4.4 Design input	7.2.1 + 7.3.2
4.4.5 Design output	7.3.3
4.4.6 Design review	7.3.4
4.4.7 Design verification	7.3.5
4.4.8 Design validation	7.3.6
4.4.9 Design changes	7.3.7
4.5 Document and data control [title only]	
4.5.1 General	4.2.3
4.5.2 Document and data approval and issue	4.2.3
4.5.3 Document and data changes	4.2.3
4.6 Purchasing [title only]	
4.6.1 General	
4.6.2 Evaluation of subcontractors	7.4.1
4.6.3 Purchasing data	7.4.2
4.6.4 Verification of purchased product	7.4.3
4.7 Control of customer-supplied product	7.5.4
4.8 Product identification and traceability	7.5.3
4.9 Process control	6.3 + 6.4 + 7.5.1 + 7.5.2
4.10 Inspection and testing [title only]	
4.10.1 General	7.1 + 8.1
4.10.2 Receiving inspection and testing	7.4.3 + 8.2.4
4.10.3 In-process inspection and testing	8.2.4
4.10.4 Final inspection and testing	8.2.4
4.10.5 Inspection and test records	7.5.3 + 8.2.4
4.11 Control of inspection, measuring and test equipment [title only]	
4.11.1 General	7.6
4.11.2 Control procedure	7.6
4.12 Inspection and test status	7.5.3
4.13 Control of nonconforming product [title only]	

continued

continued

ISO 9001:1994	ISO 9001:2000
4.13.1 General	8.3
4.13.2 Review and disposition of nonconforming product	8.3
4.14 Corrective and preventive action [title only]	
4.14.1 General	8.5.2 + 8.5.3
4.14.2 Corrective action	8.5.2
4.14.3 Preventive action	8.5.3
4.15 Handling, storage, packaging, preservation and delivery [title only]	
4.15.1 General	
4.15.2 Handling	7.5.5
4.15.3 Storage	7.5.5
4.15.4 Packaging	7.5.5
4.15.5 Preservation	7.5.5
4.15.6 Delivery	7.5.1
4.16 Control of quality records	4.2.4
4.17 Internal quality audits	8.2.2 + 8.2.3
4.18 Training	6.2.2
4.19 Servicing	7.5.1
4.20 Statistical techniques [title only]	
4.20.1 Identification of need	8.1 + 8.2.3 + 8.2.4 + 8.4
4.20.2 Procedures	8.1 + 8.2.3 + 8.2.4 + 8.4

KEY ISO/TS 16949:2000 TRANSITION CHANGES FROM QS-9000

Standard	Element	Opportunities
ISO 9001:2000	4.1, Quality management system—General requirements	Requirements for process map (or equivalent), process management, customer-oriented processes, support processes, and process characteristics.
ISO 9001:2000	5.2, Management responsibility—Customer focus	Decision on customers vs. interested parties. Need for process to gather "needs and expectations" of customer/interested parties.
ISO 9001:2000 & TS 16949:1999	5.4.1, Planning—Quality objectives	Deployed objectives addressing customer expectations.

continued

continued

Standard	Element	Opportunities
ISO 9001:2000	5.5.3, Internal communication	Creation of internal communication processes suitable to organization.
ISO 9001:2000 & TS 16949:1999	5.6, Management review	Revision of previous management review process. TS adds additional items to be reviewed.
ISO 9001:2000	6.1, Resource management—Provision of resources	Establishment of a resource allocation process.
ISO 9001:2000 & TS 16949:1999	6.2, Human resources (particularly 6.2.2.3 and 6.2.2.4)	Provision of job competency, on-the-job training, and employee motivation and empowerment.
ISO 9001:2000	7, Product realization	Documents for "effective control" of all processes in process map.
New (actually Ford's QI 2002)	7.1.4, Change control	Minor change for most suppliers.
New	7.3, Design and development	Inclusion of design and development of processes, not just product (note required development and use of FMEAs).
New	7.4, Purchasing	Inclusion of service suppliers in coverage and use of supplier monitoring indicators. ISO 9001:2000 registration of suppliers.
ISO 9001:2000	8.2.1, Monitoring and measurement—Customer satisfaction	Customer rating for quality and delivery insufficient; monitoring of "customer perceptions" of quality. Importance of customer satisfaction—supplemental requirements, including delivered part quality and schedule performance to IATF.
TS 16949:1999	8.2.2, Internal audit	Manufacturing process and product audits and audits based on COPS and process approach.
ISO 9001:2000 & TS 16949:1999	8.2.3, Monitoring and measurement of processes	Process studies on manufacturing processes. Measurement of all processes in process map.
ISO 9001:2000	8.4, Analysis of data	Increased scope from QS-9000.

Appendix F
Statistics in Auditing

STATISTICAL SYMBOLS AND
NOTATIONS USED IN AUDITING

While in statistics we use many symbols and notations for expedience, in auditing, especially for sample definition, selection, and analysis, we use some statistical notation. This appendix identifies some of the most common symbols and notations.*

Capital (and sometimes small) letters are used to denote the universe values of the study and ancillary variables (such as $Y_1, Y_2, \ldots, Y_N; X_1, X_2, \ldots, X_N$), and small letters (such as $y_1, y_2, \ldots, y_N; x_1, x_2, \ldots, x_N$). N is the universe size (that is, the total number of units in the universe), and n the sample size. Universe parameters are denoted by capital or Greek letters (such as $\overline{Y}$, the universe mean σ^2; the universe variance per unit ρ; the universe correlation coefficient of two variables), and the sample estimators by small letters (with circumflex [~] or "hat" [^] on the corresponding universe parameters) such as y, s^2, and $\hat{\rho}$ respectively for the sample mean, sample estimator for variance, and sample correlation.

In general, the following *subscripts* are used:

- h for stratum, $h = 1, 2, \ldots, L$

---

* Note: Some of the material in this appendix has been adopted from 1) R. K. Som. 1996. *Practical Sampling Techniques*. 2nd ed. revised and expanded. New York: Marcel Dekker, pp. 19–21, 31, 147, 229; and 2) J. Willburn. 1984. *Practical Statistical Sampling for Auditors*. New York: Marcel Dekker, pp. 55–67. The material is used here with written permission from Marcel Dekker, Inc.

- i for a first-stage unit, $i = 1, 2, \ldots, N$ for the universe, and $i = 1, 2, \ldots, n$ for the sample

- j for a second-stage unit, $j = 1, 2, \ldots, M_i$ for the universe, and $j = 1, 2, \ldots, m_i$ for the sample

- k for a third-stage unit, $k = 1, 2, \ldots, Q_{ij}$ for the universe, and $k = 1, 2, \ldots, q_{ij}$ for the sample

y denotes a *study variable* (also an unbiased estimator of the total Y of the study variable for the universe);

x denotes *another study variable;* and

z denotes an *ancillary variable* either for selection with probability proportional to size or for ratio or regression estimation.

The following *symbols* are used with additional subscripts, as required:

	Universe Parameter	Sample Estimator
Total of y	Y	y_0^* (or y)
Mean of y (per first-stage unit)	$\bar{Y}$	y_0^*/N
Proportion	P	p
Ratio	R	r
Sampling variance of estimator t	σ_t^2	s_t^2
Standard error of t	σ_t	s_t
Covariance of t and u	σ_{yu}	s_{yu}
Correlation coefficient	ρ	$\hat{\rho}$
Intraclass correlation coefficient	ρ_c	$\hat{\rho}_c$
Regression coefficient	β	$\hat{\beta}$

Other Notations and Symbols

ea	Enumeration unit
f	Sampling fraction (with subscripts added for strata and stages)
fsu	First-stage sample unit
pps sampling	Probability proportional to size sampling
ppswr	pps sampling with replacement
srs	Simple random sample or simple random sampling
srswor	srs without replacement
srswr	srs with replacement

continued

continued

Other Notations and Symbols

ssu	Second-stage unit
tsu	Third-stage unit
SS_{yi}	Sum of squares of deviations of y_i from the mean $\bar{y}$
SPy_ix_i	Sum of products of deviations of y_i and x_i from their respective means

Greek Letters Used. A number of events are considered.

α (alpha)	Probability point of the t or the normal distribution
β (beta)	Regression coefficient
π (pi, small)	Probability of selection
Π (pi, capital)	Product notation
ρ (rho)	Correlation coefficient
σ (sigma, small)	Universe standard deviation
Σ (sigma, capital)	Summation notation

CONCEPTS OF SAMPLING

Universe Parameters

A parameter is a function of the frequency values of the study variable. Some important parameters are the universe total and mean.

The total of the values Y_i is denoted by Y and is represented as

$$Y_i + Y_2 + \ldots + Y_N = \sum_{i=1}^{N} Y_i = Y$$

The universe mean is the universe total divided by the number of universe units, denoted by $\bar{Y}$, and is represented by

$$\bar{Y} = \frac{Y}{N}$$

Variability of the universe is measured by the mean of the squared deviations of the values from the mean and is called the universe variance per unit, is denoted by σ_Y^2, and is represented by

$$\sigma_Y^2 = \sum_{i=1}^{N} \frac{\left(Y_i - \overline{Y}\right)^2}{N}$$

The positive square root is known as the universe standard deviation per unit.

To obtain a measure of the universe variability independent of the unit of measurement, the universe standard deviation is divided by the universe mean; the ratio is called the universe coefficient of variation, is denoted by *CV*, and is represented by

$$CV_Y = \frac{\sigma_Y}{\overline{Y}}$$

This expression is usually expressed as a percentage. The square of the *CV* is called the relative variance and is used in auditing to compare the variability of different items.

Another universe measure is the ratio of the totals or means of the values of two study variables. This measure *R* (do not confuse this with range, which is maximum minus minimum) band is represented by

$$R = \frac{Y}{X} = \frac{\overline{Y}}{\overline{X}}$$

where *X* is the universe total and $\overline{X}$ the universe mean of another study variable, similarly defined as *Y* and $\overline{Y}$.

If we denote the universe standard variable of the second study by σ_X then the universe covariance between two study variables is obtained on taking the mean of the products of deviations from their respective means, is denoted by σ_{YX}, and is represented by

$$\sigma_{YX} = \sum_{i=1}^{N} \frac{\left(Y_i - \overline{Y}\right)\left(X_i = \overline{X}\right)}{N}$$

The universe linear (product moment) correlation coefficient between two study variables is obtained on dividing the product of the two respective standard deviations into the covariance, is denoted by ρ_{YX}, and is represented by

$$\rho_{YX} = \frac{\sigma_{YX}}{\sigma_Y \sigma_X}$$

This correlation coefficient is a pure number and it varies from −1 (perfect negative correlation) through zero (no linear correlation) to +1 (perfect linear correlation). If N' of the total N units posses a certain attribute or belongs to a certain category, the universe proportion P of the number of such units is

$$P = \frac{N'}{N}$$

Sample Estimators

An estimator is a rule or method of estimating a universe parameter. Usually expressed as a function of a sample value, it is called a sample estimator (or an estimator). There may be more than one estimator for the same universe parameter. The particular value yielded by the sample estimator for a given sample is called a sample estimate or an estimate.

If a simple random sample of n units is selected from the universe of N units, the value of a study variable for the *ith* sample unit is denoted by y_i ($i = 1, 2, \ldots, n$). The *ith* sample unit may be any of the N universe units. The sample mean is

$$\bar{y} = \frac{(y_1 + y_2 + \ldots y_n)}{n} = \sum_{i=1}^{n} \frac{y}{n}$$

A sample estimator of the universe total Y is

$$y = N\bar{y}$$

The sampling variance of the sample mean in sampling with replacement is

$$\sigma_{\bar{y}}^2 = \frac{\sigma_y^2}{n}$$

The sample estimator is

$$s_y^2 = \sum_{i=1}^{n} \frac{(y_i - \bar{y})^2}{n-1}$$

If sampling is made with replacement, then the estimator of the variance of the sample mean $\bar{y}$ in simple random sampling is

$$s_{\bar{y}}^2 = \frac{s_y^2}{n}$$

The sample estimator of the universe covariance of two study variables is

$$s_{yx} = \sum_{i=1}^{n} \frac{(y_1 - \bar{y})(x_i - \bar{x})}{n-1}$$

The ratio of the estimator of two variables is

$$r = \frac{y}{x} = \frac{\bar{y}}{\bar{x}}$$

The sample correlation coefficient is

$$\hat{\rho}_{yx} = \frac{s_{yx}}{s_y s_x}$$

Criteria for Estimators

A sample estimator is unbiased if the average value of the sample estimates for all possible samples of the same size is mathematically identical with the value of the universe parameter. This average over all possible samples of the same size is also known as mathematical expectation. This is shown as $\bar{y}$ and $\bar{x}$ of the universe parameters Y and X, respectively.

A second criterion is consistency. An estimator is said to be consistent if it tends to the universe value with increasing sample size.

A third criterion is precision (efficiency). There are two estimators based on the same sample size, for the same universe parameter, one is said to be more efficient than the other when its sampling variance is smaller than the other's. The precision of the estimator t relative to that of t' is defined as

$$\text{precision } (t,t') = \frac{\sigma_{t'}^2}{\sigma_t^2}$$

The efficiency of the estimator t relative to that of is defined as

$$\text{efficiency } (t,t') = \frac{MSE_{t'}}{MSE_t}$$

where MSE_t is the mean square error.

In large samples (simple random) the variance of the median as an estimator of the universe mean Y is

$$\frac{1}{2}\pi\sigma_Y^2 / n$$

(where π is the ratio of the circumference of a circle to that of its diameter = 3.14159 . . . , so that the efficiency of the mean relative to the median is

$$\frac{\left(\frac{1}{2}\pi\sigma_Y^2 / n\right)}{\left(\frac{\sigma_Y^2}{n}\right)} = \frac{1}{2}\pi = 1.5708$$

or 1.57 approximately. This means that for a simple random sample of the same size, the same mean is 57 percent more efficient than the sample median in estimating the universe mean.

Special note: A relative concept known as minimum variance estimator (Cramer–Rao inequality) states that the variance of an estimator of Y cannot be smaller than σ_Y^2 / n. But as the sample mean itself has sampling variance σ_Y^2 / n in simple random sampling (with replacement), we can say that under this sampling plan, the sample mean is an unbiased, consistent, minimum variance estimator of the universe mean.

Mean Square Error

If the sample estimator t has a mathematical expectation T' different from the universal parameter T that the sample estimator t seeks to measure, the sampling variability of the estimator t around its mathematical expectation T' is given by the sampling variance σ_t^2; but the variability of the estimator t around the true value T is given by the mean square error. The sampling variance and the mean square error of t are connected by:

$$\text{mean square error } (MSE) = \text{sampling variance } + (\text{Bias})^2$$

$$MSE_t = \sigma_t^2 + B_t^2$$

where $Bt = T' - T$ is the bias in the estimator t.

Symbols and Notations

$$SS_{y_i} = \sum_{i}^{n}(y_i - \bar{y}) = \sum_{i}^{n} y_i^2 - \left(\sum_{i}^{n} y_i\right)^2 / n = \sum_{i}^{n} y_i^2 - n\bar{y}^2 = \sum_{i}^{n} y_i^2 - \bar{y}\left[\sum_{i}^{n} y\right]$$

will be termed the corrected sum of squares. The choice of the particular expression for SS_{yi} in the equation will depend on computational convenience. Similarly,

$$\sum_{i}^{n} y_i x_i$$

will be called the raw or crude sum of products of the y_i and x_i values and the sum of products of deviations from the perspective means

$$\sum_{i}^{n} y_i x_i = \sum_{i}^{n}(y_i - \bar{y})(x_i - \bar{x}) = \sum_{i}^{n} y_i x_i - \bar{x}[\sum_{i}^{n} y_1]$$

the corrected sum of products. Thus, the sample variance is given by

$$s_y^2 = \sum_{i}^{n}(y_i - \bar{y})^2 /(n-1) = SS_{y_i} /(n-1)$$

and the sample covariance given by

$$s_{yx} = \sum(y_i - \bar{y})(x_i - \bar{x})/(n-1) = SPy_i x_i /(n-1)$$

Simple Random Sampling

$$\text{Average} = \bar{y} = \sum_{i=1}^{n} y_i / n$$

Variance per unit:

$$s_y^2 = \sum_{i}^{n}(y_i - \bar{y})^2 /(n-1)$$

Variance of sample mean (depending on convenience of computation):

$$s_y^2 = \sum_{i}^{n}(y_i - \bar{y})^2 /(n-1) = [\sum_{i}^{n} y_i^2 - [\sum_{i}^{n} y_i]^2 / n]/ n - 1$$

$$= (\sum_{i}^{n} y_i^2 - n\bar{y}) /(n-1) = (\sum_{i}^{n} y_i^2 - \bar{y})[\sum_{i}^{n} y_i]/(n-1)$$

Coefficient of variation of the sample mean is

$$CV(\bar{y}) = \frac{\sigma_{\bar{y}}}{\bar{Y}} = \frac{\sigma}{\bar{Y}\sqrt{n}} = \frac{\text{universe } CV \text{ per unit}}{\sqrt{n}} \quad \text{in srswr}$$

$$= \left[\frac{\text{universe } CV \text{ per unit}}{\sqrt{n}}\right]\sqrt{\frac{N-n}{N-1}} \quad \text{in srswor}$$

$$= \frac{\sigma}{\bar{Y}\sqrt{n}}\sqrt{\frac{N-n}{N-1}}$$

In sampling with replacement, and also in sampling without replacement when the sampling fraction is relatively small, the sampling variance of the sample mean is inversely related to the sample size, and does not depend on the size of the universe.

STANDARD ERROR OF ESTIMATORS AND SETTING CONFIDENCE LIMITS

If $\bar{t}$ is an unbiased estimator of universe T and its sampling distribution moderately normal (which will happen when the sample size is not too small) $\sigma_{\bar{t}}$ and the standard error of $\bar{t}$ is estimated from the sample data, then the statistic student's t-distribution with $(n-1)$ degrees of freedom is

$$t' = \frac{\bar{t} - \bar{T}}{s_{\bar{t}}} = \frac{(\bar{t} - T)\sqrt{n}}{s_t}$$

then, the

$$s_{\bar{t}}^2 = \frac{\sum_{}^{n}(t_i - \bar{t})^2}{(n-1)}$$

Denoting by $t'_{\alpha,\,n-1}$ the 100α percentage point of the t-distribution corresponding to $(n-1)$ degrees of freedom, we see that the inequality

$$\frac{|\bar{t} - T|\sqrt{n}}{s_t} \le t'_{\alpha, n-1}$$

is expected to occur on an average with probability $(1 - \alpha)$. The chances are therefore $100(1 - \alpha)$ percent that the universe value T will be contained by the limits

$$\frac{\bar{t} \pm \left(t'_{\alpha, n-1}\, s_t\right)}{\sqrt{n}}$$

It should be noted here that if the standard error of $\bar{t}$ is known

$$\sigma_{\bar{t}} = \frac{\sigma}{\sqrt{n}}$$

then the statistic is

$$\frac{(\bar{t} - T)}{\sigma_{\bar{t}}}$$

Of course when the sample size is small, the t-distribution may still be used in setting probability limits to the universe values, but with the additional assumption that the sample itself comes from a normal distribution.

COMPARISON OF SYSTEMATIC AND SIMPLE RANDOM SAMPLING

From a universe comprising $N = nk$ units, it is proposed to select a systematic sample of 1 in k. The universe units are set in k columns and n rows, the columns 1 to k showing the random starts (clusters), each column containing n units. A random number is chosen between 1 and k and the set of n units in the selected column constitutes one systematic sample. In other words, every one of the k columns representing the k possible systematic samples has an equal chance ($= 1 / k$) of being selected.

Let y_{rj} denote the value of the unit with the serial number $r + (j - 1) k$ in the universe ($r = 1, 2, \ldots k; j = 1, 2, \ldots n$). If r is the chosen random number then the intraclass correlation coefficient is

$$\rho_c = \frac{\sum_{r=1}^{k} \sum_{j' \neq j=1}^{n} \left(y_{rj} - \bar{Y}\right)\left(y_{rj'} - \bar{Y}\right)}{kn(n-1)\sigma^2} \quad \text{so that}$$

$$\sigma_b^2 = \frac{\sigma^2}{n}\left[1 + (n-1)\rho_c\right]$$

Remember that $\sigma^2 = \sigma_b^2 + \sigma_w^2$ (between variance + within variance), and since $\sigma^2 \geq \sigma_b^2$ we will get the ρ_c to lie between $-1/(n-1)$ and 1.

As the sampling variance of the sample mean in srs is σ^2/n in sampling with replacement and $[(N-n)/(N-1)]\sigma^2/n$ in sampling without replacement, the relative efficiency of systematic sampling compared to srs with replacement is

$$\frac{1}{1 + (n-1)\rho_c}$$

where ρ_c is the intraclass correlation coefficient and compared to srs without replacement is

$$\frac{N-n}{N-1}\left(\frac{1}{1 + (n-1)\rho_c}\right)$$

where ρ_c is the intraclass correlation coefficient.

Cluster Sampling

The required sample size due to sampling clusters is approximately $n_c = n$ $(1 + M_o\rho_c)$ where n = sample M_o is the jth unit $(j = 1, 2, \ldots M_o)$ in the ith cluster $(i = 1, 2, \ldots n)$ of the y_{ij}, which is the value of the study.

Sampling for Proportions

$N = [(CV \text{ per unit}/e]^2$ where

$$e = \frac{\sigma_p}{P} = \sqrt{\frac{1-P}{nP}}$$

P is the universe proportion and p is the sample proportion.
   The optimal cluster size is

$$M_0 = \sqrt{\left[\frac{c_1}{c_2}\frac{1-\rho_c}{\rho_c}\right]}$$

where c_1 and c_2 are the individual costs of the specific items identified for comparison.

STRATIFIED SAMPLING

Stratified sampling is adopted in a number of situations:

1. When estimates are required for each subdivision of the universe separately, such as for geographic subdivisions

2. When estimates of universe characteristics are required with increased efficiency per unit of cost

3. When a greater weightage is required to be given to some units that occur infrequently in the universe; when the universe has a large variance, that is, the units vary greatly in the values

4. When different sampling procedures are to be adopted for different subuniverses, in which case the field work is easier to organize in the different strata, formed according to the nature of the available ancillary information required for sample selection

MULTISTAGE SAMPLING

Multistage sampling is adopted in a number of situations:

1. Sampling frames may not be available for all the ultimate observational units in the universe, and it is extremely laborious and expensive to prepare such a complete frame.

2. Even when suitable sampling frames for the ultimate units are available for the universe, a multistage sampling plan may be more convenient than a single stage sample of the ultimate units, as the cost of surveying and supervising such a sample in large-scale surveys can be very high.

3. Multistage sampling can be a convenient means of reducing response errors and improving sampling efficiency by reducing the intraclass correlation coefficient observed in natural sampling units.

Glossary

E ven individuals with ISO 9000 experience are challenged to keep up with the changing terminology. If you are new to the game, it can be especially daunting. Therefore, we offer these terms and their definitions to help explain ISO and its derivative standards as well as the process of implementing and auditing. The basis for these definitions is ISO 9000:2000.

GENERAL TERMS

continual improvement—Optimization of characteristics and parameters of a product or process at a target value. Note: Continual improvement is only applicable where conformance has been established.

control plan—Documented descriptions of the systems for controlling parts and processes to provide control of all characteristics important for quality and engineering requirements.

customer—Organization, department, process, or person that receives a product and or service.

customer satisfaction—Customer's perception of the degree to which the customer's requirements have been fulfilled.

design responsible organization—Organization with authority to establish a new or change an existing product specification for product delivered to a customer. Note: This responsibility includes testing and verification of design performance within the customer's specified application.

effectiveness—The extent to which planned activities are realized and planned results achieved.

efficiency—The relationship between the result achieved and the resources used.

error-proofing—Use of product and process design and development features to prevent manufacture of nonconforming products. [Note: Generally, error-proofing is associated with design, whereas mistake-proofing is associated with process.]

laboratory—Test facility that may include chemical, metallurgical, dimensional, physical, electrical, reliability testing, or validation.

laboratory scope—Quality records containing the following:

- Specific test, evaluations, and calibrations that a laboratory is qualified to perform
- List of the equipment that it uses to perform the tests
- List of methods and standards to which it performs the above

manufacturing—Refers to the processes making or fabricating production materials, or production or service parts, or assemblies, or heat-treating, painting, plating, or other finishing services.

nonconformity—The nonfulfillment of a requirement.

organization—Group of people and facilities with an arrangement of responsibilities, authorities, and relationships. Example: company, corporation, firm, enterprise, charity, sole trader, association, or parts or combination thereof.

outsourcing—Process of acquiring products from outside the organization.

predictive maintenance—Activities based on product data aimed at the avoidance of maintenance problems by prediction of likely failure modes to prevent disruption of production.

management—Coordinated activities to direct and control an organization.

premium freight—Charges incurred additional to contracted delivery.

process—Set of interrelated or interacting activities that transform inputs into outputs.

quality—Degree to which a set of inherent characteristics fulfills requirements.

quality management system (QMS)—Management system to direct and control an organization with regard to quality.

remote location—Location that supports sites and at which nonproduction processes occur.

site—Location at which value-added processes occur. [Note: Includes distribution of parts manufactured by other companies. However, it does not include suppliers of indirect material, products]

special characteristics—Product characteristics or manufacturing process parameters subject to variation that may affect safety or compliance with regulations, fit, function, performance, or subsequent processing of product. [Clarification: Special characteristics are two: critical and significant]

supplier—Organization or person that produces a product.

top management—Person or group of people who direct and control an organization at the highest level.

validation—Confirmation, through the provision of objective evidence, that the requirements for a specific intended use or application have been fulfilled. [Note: The use conditions for validation can be real or simulated.]

verification—Confirmation, through the provision of objective evidence, that specified requirements have been fulfilled. [Note: Confirmation can comprise activities such as: performing alternative calculations, comparing a new design specification with a similar proven design specification, undertaking tests and demonstrations, and reviewing documents prior to issue.]

SPECIAL TERMS AS THEY RELATE TO SPECIFIC CATEGORIES

Introduction to Management Systems

assessment—A verification of the effectiveness of the management system operated by an organization through examination of materials, processes, finished product, methods of test, records, systems, services, and other activities established by an organization.

audit—A planned, independent, and documented assessment to determine whether agreed-upon requirements are being met by the organization. It is a system (holistic) orientation to effectiveness. A complete system audit generally is conducted every three to four years. The outcome of the audit is registration. See also: *assessment* and *surveillance audit.*

ISO—A Greek word that means "equal" or "harmonizing." The International Organization for Standardization is responsible for coordinating and publishing ISO 9000, ISO 14001, and other international standards.

ISO 9000—A generic name given to the standards developed to provide a framework around which a QMS can effectively be planned and documented.

ISO 9001:2000—Every five years, international standards have to be revised. ISO 9001:2000 was published in December 2000, after two years of development. It is simpler and more flexible for organizations to adopt and use, and builds on the merits of its predecessor. The primary difference is a shift from procedure to process-based activity.

management system—The manner in which an element of your organization is managed. It could be quality, environment, information security, health, or safety. Because they can be systemized, they can be standardized and benchmarked/audited.

quality management system (QMS)—A commonsense, well-documented system that ensures consistency and improvement of working practices, including the products and services produced.

registration/certification—What you achieve when you pass the assessment of your management system against a standard. The author prefers to use the term registration, as certification is often misunderstood to refer to each product being guaranteed.

standard—The document produced by an international committee of experts setting the guidelines on how things should be done that enables organizations to link business objectives with business effectiveness more directly.

surveillance audit—The regular audit conducted by registrars to confirm that a company already registered to the ISO standard still complies. A surveillance audit is a random audit of particular areas deemed important or trouble spots by the registrar. Typically, a surveillance audit is conducted every six to 12 months. A surveillance audit does not audit the entire system, it verifies compliance to the registration.

Management System Implementation and Registration

accreditation—The accreditation bodies are the ones that make sure that the registrars are in compliance with Guide 62 and are meeting all the requirements to be a good impartial registrar. This allows registrars to come and see how you are doing, and issue a certificate that people can be confident means you are doing a good job. Some registrars operate without accreditation, but obviously there is nobody saying how good a job they are doing.

American Society for Quality (ASQ)—ASQ is a society of individual professionals who are working in the field of quality.

assessor/auditor—This is a qualified industry expert who visits your organization, and has a look at what you do and how it is managed through your management system.

consultants—These people will help you to implement a management system, and help you achieve registration. They can help you design, write, and implement your management system in accordance with the standard and provide you with immediate assistance. Organizational members dedicated to the ongoing, development, advancement, and promotion of quality concepts, principles, and techniques. Visit www.asq.org for more details.

RAB (Registrar Accreditation Board)—The primary U.S. accreditation body. They allow a registrar to issue you a certificate, and they carry out a similar assessment on the registrars to make sure they are also following the process and standards as they are meant to be. Other countries have similar organizations, for example: UKAS— the UK equivalent, RvA—the Dutch equivalent, SCC—the Canadian equivalent.

registrar—A third-party entity. An independent body who visits your organization and assesses how you are using your management system. They issue a certificate so you can demonstrate you are compliant and doing it well.

software—There is a great deal of software out there to help you implement your management system in the first place and to manage your documentation and processes in an ongoing situation.

The Quality Management System

internal audit—When a member of your own staff audits the systems and procedures you have in place in your own company. A quality manager may do this regularly to see if the quality system is being used and maintained.

ISO 9000, ISO 9001, ISO 9004—The ISO 9000:2000 series comprises three specific standards. ISO 9001:2000 itself is the core standard: *ISO 9000:2000—Quality management systems—Fundamentals and vocabulary; ISO 9001:2000—Quality management systems— Requirements; ISO 9004:2000—Quality management systems— Guidelines for performance improvement; ISO 19011:2001— Guidelines on quality and environmental systems.* [Special note: management system auditing. The standards should be used together, as recommended by ISO. By doing this, you will be able to understand the concepts and objectives more fully.]

plan–do–check (study)–act (PDC[S]A)—The model forms the basis for much of the strategy embodied in ISO 9000. A fairly commonsense process of planning, doing, checking (studying), and then acting to continually improve the quality system.

procedure—A procedure outlines what you do to complete a task, a flow of activity that describes who does what, in what order, and to what standard. Collectively the procedures make up your quality system. Your procedures will describe how you operate and control your business and meet the requirements of the standard.

process—Any activity or set of activities that uses resources to transform inputs into outputs can be considered a process.

quality manual—A high-level document that outlines your intention to operate in a quality manner. It can be used in many ways, including as a marketing tool, communication, training tools, and a document that allows third parties to understand your business and assess your activities against a particular standard, such as ISO 9001. Many organizations make their quality manual available on their intranets.

quality objectives—The organization's strategic planning and quality policy. Provides a framework for the setting of quality objectives. The objectives should be capable of being measured in order to facilitate an effective and efficient review by management. Consideration should be given to current and future needs of the organization. The quality objectives should be communicated so employees can contribute to their achievement.

quality policy—Shall be defined by top management and written so that it is appropriate to the purpose of the organization. Includes a commitment to comply with requirements and continually improve the effectiveness of the quality management system. Provides a framework for establishing and reviewing quality objectives and is communicated and understood within the organization. It should be reviewed for continuing suitability.

work instructions—You may need more detail than that described in the procedures. The complexity of your business helps you to determine whether you need detailed work instructions in addition to your procedures. Many businesses use work instructions in training: to clarify how a job is performed; to reduce mistakes; to review the process; and to point to specific tasks that are not carried out.

The Assessment

accreditation marks—The marks associated with the accreditation bodies that monitor the registrar's activities. These marks can only be used in conjunction with the registrar's marks.

appendix—Supporting sheets to a certificate that define the activities and locations assessed and certified under one quality system.

certificate—Awarded following recommendation after the initial assessment, and maintained through continuing assessments.

continuing assessment—The periodic (every six months) visits a registrar makes to your company to ensure you are still using your system effectively. At each visit, they review 25 percent of the system and certain critical elements, for example, internal audits, customer complaints, a procedure.

corrective action—Short-term action to address a nonconformity.

initial assessment—The first full assessment of your whole quality management review(s) and corrective action requirements from the previous visit.

nonconformity—When something in your system doesn't meet the standards requirements, we call that a nonconformity. Sometimes the following two terms are used. Minor nonconformity: there is a single lapse in following a procedure. Major nonconformity: failure to implement and maintain a required management system element.

observations—Verbal or written comments that are made by assessors to clients concerning potential nonconformities or areas of concern.

opening/closing meeting—The formal meetings at the beginning and the end of the assessment between the client and the assessment team. The opening meeting sets the scene, schedule, and expectations of the assessment. The closing meeting addresses the findings and makes recommendations for improvement.

preassessment—This is an optional service to ensure that you implemented the standard. It is a dry run to make sure that there are no major problems with you achieving registration. For clients that use this service, the pass rate is 95 percent if all the information supplied to them is addressed prior to the initial assessment.

preventive action—Action taken to address the root cause and prevent the occurrence of a nonconformity.

registered logo—This is the unique registrar's logo, which can only be used by the registrar's clients to promote their registration. Examples of where clients use the logo are on letterhead, business cards, or company literature.

scope of registration—A precise definition of a client's activities that are the subject of assessment.

strategic review—A typical biennial review, at no additional cost, of your whole system and past performance that allows you to retain your certification without having to go through a full reassessment/ certification. The registrar looks back at lessons learned, changes, and trends, and also looks forward and links to your business plan. This registrar practice is adding value by helping you meet your own goals and objectives as a business.

Fee Structure

annual management fee—A cost per year for the work that a registrar charges when they are not visiting your site, primarily the maintenance of your account, and planning and preparation for visits.

application/document review fee—This is a one-time, nonrefundable payment to cover the administrative costs of advancing your application to the point of initial assessment.

assessment fee—This is the charge for the assessor's time. This is worked out on a daily basis. You are charged based on how many days the auditor spends at your location.

expenses—The travel costs associated with the assessor coming to your location. Some registrars use an all-inclusive assessment fee, so you do not have to pay the expenses on top. This makes it easier for you to budget, as you always know how much a third-party assessment is going to cost.

report fee—A fee that some registrars charge separate from the visit, so you can receive a report of what occurred either during the pre-, initial, or continuing assessment visit.

Other Management Systems

TL 9000 (Telecommunications), AS9100 (Aerospace), ISO 9000-3 TickIT (Software Development)—Industry-specific variations on ISO 9000 where industry experts have tweaked or added to ISO 9001 to make it more appropriate or applicable to a particular industry.

CE mark—This is a product certification mark required on certain products to be sold in Europe; for example, medical devices.

environmental management system (ISO 14001)—A management system designed to help organizations manage their environmental impact.

information security management system (BS 7799/ISO 17799)—A management system designed to help organizations manage their information security risks. This addresses all company information, not just IT systems.

product certification—A process of confirming that a product has been manufactured to a product standard and has been independently tested and certified. This differs from management system certification because the product performance is assessed, not just the system through which it was produced.

Selected Bibliography

Alexander Hamilton Institute, Inc. 1978. "Management by Objectives: A Modern System for Getting Results," *Modern Business Reports.* New York.

Barker, E. M. 2002. "Aerospace's AS9100 QMS Standard." *Quality Digest* (May): 35–39.

Bravener, L. C. 1997. "Aerospace Launches AS9000." *Quality Digest* (December): 24–26.

Bullington, K. E. 2003. "5S Suppliers." *Quality Progress* (January): 56–59.

Burr, J. T. 1997. "Keys to a Successful Internal Audit." *Quality Progress* (April): 76–78.

Chen, C. C., and C. C. Yang. 2002. "Cost-Effectiveness Based Performance Evaluation for Suppliers and Operations." *Quality Management Journal* 9, no. 4: 59–73.

Cochran, C. 2002. "Six Problem-Solving Fundamentals." *Quality Digest* (September): 29–34.

———. 2002. "Document Control Made Easy." *Quality Digest* (June): 29–35.

Coens, T., and M. Jenkins. 2001. "Say Goodbye to the Performance Review—Really." *The Human Element* 18, no. 3: 8–11.

Conway Quality, Inc. 1986. *The Right Way to Manage.* Videotapes. Nashua, NH.

Dalgleish, S. 2003. "Design Engineering: A Goldmine for Quality Improvement." *Quality* (January): 14.

———. 2003. "Registrars and ISO 9000 credibility." *Quality* (February): 14.

Decker, D. C., and J. A. Belohlav. 1997. "Managing Transitions." *Quality Progress* (April): 93–98.

Detert, J., and R. Jenni. 2000. "A Instrument for Measuring Quality Practices in Education." *Quality Management Journal* 7, no. 3: 20–37.

Eckes, G. 2003. *Six Sigma for Everyone.* New York: John Wiley & Sons.

Fellenstein, S. J. 1999. "Harmonizing Standards: TS 16949 Puts International
Suppliers on the Same Road." *Quality in Manufacturing* (Nov./Dec.): 14.

Frieswick, K. 2003. "How Audits Must Change." *CFO* (July): 42–50.

Gordon, D. K. 2002. "AS9100: Aerospace Thinks Globally." *Quality Digest*
(December): 37–40.

Gould, L. S. 2003. "Automotive Supply Chain Management As Good As It Gets?"
Automotive Design and Production (February): 60–62.

Hutchins, C. 2001. "The State of Quality Auditing." *Quality Progress* (March):
25–32.

Hutchins, G. 2002. "Value-Added Auditing: Your Best Assessment Tool." *Quality
Digest* (October): 39–43.

———. 2002. "Add Value to Quality Audits." *Quality Progress* (September):
74–75.

Kaganov, M. 2003. "ISO 9000:2000; A Quality Manual for the Transition and
Beyond." *Quality Progress* (March): 27–31.

Ketola, J., and K. Roberts. 2000. "Product Realization." *Quality Progress* (May):
39–44.

———. 2001. "Demystifying ISO 9001:2000, Part 1." *Quality Progress*
(September): 65–71.

———. 2001. "Demystifying ISO 9000:2000, Part 2." *Quality Progress*
(October): 44–48.

Krass, P. 2002. "The Never-Ending Audit." *CFO* (October): 25–26.

Kymal, C., and D. Watkins. 2001. "Making the Transition from QS-9000 to
ISO/TS 16949." *Quality Digest* (December): 31–37.

Landon, T. 2003. "13 Steps to Certification in Less Than a Year." *Quality
Progress* (March): 32–41.

Levy, P. S., and S. Lemeshow. 1991. *Sampling of Populations: Methods and
Applications.* New York: John Wiley & Sons.

Marabotti, D. 2003. "Build Supplier Metrics, Build Better Product." *Quality*
(February): 40–43.

Okes, D., and R. T. Westcott, eds. 2001. *The Certified Quality Manager
Handbook,* 2nd ed. Milwaukee: ASQ Quality Press.

Osterland, A. 2002. "No More Mr. Nice Guy." *CFO* (September): 48–58.

Reichardt, E., and L. J. Nichols. 2003. "Score Your ISO Certification." *Quality*
(February): 44–47.

Romano, P. 2000. "ISO 9000: What Is Its Impact on Performance?" *Quality
Management Journal* 7, no. 3: 38–56.

Salot, S. H., and A. Downey. 2001. "Tomorrow's Document Management."
Quality Digest (February): 43–58.

Shipley, D. 2002. "Destination ISO 9001." *Quality Progress* (March): 32–34.

Slickers, K. A. 2003. "Harmonizing Standards." *Quality* (January): 58–60.

Smith, R. M. 2002. "Making the Transition from QS-9000 to ISO/TS 16949."
Quality Digest (March): 29–34.

———. 1999. "ISO/TS 16949: Successor to QS-9000." *Quality Digest* (August):
39–42.

Stahan, J. 2002. "Transition to ISO 9000:2000." *Quality Progress* (March): 27–31.

Stamatis, D. H. 2003. *Six Sigma Fundamentals.* New York: Productivity Press.

Stein, B. 1989. "A Program to Revitalize a Corporate Culture for Competitiveness." Annual meeting of the National Association of Suggestions Systems, Orlando, FL (September).

Teach, E. 2002. "Working on the Chain." *CFO* (September): 83–90.

Umble, E. J., and M. Umble. 2000. "Developing Control Charts and Illustrating Type I and Type II Errors." *Quality Management Journal* 7, no. 4 (September): 23–31.

Vavra, T. G. 2002. "ISO 9001:2000 and Customer Satisfaction." *Quality Progress* (May): 69–75.

Warnack, M. 2003. "Continual Improvement Programs and ISO 9000:2000." *Quality Progress* (March): 42–49.

Weiss, L. A. 1998. "AS9000 Takes Flight: One Company's Story." *Quality Digest* (April): 53–56.

West, J. E. 2002. "Three Strategies for Aligning Quality Policies, Objectives, and Processes." *Quality Digest* (June): 41–45.

———. 2002. "Should You Transition to ISO 9000:2000?" *Quality Progress* (September): 58–65.

Whitmore, K., and C. Kalogeridis. 2002. "ISO/TS 16949: Here at Last." *Quality Digest* (October): 21–26.

Wright, T. 2001. "ISO 9001 without Tears." *Quality Progress* (August): 57–61.

Zuckerman, A. 2003. "Transition to ISO/TS 16949." *Quality Digest* (April): 35–38.

BIBLIOGRAPHY OF STANDARDS

For information on these standards please contact ASQ.

ANSI/ISO/ASQ Q9000-2000, Quality management systems—Fundamentals and vocabulary.

ANSI/ISO/ASQ Q9001-2000, Quality management systems—Requirements.

ANSI/ISO/ASQ Q9004-2000, Quality management systems—Guidelines for performance improvements.

ANSI/ISO/ASQ Q10005-1995, Quality management—Guidelines for quality plans.

ANSI/ISO/ASQ Q10007-2003, Quality management systems—Guidelines for configuration management.

ANSI/ISO/ASQ Q10011-1-1990, Guidelines for auditing quality systems—Part 1: Auditing

ANSI/ISO/ASQ Q10011-2-1991, Guidelines for auditing quality systems—Part 2: Qualification criteria for quality systems auditors

ANSI/ISO/ASQ Q10011-3-1991, Guidelines for auditing quality systems—Part 3: Management of audit program.

ANSI/ISO/ASQ Q10015:2001, Quality management—Guidelines for training.

ANSI/ISO/ASQ Q14001-1996, Environmental management systems—Specification with guidance for use.

BSR/ISO/ASQ QE19011-2002, Guidelines for quality and/or environmental management systems auditing.

IEC 60300-1: 2, Dependability management—Part 1: Dependability programme management.

ISO 10006:2003, Quality management systems—Guidelines for quality management in projects.

ISO 10012:2003, Measurement management systems—Requirements for measurement process and measuring equipment.

ISO/IEC 9000-3:2004, Software engineering—Guidelines for the application of ISO 9001:2000 to computer software.

ISO/TR 10013:2001, Guidelines for quality management system documentation.

ISO/TR 10014:1998, Guidelines for managing the economics of quality.

ISO/TR 10017:2003, Guidance on statistical techniques for ISO 9001:2000.

ISO/TS 16949:2002, Quality management systems—Particular requirements for the application of ISO 9001:2000 for automotive production and relevent service part organization.

IWA 1:2001, Quality management systems—Guidelines for process improvements in health service organizations.

IWA 2:2003, Quality management systems—Guidelines for the application of ISO 9001:2000 in education.

ISO Management Systems. *ISO 9000 and ISO 14000 News.* This is a bimonthly publication that provides comprehensive coverage of international developments relating to ISO's management system standards, including news of their implementation by diverse organizations around the world.

Index

A

acceptance criteria, ISO/TS 16949, 68, 105
acceptance testing procedures, 321
action plan, 224
active part, 86, 88
administrative manuals, 159
advanced product quality and control plan, 218–20
  key characteristics, 220
advanced product quality planning process, 91, 105
affinity diagram, 8
aftermarket parts, 86, 88
Americas Aerospace Quality Group, 137
analysis of data,
  ISO 9001:2000, 56–57
  ISO/TS 16949, 80–81
annual layout inspection, 92
appearance items, 80, 117
appearance masters, 94
AS9100, 137–49
  checklist, 148
  development, 139
  elements added to basic standard, 141–47
  implementation, 140–41
  important characteristics, 209
  registration, 147–49
  registration benefits, 139

  requirements, 139
  variations, 138
AS9101, 148
  purpose, 210
assessment summary sheet, 128
assurance system, 273
assurance system assessment, 275
attribute sampling, 308–10
audit,
  conducting, 252
  defined, 231
  documenting, 253
  physical visit, 234–35
  planning, 250
  process inputs, 251–52
  scope, 250–51
audit appraisal, 291–92
audit checklist, 233, 245
audit planning tools, 233–34
audit process, steps, 234–37
audit program,
  establishing, 255
  implementing, 255
  improving, 256
  monitoring, 255
audit risk, 303
audit stratification, 293
audit summary report, 236–37
audit team, tasks, 244–45
auditing, communication, 312
auditing methodologies, 286–87
  nonstatistical approaches, 286–87